YES
PRIME
MINISTER

YES PRIME MINISTER

The Diaries of
the Right Hon. James Hacker

VOLUME I

Edited by Jonathan Lynn and Antony Jay

BBC PUBLICATIONS

The BBC TV series *Yes Prime Minister* was written
by Jonathan Lynn and Antony Jay and
produced by Sydney Lotterby.
The part of *James Hacker* was
played by Paul Eddington, *Sir Humphrey
Appleby* by Nigel Hawthorne and *Bernard
Woolley* by Derek Fowlds.

Photographs of Harold Wilson on page 101
from BBC Hulton Picture Library and
The Photo Source (Central Press)

Published by BBC Publications
A Division of BBC Enterprises Ltd
35 Marylebone High Street
London W1M 4AA

First published 1986

ISBN 0 563 20469 9

Typeset by Phoenix Photosetting, Chatham
Printed in England by
Mackays of Chatham Ltd

Contents

EDITOR'S NOTE *7*

1 PARTY GAMES *9*

2 THE GRAND DESIGN *59*

3 THE MINISTERIAL BROADCAST *86*

4 THE KEY *114*

5 A REAL PARTNERSHIP *138*

6 A VICTORY FOR DEMOCRACY *161*

7 THE SMOKESCREEN *187*

8 THE BISHOP'S GAMBIT *212*

9 ONE OF US *235*

Editor's Note

Hacker's unexpected elevation to the Premiership, which occurs at the end of the first chapter of this volume, created almost as many problems for his editors as it did for Britain. He was determined that his diaries should portray his period in office as a series of triumphs, even though the task would have defeated a far more skilful diarist. History dealt somewhat roughly with Hacker as Prime Minister; but readers of his full diaries will see some justice in this, since Hacker as an author dealt even more roughly with history. It may be that the office of Prime Minister encouraged in him – as in others – a progressive separation from reality, and a breaking down of the barrier between fact and imagination as he dictated, alone with his customary glass of Scotch and his cassette recorder, a version of the day's events in which he relived his successes and reinterpreted his failures.

As the months went on it seems as if Hacker found in his taped memoirs something of the solace a medieval monarch would have gained from the confessional, without the inconvenience of having to admit to any sins, let alone repent of them. It may have been effective therapy, but it does not make for good history. For this reason the editors have had to have even greater recourse than previously to corrective versions of events drawn from the papers of those whose recollections are perhaps more trustworthy than his. Happily many of these documents have been released under the Thirty Year rule, and others have been generously supplied to us by executors and trustees.

As before we have made extensive use of the Appleby Papers, and we are as grateful as before to Sir Bernard Woolley, formerly Hacker's Principal Private Secretary at Number Ten Downing Street, who gave us at great length his own recollections of the period, and generously checked the first draft for us. But the responsibility for any inaccuracies or inadequacies remains our own.

Hacker College, Oxford   Jonathan Lynn
August, 2022 AD   Antony Jay

1
Party Games

December 6th
December 6th
Sir Humphrey's up to something. When I saw him yesterday at the
Department of Administrative Affairs he was in a sort of dream and
he seemed quite unable to concentrate on my problems with the
Eurosausage, which is the latest idiotic standardisation fight that I
have to have with our European enemies. [*Or European partners, as
Hacker referred to them in public – Ed.*]

But more of that in a moment. Sir Humphrey normally has a real
zest and enthusiasm for bureaucratic battles, and he has been
strangely subdued recently. No doubt he's plotting something. I
suppose I'll find out soon enough – if not, I'm in trouble!

Meanwhile, today was mostly spent on routine business. I was
wading through some Cabinet Defence Papers in the office this morning when Bernard interrupted me.

'Excuse me, Minister, but I'm afraid you have to deal with something that is much more urgent.'

I asked what.

'Your Christmas cards, Minister. They cannot be postponed any
longer.'

Bernard was right. Getting the Christmas cards out *is* much more
important than reading Cabinet Defence Papers – unless you're the
Secretary of State for Defence, I suppose.

[*Hacker, like many politicians, was apparently unable to distinguish
between 'Urgent' and 'Important'. Bernard had described the Christmas cards as the former. Hacker assumed that he meant the latter. On the
other hand, the possibility exists that Hacker was right in describing the
Christmas cards as more important. As a mere member of the Cabinet
his influence over defence matters would be negligible. So would the
information contained in the papers he would be shown – Ed.*]

Bernard had laid out large piles of DAA[1] Christmas cards along

[1] Department of Administrative Affairs.

the conference table. The piles were all different sizes. Clearly they were divided for a reason.

Bernard proffered the reason. 'They're all clearly labelled, Minister.' He strolled along the table, casually indicating each pile in turn as if he were reviewing a Guard of Honour. 'These you sign Jim. These you sign Jim Hacker. These, Jim and Annie. These are Annie and Jim Hacker. These, love from Annie and Jim. These Mrs Hacker should write, and you should append your name.'

I spotted two more piles. 'What about those?'

'Those are printed. And those have cyclostyled signatures, so you needn't write anything. Just check to whom they're being sent, to make sure they're not going to people to whom you should have sent a *personally* signed card. You know,' he added in explanation, 'signed Jim, or Jim Hacker, or Jim and Annie, or Annie and Jim Hacker.'

There was yet another large batch at the end of the table, sub-divided into several more piles. 'What are those?'

Bernard was completely in command. 'Those are the constituency cards. Your election agent dropped them off this morning.'

I hadn't realised that they were divided up into different sections like that. But of course, constituency mail is considered political, not governmental. The Civil Service would never help with that, because it mustn't take sides in party politics. At least, that's their excuse.

However, Bernard was more than happy to explain about the con-stituency Christmas cards. 'Those you sign Jim, these Jim Hacker, these Jim and Annie, these love from Annie and Jim . . .'

I told him that I'd got the gist. But it was clearly going to take up much of the day. What a bore.

In fact, I hadn't yet been shown the full magnitude of the task. Bernard suddenly produced a bulging carrier bag.

'And Mrs Hacker left these,' he murmured sympathetically. 'Your personal cards. But it won't take too long. Only eleven hundred and seventy-two.'

I was appalled. 'Eleven hundred and seventy-two?'

'Apart from', he added, 'the cards that are waiting for you at Party Headquarters.'

My heart sank. Party Headquarters. I'd forgotten about all that. I didn't sign any Party Christmas cards last year. But last year I wasn't Party Chairman. This year I am.

I started signing the cards. To my surprise I noticed that there were two kinds: DAA cards and House of Commons cards.

Bernard explained. 'Departmental cards bestow a slightly higher status on the recipient than a mere House of Commons card.' Quite right too – a departmental card can only be sent by a member of the Department, whereas a House of Commons card can be sent by any ordinary backbencher.

I asked why we didn't send departmental cards to everyone.

'They cost 10p more, Minister.'

'But aren't people who get mere House of Commons cards going to be offended at being downgraded?'

'No, Minister, we've worked it out quite carefully. For some people you can get away with a House of Commons card if you sign it Jim instead of Jim Hacker, or Jim and Annie instead of Jim and Annie Hacker, or add "with love", or sign it instead of cyclostyling, or . . .'

I silenced him with a look.

There was one card I particularly resented sending. It was to the EEC Agriculture Commissioner in Brussels. I would rather have sent him a redundancy notice. He's even worse than his colleagues, and I can't speak any worse of anybody than that. He's the fool who has forced through the plan to standardise the Eurosausage. By the end of next year we'll be waving goodbye to the good old British sausage, and we'll be forced to accept some foreign muck like salami or bratwurst in its place.

Of course, they can't actually *stop* us eating the British sausage. But they can stop us calling it a sausage. It seems that it's got to be called the Emulsified High-Fat Offal Tube. And I was forced to swallow it. I mean, it is a perfectly accurate description of the thing, but not awfully appetising. And it doesn't exactly trip lightly off the tongue. It sticks in the throat, as a matter of fact. There's going to be frightful trouble over it.

But it's my job to implement EEC regulations. And, in exchange for getting a new deal on farm prices and on Britain's reduced contribution to the community budget, a concession had to be made. The PM didn't seem to mind, nor did the FO, nor did Agriculture – presumably because I'm the one who is to be landed with trying to sell this to the British people. It could ruin my career.

Bernard asked me what the EEC has against our sausage. Apparently he doesn't read the papers he puts into my red box.[1]

'Didn't you read this analysis?'

'I glanced at it, Minister, but I'm afraid it rather put me off.'

I re-read it, there and then.

[1] The official briefcase containing government papers, which members of the government are given each evening and weekend as their homework.

11

```
                            - 3 -


   a lack of healthy nutrition.  The average British

   sausage consists of:


               32 %  ..... Fat

                6 %  ..... Rind

               20 %  ..... Water

                5 %  ..... Seasoning, preservatives

                           and colouring

               26 %  ..... Meat

   The 26% meat is mostly gristle, head meat, other

   off cuts, and mechanically recovered meat steamed

   off the carcass.
```

I felt slightly sick. I had had one for breakfast.

Bernard read the analysis. 'Perhaps the EEC Commissioner is right about abolishing it.'

Bernard sometimes misses the point *completely*. 'He *may* be right,' I explained wearily, 'but it'll be dreadfully unpopular with the voters.' Bernard nodded gloomily. 'Ah well,' I added, 'it seems we'll just have to grit our teeth and bite the bullet.'

[*We have kept Hacker's mixed metaphors in the text of this document because we feel it gives an insight into the mind of one of our great national leaders – Ed.*]

Bernard tactfully suggested that I should send Maurice a Christmas card, nonetheless. I toyed with the idea of wishing him an offal Christmas and a wurst New Year, but Bernard advised me against it.

[*One of the reasons for trying to maintain impenetrable secrecy around Government Ministers is that without it many would make themselves laughing stocks within days or – at most – weeks. Bernard's advice in this case was clearly wise – Ed.*]

I asked Bernard what Christmas presents it would be appropriate to give to the Private Office.

Bernard said that it was entirely up to me. But he recommended bottles of sherry for the Assistant Private Secretaries, large boxes of House of Commons mints for the Diary Secretary and the Correspondence Secretary, and small boxes of House of Commons mints for the rest.

'What about the Principal Private Secretary?' I asked absent-mindedly.

'That's me,' he replied, slightly startled.

I explained that I knew who he was. But I wondered what I should give him.

'You don't have to give me anything, Minister.'

'I know that,' I said with real warmth. 'But I'd *like* to.'

Bernard seemed quite touched. 'Oh, Minister,' he replied.

'Well?' I asked.

'Well, anything really.'

He obviously didn't want to say. But I had *no idea* what he'd like.

'Such as?' I prompted.

'Really,' he said, 'I'd like a surprise.'

I still didn't have a clue. 'What *sort* of surprise should I give you?'

'Well,' he said cautiously, 'a bottle of champagne is the customary surprise.'

I spent the rest of the day signing these bloody cards. I was supposed to have a big meeting with Humphrey, but it was cancelled because he had some unexpected meeting with Sir Arnold.[1] I think Bernard knows that there's something going on with Sir Humphrey because I got one of his less-than-completely-straightforward replies when I asked him if the meeting was about something I should know about.

'Well,' he answered evasively, 'I'm sure that if, you know, it's about something you should know, assuming that, you know, you *didn't* know about it already, then, obviously, *when* you can know will be when Sir Humphrey really knows.'

'I don't like being kept in the dark,' I complained.

'Well, quite honestly, Minister, Sir Humphrey may not know what it's about. Only Sir Arnold may know what it's about. And they do have meetings that aren't just about this Department.'

Bernard may be right. But Sir Arnold always makes me feel nervous. The Cabinet Secretary is, in some ways, the most powerful man

[1] Sir Arnold Robinson, the Secretary of the Cabinet.

in the country. He's the Prime Minister's right-hand man. He controls Cabinet Agenda. He can control access to the PM.

[*Sir Humphrey Appleby's meeting with the most powerful man in the country was to have a momentous effect on the future of them all: Hacker, Appleby and Bernard Woolley. A note of the meeting has been found among Sir Humphrey's private papers – Ed.*]

Had an astonishing and nerve-wracking meeting with AR[1] today. The CS[2] fixed me with an eagle-eyed stare.

'Humphrey,' he murmured, 'I've been giving some thought to the matter of early retirement.'

I was shocked. I had no wish to retire. I couldn't see what I'd done wrong. But he seemed very firm. 'The time has come, Humphrey. Enough is enough.'

I told him that this was a bit of a bombshell.

'I'm well aware of that, Humphrey,' he replied firmly, 'but no one is indispensable.'

I was hesitating, wondering whether I should launch into a defence of my own recent conduct, pointing out that there were severe limits to one's achievements when one has a Minister such as Hacker to contend with, when Arnold added: 'Don't try to persuade me, Humphrey, the die is cast. I shall retire six months early, in the New Year.'

I reflected how fortunate it was that thirty years of training in Civil Service methods had triumphed over my initial impetuosity. So long as there is anything to be gained by saying nothing, it is always better to say nothing than anything.

But why was Arnold taking me into his confidence? The answer became clear immediately. 'My successor, Humphrey, has to be someone who can be firm with our political masters.'

I hastened to agree. We can't put up with too much nonsense from that lot. I said as much. But we both agreed that Sir Arnold's successor, while not putting up with any nonsense, had to be tactful, suave, charming and emollient. But, above all, he has to be *sound*. There was no doubt in my mind that I embodied all the necessary qualities in full measure. And indeed, Arnold went on to say that it is his heavy duty to convey a recommendation to the Prime Minister as to which of the present Permanent Secretaries best meets these stringent criteria.[3]

He came to the point. He remarked that in his job, the problem isn't really finding the answers. It's finding the questions. 'We need the man who can find the key questions.'

[1] Sir Arnold Robinson.

[2] Cabinet Secretary, the same AR.

[3] A small committee, including the Permanent Secretary of the Treasury and the Head of the Civil Service would have made this recommendation. In practice, the Prime Minister was likely to follow Sir Arnold's recommendation, especially if Sir Arnold ensured that his colleagues endorsed it.

So this was it! This was my test. As I'd been given no warning of this oral examination I had to think fast. Fortunately I collected my thoughts in a matter of moments, and the key question popped into my mind.

But it had to be asked with taste and discretion. So I remarked that I was changing the subject completely, and then enquired what he intended to do when he retired.

Arnold was delighted. He congratulated me on asking such a good question. But it was immediately clear to me that there would be ways in which he might serve the country [*i.e. jobs that Sir Arnold might pick up – Ed.*] that his successor as Cabinet Secretary might persuade him to undertake [*i.e. slip his way – Ed.*]

It transpired that Sir Arnold had given this matter some thought already, and had been offered the Chairmanship of Banque Occidentale, plus directorships of BP and IBM.

However, I made careful notes of a few other ways in which Sir Arnold suggested that he could serve his country, and which were on his mind. The Chairmanship of the Royal Opera House Trust is coming up next year, and the Chancellorship of Oxford. We agreed that the Deputy Chairmanship of the Bank of England would be a challenge, as would being Head of the Security Commission. And the Presidency of the Anglo-Caribbean Association would also give Arnold a chance to be of service. Especially in the winter months.

I assured Arnold that any successor worth his salt would be able to arrange those matters satisfactorily. I could tell that Arnold found my positive approach extremely reassuring.

However, it transpired that he had other matters on his mind as well. He was concerned that certain advice that he might have given the Prime Minister in the past could, if it comes out, be misinterpreted. [*In other words, could be understood perfectly – Ed.*] Naturally we are, all of us, in the Service, concerned that advice that one has given could be misunderstood if it were to come into the public domain.

Arnold was particularly concerned because it appears that papers exist recording his reasonable and sensible advice to use troops during strikes, and suggesting the equally reasonable precaution that such troops should be armed. Of course, taken out of context [*i.e. placed in the correct context – Ed.*] such information could be damaging to him.

He has also, in the distant past, suggested we ensure that sanctions against Rhodesia [*as it then was – Ed.*] never happened, and in the recent past he proposed negotiations with South Africa about reactivating the Simonstown naval base. This was all perfectly sensible strategically, and of course would be a great help with the Falklands. But it could be an embarrassment for somebody in line for the Secretary-Generalship of the Commonwealth. And I was able to confirm that Arnold *would* be in line for the Secretary-Generalship of the Commonwealth.

He was gratified, especially when I told him that in my opinion the right successor would see no problem in keeping the relevant files under wraps.

So we reverted to the original subject of discussion, namely Arnold's retirement. He told me that he could now see his way forward to placing my name at the head of the list. Good news – and better news followed at once, as careful questioning elicited the hint that there would be no other names on that list.

As I left, on cloud nine, Arnold mentioned that he had already accepted the Presidency of the Campaign for Freedom of Information. I was rather stunned. But then I quickly saw the wisdom of it. The Campaign is always very popular with the Opposition. And today's Opposition is tomorrow's government. Also his Presidency of the Campaign will ensure that the Freedom of Information is not abused. Hopefully he will be in a good position to help keep those files of advice given to the PM – and to Ministers – under wraps.

We drank a toast to the continuity of sound government, and to freedom of information – whenever it's in the national interest.
[*Appleby Papers/PPC/MPAA*]

[*Hacker's diary continues – Ed.*]

December 9th

The day began with a frightful misunderstanding about Humphrey's future. The resulting embarrassment could have been ghastly, but for the fact that I covered up the situation with my customary skill.

He came in to see me first thing this morning. He told me that he had very grave news, and he said it in a profoundly sepulchral tone. In fact, the misunderstanding that ensued came about entirely because he speaks in gobbledegook instead of plain English.

Later today I asked Bernard what Humphrey had said, and he remembered it perfectly. Apparently Humphrey had said gravely that 'the relationship, which I might tentatively venture to aver has not been without a degree of reciprocal utility and even perhaps occasional gratification, is approaching the point of irreversible bifurcation and, to put it briefly, is in the propinquity of its ultimate regrettable termination'.

I asked him if he would be so kind as to summarise what he's just said in words of one syllable.

He nodded in sad acquiescience. 'I'm on my way out,' he explained.

I couldn't believe my ears. Did he mean what I thought he meant?

'There comes a time,' he continued, 'when one must accept what fate has in store, when one passes on . . .'

'Passes on?' I interrupted softly, aghast.

'. . . to pastures new,' he continued, 'perhaps greener, to put oneself finally at the service of one who is greater than any of us.'

I was shattered. I told him I was frightfully sorry. He thanked me. I

asked him if his wife knew. He said that, apparently, she had suspected for some time. I asked him when they had told him. He said
this afternoon. Finally, I asked him how long they'd given him.

'Just a few weeks,' he said.

I was appalled. And very moved. It did strike me at the time that he
was being awfully brave, but . . . I just thought he was being awfully
brave.

'Humphrey, you're being awfully brave,' I said.

'Well, I am a little anxious, I must admit – one is always frightened
of the unknown – but I have faith. Somehow I'll muddle through.'

I was overcome. Overwhelmed. In fact, I am not ashamed to admit
that I wept. Fortunately, Humphrey couldn't quite see that, as I had
the good sense to cover my eyes with my handkerchief.

But he certainly noticed I was upset, and he asked me what the
matter was. I was hopelessly inarticulate. I tried to explain how sorry
I was, that we'd had our ups and downs but they were nothing really.
Then I sort of noticed Humphrey eyeing me as if I were emotionally
unstable.

'Minister, don't take on so,' he remonstrated. 'We'll see each other
regularly – once a week at least.'

I thought I'd misheard him. But he was smiling a confident smile.
My brain was in a whirl. What could he possibly mean? Had I totally
misunderstood him?

'I haven't told you where I'm going yet.'

I goggled at him.

'I've been appointed Secretary of the Cabinet.'

I *had* totally misunderstood him. 'Secretary of the Cabinet?'

'Yes.' Now he looked as confused as I must have looked. 'Why,
what did you think I meant?'

I could hardly tell him, could I? 'I thought . . . I thought . . .' Then
I gave up and tried to explain it all away by hinting that I wasn't quite
myself, tired, overwrought, that sort of thing. I've honestly never
been so embarrassed in the whole of my life.

Sir Humphrey's sympathy, unlike mine, is to be avoided at all
costs. 'I'm so sorry,' he murmured. 'Perhaps as Cabinet Secretary
designate I should suggest to the Prime Minister some lightening of
the load.'

That'll teach me to have kindly feelings towards him. I'll never
make *that* mistake again! I hastened to reassure him that I was absolutely fine. I congratulated him warmly, even effusively, on his elevation. I may even have been too effusive, but I don't think so. I even

17

flattered him a little, by asking how I would manage without him.

'You'll probably manage even better without me,' he replied with uncharacteristic honesty. I was about to agree enthusiastically, but I realised, just in time, that it would be a little tactless.

Also, it was already clear to me that Humphrey, when it was time for a reshuffle, would inevitably be advising the Prime Minister on his Cabinet colleagues. The PM would be bound to question Humphrey about me.

So I gave him a lot of soft soap about how wonderful he'd been, how I had tremendous admiration for all he'd done, wonderful work in the highest traditions of the service. Fulsome twaddle, but he lapped it up and told me I was too kind. Too true!

Carefully, I gave him the chance to reciprocate, by saying that in my opinion we'd done a pretty good job together. 'I couldn't have wished for a better Minister, Minister,' he said. Jolly nice, that. And I think he means it. Humphrey's pretty devious but I've never caught him out in an actual lie.

[*Sir Humphrey Appleby's diary reveals a somewhat different view of the conversation that Hacker describes above – Ed.*]

I told the Minister that I had to pass on to pastures new, and put myself at the service of the PM. I tried to express it with a sadness that I did not feel, in order that Hacker should not perceive the sense of delight and relief that I was experiencing now that my sentence of several years' hard labour with him was nearly over. I had not been expecting to be paroled.

He reacted in a way which genuinely makes me wonder if he is emotionally unbalanced. He seemed to be weeping. He is obviously a serious hysteric. This had not been clear to me until today.

It took him some time to understand my new job, so upset was he at the thought of losing me. But then he grovelled in a deeply embarrassing fashion. He asked if I'd be doing for the Prime Minister what I did to him. He must have meant *for* him. [*We don't think so – Ed.*] He smarmed and greased his way through a bootlicking speech about how much he admired me and how wonderful I'd always been. Perfectly true, of course, but his motives were completely transparent.

He invited me to return the compliment. The best I could manage was to assure him that I couldn't have wished for a better minister. He seemed positively thrilled. Remarkably, he still takes everything I say at face value.

We agreed that I'd tell the DAA staff of my departure on Friday evening, just before my new appointment is promulgated. Then I can bid them all farewell at the Christmas drinks party.

Hacker said that that will certainly make it a happy occasion. Obviously he means for me. Of course it will be sad for him.
[*Appleby Papers 928/2033/NT*]

[Hacker's diary continues – Ed.]

December 18th

This has been a highly dramatic weekend. It all started on Friday evening. We had a little drinks party in my offices at the end of the day. We had all the chaps from my private office and Humphrey's private office in for some Christmas cheer, plus Roy my driver and a couple of messengers and cleaners. These are egalitarian times.

I gave them all their House of Commons mints, or bottles, and they all seemed pleased though not a bit surprised. Then we all had a few drinks, not too much, and I proposed Humphrey's health in a charming speech which, though I say it myself, went very well. He complimented me in turn and we all drove home.

SIR BERNARD WOOLLEY RECALLS:[1]
Hacker's diary is a less than accurate account of that Christmas party. I remember it well. It was the usual initial embarrassment – all of us standing around in a inarticulate circle, clutching sticky sherry glasses, in a freezing room because the central heating had already been turned off for the Christmas break. As at all office parties, we had nothing to say to each other socially, and foolish grins predominated until we realised that the Minister was, predictably, getting drunk.

He poured lavish drinks and finally asked us all, not once but several times, if we were having a good time.

I recall that he asked Sir Humphrey if he were looking forward to the Cabinet Office. Sir Humphrey enthused, but added kindly that everyone was still very excited over the vexed question of the Eurosausage.

'Ah yes,' slurped the Minister, 'the Eurobanger.'

Sir Humphrey was unable to resist a little joke at Hacker's expense and replied that surely the Eurobanger was NATO's new tactical missile.

'Is it?' asked Hacker, confused, not getting the joke. This increased the general embarrassment factor tenfold.

Then, at last, the moment we all dreaded: Hacker's speech of farewell to Sir Humphrey. Hacker's belief, revealed in his diaries, that he made a charming speech which went well is a startling example of self-deception even by his own unique standards.

He began by saying that he had to say 'a few words' – always an understatement, I fear. He babbled on about how Christmas is a special time for us all, peace and goodwill to all men and so forth, and how it is always a pleasure to have a little seasonal get-together for those who serve him. He clumsily amended 'serve' to 'help'.

He thanked them all for their help, 'everyone from the Permanent Secretary right down to my messenger, my driver, the cleaner . . . not *down* to, that is, at least only down in the sense that Humphrey's up here on the fourth floor, oh no! we don't have any élitism here.'

[1] In conversation with the Editors.

He must have noticed that we were staring at him in some disbelief, as he hastened to explain himself still further. 'We're all equals,' he said with transparent dishonesty. 'A team. Like the Cabinet, except that we're all on the same side. No backstabbing, no leaking to the press.' Realising that he was being quotably disloyal to his Cabinet colleagues, and that even though he was arguing that we were all on the same side with no backstabbing or leaking there might nevertheless be amongst the gathering an unofficial spokesman or an informed source, or perhaps a feeling that *he* was being a bad team player by criticising his Cabinet colleagues, he added, 'I mean, the *Shadow* Cabinet'. Then he retracted even that. 'No. No. *Must keep politics out of it*. Peace and goodwill. Even towards one's officials, especially those who are leaving. So . . . to Humphrey.' He raised his glass unsteadily.

It is hard to describe the sense of relief that swept around the frozen room as Hacker finished his speech. We sipped our drinks and Sir Humphrey replied briefly and elegantly thanking everyone for their hard work over the past years. He remarked that such an occasion engenders a certain emotional ambiguity and personal ambivalence, because though honoured by the cause of his departure he was saddened by the fact of it.

He added that he was particularly sad to leave the service of a Minister without parallel in his experience. Perhaps it was this remark that Hacker mistook for a compliment.

We all agreed that an absolutely unique partnership had come to an end.

[Hacker's diary continues – Ed.]

I sent our detectives home early, before the party. They shouldn't have gone off duty, but I insisted. Season of goodwill and all that. So they weren't on hand when the police stopped me. I don't know why they did. I was driving perfectly safely. I was going slowly and carefully home to the constituency. I do dimly remember being overtaken by a middle-aged lady on a bicycle, which may suggest that I was overdoing the safety bit, but that is hardly a reason to accuse me of drunken driving. I mean, there's nothing wrong – I mean morally, of course, not legally – with being drunk. The danger comes if you're *dangerous* with it, which I never am.

Anyway, a couple of bobbies appeared from nowhere in a panda car, but when I mentioned that I had a Silver Badge[1] there was no more trouble. I don't think Annie's much of a driver, but in the circumstances I had to let her drive the rest of the way home.

[Our researches have not revealed the notebooks of the policemen who stopped Hacker that night. But we were fortunate enough to find, in the Home Office files, a letter from the Commissioner of Police in which their report was quoted. We reproduce it opposite – Ed.]

[1] See page 22 below.

NEW SCOTLAND YARD
BROADWAY. LONDON. SW1H 0BG

Permanent Secretary
Home Office
Whitehall
London SW1   19 December

Dear Richard,

We regret to inform you that the Rt Hon. James Hacker, MP, Minister for
Administrative Affairs, was stopped while driving home on Friday night.
He was driving at approximately nine miles an hour, and his breath smelled
strongly of alcohol. Since he immediately produced his Silver Badge
my two officers did not breathalyse him, a serious error which I can only
put down to inexperience.

They reported that when they approached Mr Hacker he began the conversation
with the words 'Good evening, Cinstable, Happy Chrostmas.' When asked
why he was driving so slowly he replied, 'I didn't want the kerb to
hit me.' Mrs Hacker, who had apparently not been drinking, offered to
drive the rest of the way home.

I would be obliged if you would make the Minister aware of the seriousness
of this matter and warn him that, in the event of a further breach of the
law, his Silver Badge will afford him no protection. For my part, I shall be
disciplining the detectives responsible for his 'protection', and ensuring
that in future they understand that their job includes protecting politicians
from themselves.

Yours sincerely

December 20th

Imagine my surprise when after the next Cabinet meeting – Humphrey's first as Cabinet Secretary – he buttonholed me as we were leaving the Cabinet Room and asked me if I'd pop over to his office and have a word with him.

I congratulated him on the conduct of his first Cabinet meeting and asked him how it felt, sitting there at the PM's right hand.

He ignored my question, asked me to take a pew and, absolutely without any warning and not even pausing to offer me a drink, told me that he wanted to have a word about a traffic incident.

Well, a nod is as good as a wink. I realised at once that it must be my little incident to which he was referring.

'I've had a report from the Home Office. Of course, it's entirely your affair . . .'

I interrupted him firmly. 'Precisely,' I said.

'But,' he continued, 'the Home Office take a very grave view. They feel that Ministers should set an example. There's a lot of damage to police morale if people get away with things just because they happen to hold an office of trust, however temporarily.'

The threat in the last two words was unmistakeable. I could hardly believe my ears. Two days as Cabinet Secretary and he was really getting rather uppity.

'Humphrey,' I asked with some incredulity, 'are you trying to tell me off or something?'

He backtracked immediately. 'Minister! Far be it from me. I am only the servant of the members of the Cabinet. A humble functionary. But I have been asked to reassure the Home Office that it will not occur again.'

I knew I was untouchable. 'What do they give us Silver Badges for then?' I enquired loftily.

'To get police co-operation, to let us pass through police cordons and security barriers and so on. Not to protect drunks who drive cars.'

I rose above it. 'Humphrey, I am not going to be lectured by functionaries, not even those as humble as your good self. I am a Minister of the Crown.'

'Of course, Minister,' he replied pleasantly, 'I will inform the Crown of the incident, if that is your wish.'

That was *not* my wish, as he perfectly well knew. I started to explain that I was speaking purely technically when I said I was a Minister of the Crown, but he interrupted me to add that his proper course was actually to inform the Prime Minister. At which point I decided that, thinking it over, he could feel free to tell the Home Office that I'd taken the point.

He thanked me politely. I asked if the Home Secretary knew. It would obviously be rather humiliating if the rebuke had been authorised by one of my colleagues.

Humphrey said no. 'This came straight from the Permanent Secretary of the Home Office.'

I was relieved. 'So there's no need for the Home Secretary to be . . . I mean, one doesn't want one's . . . colleagues (I nearly said enemies) to know?'

Humphrey guessed what I meant. After all, my views on Ray have not exactly been a closely guarded secret. 'I think the Home Secretary is not in a position to take advantage.'

I wondered why not. I suddenly realised that Ray hadn't been at Cabinet. Then Humphrey showed me the headline in the *Standard*.

The long and the short of it is that the Home Secretary, having personally initiated the 'Don't Drink And Drive At Christmas' campaign, and having ordered a get-tough policy from the police, was picked up pissed in his car in his own constituency.

How had he got into such a situation? I asked Humphrey why his security man hadn't been with him.

'Apparently,' replied Sir Humphrey pointedly, 'he'd given him the slip. You know how cunning these drunks can be.'

It transpired that the Home Secretary had been rather less lucky than me. He'd collided with a lorry that was full of nuclear waste. Then, as if that wasn't unlucky enough, he rebounded off the lorry and smashed into a car which was being driven by the editor of the local newspaper. Fat chance of hushing *that* up. So naturally it leaked out. [*The story, not the nuclear waste – Ed.*]

That was the end of Ray. By the end of the day he would be out of office.

I looked at Humphrey. 'What'll happen to him?'

'I gather,' he replied disdainfully, 'that he was as drunk as a lord – so after a discreet interval they'll probably make him one.'

SIR BERNARD WOOLLEY RECALLS:[1]

I well remember the dramatic events of two days later. I had called at the Minister's London flat, to collect him for a dinner to which I had to accompany him.

He was late home from the office. Annie Hacker was writing her Christmas cards, and asked me if I could put stamps on them while I was waiting.

I explained that I was not able to. Not, I hastened to explain, because the task was beyond me, but because I guessed that the cards were being sent to constituents. Such Christmas cards were considered political activity rather than government business, and of course as a Civil Servant I was not allowed to help with the Minister's political activities.

'I'm only asking you to lick some stamps,' she said plaintively.

I explained that it would be government lick. [*Bernard Woolley's cautious and pedantic attitude is seen clearly here, and doubtless explains his relatively quick rise to the highest reaches of the Civil Service – Ed.*]

Mrs Hacker found an ingenious solution to her dilemma. 'Suppose all these cards were to journalists?' she asked.

'That would be all right,' I confirmed.

'They're all to journalists,' she said firmly, and of course I could not doubt her word. So I settled down on the sofa to lick stamps, reflecting privately that licking is an essential part of relationships with the press. [*Doubtless Bernard Woolley and Mrs Hacker were pleased to be only licking journalists' envelopes, for a change – Ed.*]

We discussed the opinion polls which had been released to the newspapers that morning. The Minister had been absolutely delighted with them. It seemed that the Home Secretary's misfortune had done the Government no harm in the country, even though he was the Deputy Leader of the Party.

We discussed the inevitable reshuffle, although Mrs Hacker seemed uninterested. The only thing that concerned her was the fact that Hacker might get Northern Ireland, but we agreed that the Prime Minister did not appear to dislike Hacker enough for that. Most people, of course, found Ulster a dead end, though there was always the possibility of finishing up there in a blaze of glory. [*We feel sure that Sir Bernard intended no puns here – Ed.*]

Eventually we switched on the television news. Like most Government wives, Annie Hacker liked to watch the news because it was her best chance of finding out where her husband was.

[1] In conversation with the Editors.

We were astonished by a newsflash, reporting that Number Ten Downing Street had just announced that the Prime Minister was to retire in the New Year.

According to the press release, the Prime Minister did not wish to serve through another Parliament and therefore was resigning now in order to give his successor a good run up to the next election. A historic day.

[Hacker's diary continues – Ed.]

December 22nd

When I got home Annie and Bernard were there, apparently poleaxed by the news of the PM's resignation. I knew already – the PM had held an emergency Cabinet meeting late this afternoon, to tell us. You could have knocked all twenty-four of us down with the metaphorical feather.

Annie asked me why he'd resigned. That was the question we were *all* asking. He had said, to us and to the press, that he'd done it so as to give his successor a good run up to the next election. So that's obviously not the reason.

There have also been some amazing rumours flying around Whitehall. The left are saying the PM's a secret CIA agent. The right are saying that he's a secret KGB agent.

Bernard and I discussed these rumours. Bernard had heard something quite different. 'Minister, I've heard that there is £1 million worth of diamonds from South Africa in a Downing Street safe.[1] But of course,' he added, 'it's only a rumour.'

'Is that true?' I asked.

'Oh yes,' he said authoritatively.

I was amazed. 'So there *are* all those diamonds in Downing Street.'

Bernard looked surprised. 'Are there?'

I was confused. 'You said there were,' I said.

'I didn't,' he replied indignantly.

'You did!' I wasn't going to let him get away with it. 'You said that there was this rumour. I said, is it true? And you said yes!'

'I said yes, it was true that it was a rumour.'

'No, you said you'd heard it was true.'

'No, I said it was true that I'd heard it.'

Annie interrupted us. 'I apologise for cutting into this vital discussion, but do you believe the story about the diamonds?'

I don't, and nor does Bernard (it transpires). It's not impossible,

[1] Similar rumours circulated in Whitehall at the time of the surprise resignation of Mr Harold Wilson, as he then was.

25

but it's never been officially denied so I think we can discount it. The first rule of politics is Never Believe Anything Until It's Been Officially Denied.

We discussed the likely possibilities. It was clear that there wouldn't be a general election. Our party has quite a big majority. All that will happen is that the party must choose a new leader.

Annie asked me if I wanted the job.

I hadn't really thought about it. There's no chance. It'll either be Eric [*Eric Jeffries, the Chancellor of the Exchequer – Ed.*] or Duncan [*Duncan Short, the Secretary of State for Foreign Affairs – Ed.*]. I started to explain why to Annie. 'You see, it *would* have been Ray, he was Deputy Leader, but as he's had to resign from the Home Office . . .'

I stopped dead. Suddenly I understood. *That* was why the PM resigned! He had always hated Ray. And Ray was his natural successor. So he had just hung on long enough to make sure that Ray didn't get the job.

[*The Prime Minister had probably learned this trick from Clement Attlee, who unquestionably hung on as Prime Minister until Herbert Morrison was out of the running. It has also been suggested that Harold Wilson chose the time of his own surprise resignation to coincide with a period of Denis Healey's unpopularity with the Left of the Labour Party, thus ensuring the succession for James Callaghan. Of course, there is no evidence for this allegation – Ed.*]

I explained this to Annie and Bernard. Bernard was touchingly pleased that the Prime Minister's press statement had been true. 'So the resignation *is* to give time for the new leader to be run in before the next election.'

'Now that the Home Secretary's been run in already,' said Annie with a quiet smile.

Naturally we started to discuss the two likely candidates. They had both buttonholed me after Cabinet this afternoon.

'Eric wants me to support him,' I told them. 'I think he could be the man for the job, he's been quite a successful Chancellor. I've already indicated that I'm on his side.'

Annie was surprised. 'But what about Duncan?'

Duncan is indeed a very real possibility. I nodded. 'Perhaps he should get it. He's done quite well at the Foreign Office, after all. Yes, he could be the man for the job. I think perhaps I'd better give him my support.'

'So you're supporting Eric *and* Duncan?' she enquired innocently.

I was indignant. It's obviously a very difficult choice. 'Look,' I told her, 'if I support Duncan, and *Eric* gets it . . . then, that's it, it's all over for me. But if I support Eric, and *Duncan* gets it . . . that's it too.'

'Then don't support either of them,' she suggested.

If only it were that simple. 'Then, *whichever* of them gets it, that's it!'

She understood. Then she asked me which one I actually am going to support. I told her.

I'll support Eric.

Or Duncan.

December 23rd

Eric wasted no time in lobbying me. I was in my office at lunchtime when he phoned and said he was popping over for a drink.

Eric's a charming man. Tall, elegant, greying hair, with an incisive, intelligent manner. Quite an appealing party leader to offer the electorate, I think. They never see the other side of him – mean-spirited, devious and malicious. He'd hardly set foot in the room when he started rubbishing Duncan.

'Duncan's so divisive. So it really wouldn't be for the good of the party, or the good of the country.'

I still haven't made up my mind and I was struggling to find a way to avoid committing myself. I was starting to say that I didn't see how I could offer Eric my public support, when he explained his position more fully.

His argument, quite simply, is that my support would be crucial for him because I'm universally popular. I must admit that I can see the truth of this. He also emphasised that I have a good public image and that I'm regarded as sound by everyone.

I explained my problem. Well, at least, I didn't explain that I was undecided because of my legitimate anxiety about backing the wrong horse. But I did explain, fully and frankly, that as Chairman of the Party I have to look impartial. [*We note that Hacker's definitions of 'fully' and 'frankly', though in general use in politics, would not correspond with definitions found in the* Oxford English Dictionary *– Ed.*]

Eric played on my feelings of party loyalty. He reminded me that we are both moderates, that we've always had the same objectives for the Party, and that if Duncan got it it would be a disaster.

I knew he'd say all that. But then he surprised me. 'I'll tell you one thing,' he said firmly, 'I wouldn't keep Duncan at the Foreign Office. I'd be looking for a new Foreign Secretary.'

27

The inference was clear. He means me! This is very exciting! But it's still dangerous – what if he were to lose the race? However, I must seize my opportunities. So in conclusion I said to Eric that although I must *appear* impartial I would find ways of hinting at support for him. In a completely impartial way, of course.

So I think perhaps I'll be supporting Eric.

December 24th

Duncan came round to see me at the flat last evening. I got the impression that he'd heard about my little chat with Eric.

Duncan is very different from Eric. Also very bright, he is not devious, malicious or treacherous – he is a straightforward, heavy-handed bully. I began to explain that I ought to be impartial, or at least *look* impartial, as Chairman of the Party.

He brushed that aside in his usual offhand manner. 'As Chairman of the Party you carry more weight than before. And you haven't got any real enemies. Yet.'

The threat was unmistakable. Then he went on to explain what a catastrophe it would be if Eric got into Number Ten. I nodded, which I felt could be interpreted as full agreement, but in fact could also be taken merely as an indication that I could hear what he was saying.

Then, like Eric, he tried the loyalty gambit. He bared his teeth in what he thought was a warm and friendly smile. 'Jim, we're on the same side, aren't we?'

I said yes, as I felt that a yes could simply mean that as members of the same party we must be on the same side. [*Not necessarily – Ed.*] I was scrupulously careful not to tell lies. [*There is, of course, a signifi-cant difference between not telling lies and not telling the truth. 'The truth' in politics means any statement that cannot be proved false – Ed.*]

'Good,' said Duncan. But I'm afraid that he could see my support for him was less than wholehearted, because he added: 'I'm going to win, you know. And I never forgive people who let me down.'

Really, Duncan's not awfully subtle. I pointed out that if I gave him my support I couldn't make it too public.

'It doesn't have to be public,' he answered, 'just as long as every-body knows. Then, when I'm in Number Ten and Eric's in Northern Ireland,' here he chuckled maliciously, 'we know who'll be the next Chancellor, don't we?'

Another job offer! He means me! But, predictably, he couldn't finish the conversation without a threat. 'Unless you fancy Northern Ireland yourself?'

I think perhaps I'll be supporting Duncan.

[*There the matter rested until after the Christmas break. Hacker gave himself a well-earned holiday, and even stopped dictating his notes for his diary. There are one or two undecipherable, slightly slurred cassettes that may have been dictated over the festive season, but we have ascribed their lack of clarity to a faulty cassette recorder.*

Early in the New Year Sir Humphrey Appleby met Sir Arnold Robinson for lunch at the Athenaeum Club. Appleby refers to the lunch in his private diary – Ed.]

It was my first meeting with Arnold since he retired from the Cabinet Office and took on his other onerous duties. I asked him, mischievously, how things are at the Campaign for Freedom of Information. 'I'm sorry,' he said, 'but I can't talk about that.'

Fair enough. Arnold wanted to know whether the new PM was likely to be our eminent Chancellor or our distinguished Foreign Secretary. [*Sir Humphrey used irony extensively, even in his private notes – Ed.*] Funnily enough, this was what I wanted to discuss with Arnold: who, in his opinion, should get Number Ten?

He takes a fairly dim view of them both. He's right, it is a difficult choice, rather like asking which lunatic should run the asylum.

We both agreed that they would present the same problems. They are both interventionists and they would both have foolish notions about running the country themselves if they became Prime Minister.

Arnold asked me if we had any allies. [*Allies, that is, in helping to find a third, more suitable candidate for Number Ten – Ed.*] There is the Chief Whip, of course. He is worried that whichever gets the job will antagonise the other one's supporters and split the party. A very real fear, in my view.

As this could lead to a period of real instability and change [*two things that the Civil Service wishes to avoid at all cost – Ed.*] it is clearly advisable to look for a compromise candidate.

We agreed that such a candidate must have the following qualities: he must be malleable, flexible, likeable, have no firm opinions, no bright ideas, not be intellectually committed, and be without the strength of purpose to change anything. Above all, he must be someone whom we know can be professionally guided [*manipulated – Ed.*], and who is willing to leave the business of government in the hands of the experts.

Only one person seemed to have all these qualifications . . . Hacker! But the idea of his becoming Prime Minister seems, on the face of it, completely laughable. And, what is worse, it would be difficult to achieve.

Nonetheless, we felt that it should be seriously considered for several reasons. Many of the government would welcome a less interventionist leader. The real obstacle will undoubtedly be the two front-runners for the job, but Arnold feels that they might be persuaded to stand aside.

The key to this lies in their MI5 files. I have not yet had a chance to glance at them but Arnold advised me that one should always send for the MI5 files of Cabinet Ministers if one enjoys a good laugh. [*The Cabinet Secretary is the centre of all security operations, and the Cabinet Office contains rooms full of top-secret security information – Ed.*]

BW[1] joined us for a brief cup of coffee, as he had some final DAA files for me to look at. We wished each other a Happy New Year, and then I raised the matter with him.

He was quite astonished when I asked him what he would think of his present master as the next Prime Minister. In fact, he seemed unable to grasp the question for some moments. He kept asking if I meant Mr Hacker, *his* Minister?

AR wanted to know if BW was suggesting that JH was not up to the job of PM. BW seemed unable to frame an appropriate reply. So we explained that there is a considerable body of opinion that can see many advantages in such an appointment. Advantages for Britain. [*By which Sir Humphrey meant advantages for the Civil Service, which in his view represented all that was best about Britain. It is also worth noting that Sir Arnold Robinson's statement that there was a considerable body of opinion in favour might not have been true at that moment, but would definitely have been true by the following morning – Ed.*]

We concluded the meeting by giving BW some firm and clear advice as to what Hacker should not do in the next few weeks if he was to succeed. Essentially, Woolley has to ensure that his Minister does nothing incisive or divisive in the next few weeks, avoids all controversy, and expresses no firm opinion about anything at all.

Bernard felt that this would be no problem. He believes that this is probably what Hacker was planning to do anyway.

[*Hacker's diary continues – Ed.*]

January 2nd

There was a drinks 'do' at the FCO[2] this evening. It was for our European friends. With friends like them . . .

I met an EEC official who seemed awfully Teutonic, and I asked him where he was from.

'From Brussels I have just arrived,' he told me.

I was surprised. 'You're from Belgium?'

'Brussels is in Belgium. That is correct.' The Teutonic mind!

Bernard came to the rescue. 'I think the Minister is asking if you are Belgian?'

The official nodded and smiled. 'No, I am German.'

'And what are you at the EEC?' I asked pleasantly.

'I am still German.'

I reminded myself that patience is a virtue. 'I *know* that,' I said, and looked to Bernard to rescue me again.

[1] Bernard Woolley.
[2] Foreign and Commonwealth Office.

30

'I think the Minister means,' said Bernard carefully, 'what is your job?'

'Ah,' said the Kraut. 'I am a Chef du Division.'

'It's a sort of Assistant Secretary,' Bernard whispered to me.

I wondered, to Bernard, if our German friend (as I have to call him) can help us with our sausage problem. Bernard nodded, and asked him *exactly* what his job is.

He was only too happy to explain. 'My job is concerned with the Common Agricultural Policy. I have to see that the farmers are paid enough money to produce more food.'

This came as a considerable surprise to me. I thought we were producing too much food in the EEC – hence the surpluses. I said as much.

The German nodded significantly. 'Too much food to *eat*, yes!'

I was baffled. 'What else is food for?' I asked him. His eyes lit up with pleasure.

'We do not produce food for eating. Food is a weapon!'

I couldn't exactly see what he meant. 'A weapon?' I said. 'You mean . . .' I searched for the right response, but answer came there none. 'You mean . . . what *do* you mean, exactly?'

It was obvious to him. 'Food is power. Green power.'

I asked if he meant that we fight the Russians with food. He became impatient, and explained that we don't fight the Russians. They are our friends, our customers. We fight the Americans!

I asked him to expand on this theme. He was delighted. His eyes gleamed as he discussed his nation's favourite pastime. 'It is a war,' he began. 'A trade war. Using food we can increase our spheres of influence over Third World countries. You should have seen Dr Kissinger's face when we threatened to sell wheat to Egypt.' He chuckled merrily. 'He wanted Egypt to himself. You see, if the Third World switches from American to European wheat, the US President loses millions of votes in the vest.'

It took me a moment to realise that he was speaking geographically, not sartorially.

'The *Mid*-vest,' he explained. 'So. The Common Agricultural Policy gives us great influence over America, you see? Last war, guns. This war, butter.'

'It's better, butter,' I remarked facetiously and laughed a little. He did not get the joke. [*Such as it was – Ed.*] So I asked what, *precisely*, he did in the food war.

'I ensure that our farmers are subsidised to produce all the food

31

that they can. We have underground silos bursting with agricultural missiles.' We were standing by the buffet, and he started to set up a dinner-table battlefield as an illustration. 'We move a division of butter to Bangladesh, we threaten Egypt with three brigades of wheat. But it is a decoy, you see,' he cried triumphantly. 'We have six airborne divisions of beef waiting to fly into China. Then . . .'

He suddenly paused, and then burst out laughing. Bernard and I stared at him, bemused. Finally I asked him what the joke was.

'It's better, butter,' he chortled. 'Very funny. Very funny.'

Bernard took me by the hand and led me quietly away to another part of the reception, where he presented me to a Monsieur Jean Penglet, who is also a Chef du Division in Brussels.

I speak no German, but I tried out a little French on Monsieur P. 'Vous parlez anglais, Monsieur Penglet?' I enquired poetically.

'I do,' he replied with cool politeness.

'And what do *you* do?' I asked.

'My job,' he said with a patient smile, 'is to deal with food surpluses.'

'You mean, export them or store them?'

He was confused. '*Non* – I pay farmers to see that all surplus food is destroyed.'

Now I was confused. 'Destroyed?' I repeated.

'But of course,' he said with a patronising Gallic shrug. 'Don't you know the Community produces too much food?'

I kept my temper.

'But look, sorry, I don't want to appear dense but that chap there' – I pointed to our humorous friendly German – 'pays farmers to *produce* surplus food. Green power, he says.'

'I know,' he nodded. 'He does a good job. Food is a weapon.'

This was making less and less sense. 'Then *why*,' I demanded, 'do you pay people to destroy it?'

There was no contradiction as far as our French friend was concerned. 'All weapons must be made obsolete. Then you can pay people to produce more. Simple.'

'Can't you just go on storing it?'

He thought that was a silly idea. '*Non*, it is cheaper to destroy the food than to store, liquefy or dehydrate.'

'Or send it across the world?' asked Bernard.

'Exactly.'

The whole Through-The-Looking-Glass approach was becoming clear to me. 'And', I said, 'I suppose you can't sell it at the market price because then the price would fall and the farmers would not make enough money.'

The Frenchman was delighted that I understood. 'Exactly.'

I decided to sum up. 'So, *he* pays French farmers to grow too much food – *you* pay the same French farmers to destroy it!'

He was grinning now. 'Exactly.'

There was just one thing left that I didn't understand. 'Why,' I asked, 'don't we just pay the farmers to sit there and not bother to grow the food at all?'

The Frenchman was offended. 'Monsieur Hacker,' he replied snootily, 'French farmers do not want to be paid for nothing. We do not want charity.'

[*Hacker's xenophobia*[1] *is clear from the above passage. This unattractive ability to see Germans and Frenchmen only in national stereotypes was both a personal weakness and a political strength. We shall see how it became his trump card at a crucial moment in his climb up the greasy pole – Ed.*]

January 3rd

I didn't get to the office till late afternoon today. And, although I had lots to do, somehow I just couldn't concentrate. I felt overwhelmed by the complete futility of it all, of everything we do, in the face of an EEC bureaucracy even more pointless than our own home-grown variety.

I sat behind the desk, musing, lost in my thoughts. Then I realised that Bernard was standing in front of me, trying to attract my attention in his characteristic way.

'Um,' he was saying hopefully.

I stared at him gloomily. 'What's it all *for*, Bernard?' I asked. 'What are we all doing? What's the point of it all?'

He looked momentarily nonplussed. 'I didn't read theology, Minister.'

I tried to explain my concerns to him. 'What I mean is, Bernard, the *waste* of it all. Paying a lot of people to produce masses of food. Paying another lot to destroy it. And paying thousands of bureaucrats to push paper about to make it all happen. Doesn't the futility of it all depress you?'

'Not really,' he replied, slightly puzzled. 'I'm a Civil Servant.'

'But when it's all so pointless? I entered politics to make people's lives happier.'

[1] Hatred of foreigners.

'Oh but they are, Minister.' He was concerned about me now, trying to cheer me up. 'Busy people are much happier than bored people.'

'Even if the work's futile?' I asked despairingly.

'Oh yes,' he replied encouragingly. 'Look at your private office. They're all much happier when you're here and they're busy.'

I couldn't see what he meant. I pointed out that the work in my private office has a purpose.

Bernard sort of disagreed. 'Well, most of it is drafts for statements you don't make, speeches you don't deliver, press releases nobody prints, papers nobody reads, and answers to questions nobody asks you.'

This comment, not without truth, made me even more depressed. I told Bernard that he was saying my job is as futile as the EEC.

He denied this, emphatically. 'Not at all, Minister. You went into politics to make people happy. You are making people happy. You're very popular in the private office. And everywhere else, of course,' he added hastily.

We sat in the conversation area, and discussed the race for the Premiership. 'Bernard,' I began, 'I've been talking to Eric and Duncan. I think I've promised to support Eric's candidature.'

'I see,' he said with interest.

'And then,' I continued, 'I think I promised to support Duncan.'

Bernard looked approving. 'That sounds very even-handed, Minister.'

He'd missed the point. I explained that I can't exactly keep my promise to both of them.

He didn't seem to think that this was anything to worry about. 'They were only political promises, Minister, weren't they?' I nodded. 'Well then,' he said, 'it's like your manifesto promises, isn't it? People understand.'

He's probably right about that. But there is another problem. I'm not sure, now that I think back on my conversations with Eric and Duncan, that either of them made any categorical promises to *me*.

I confessed this to Bernard, slightly concerned that it would make me seem a little inept. But Bernard felt that if they'd made no promises to me, then I didn't really have a deal with either of them. Even if he's right, I still have to decide which of them to support. It's not just a question of picking the winner, because my support may tip the balance. 'So the question is, Bernard, do I want to be Foreign Secretary or Chancellor of the Exchequer?'

I must say, I was genuinely surprised by his reply. 'Neither.'

'Neither? Why not?'

'They're both such terrible jobs.'

I thought at first that Bernard was being rather silly. After all, he was talking about two of the top three jobs in the Cabinet. I explained to him that as he was just a Civil Servant he didn't really understand politics.

He looked contrite and apologised.

'To be a success in politics, Bernard,' I continued, 'you have to be in the limelight. You have a very high political profile if you're the Chancellor. That has to be good for votes. Do you see now?'

It turned out that he saw only too well. He saw lots of things that I hadn't seen. I felt rather embarrassed that I'd patronised him, but I hoped he hadn't noticed.

'The Chancellor is Mr Killjoy,' said Bernard. 'Raising taxes on beer and cigarettes goes down awfully badly with the electorate.' He was right. 'And, Minister, have you considered working with the permanent officials of the Treasury? I believe I'm right if I suggest that you sometimes felt that Sir Humphrey, when Permanent Secretary here, did not always lay all his cards on the table?'

Good old British understatement. But I pointed out to Bernard that, nonetheless, I usually got my way. [*Here Hacker's capacity for believing his own fantasies, essential equipment for all politicians, is clearly shown – Ed.*] Bernard asked me if I had no fears at all about handling the officials at the Treasury.

I was about to reply none, when I realised that I'm not an economist, which meant that they could run rings round me. Also, it suddenly occurred to me that no new economic policy has any visible effect for at least two years – which means that for the first two years as Chancellor you are, in effect, paying for the mistakes of your predecessor. And no one realises that when the economy goes wrong there is *nothing* you can usually do about it. Especially as our economy is governed by the American economy over which I, as Chancellor, would have no control.

Bernard concurred, and added that the grapevine thought that there were shockwaves coming from America.

It was now perfectly clear to me that I shouldn't become the next Chancellor. 'There's no escape in that job, is there?' I said to Bernard.

'No, Minister. Unless, of course, you were sent to the Foreign Office as a punishment.'

I couldn't see what he meant. 'A punishment?'

'The Secretary of State for Foreign and Commonwealth Affairs is an even worse job.'

So that's what he meant. No longer so willing to dismiss Bernard's view out of hand, I stopped to consider this. Did he simply mean that there are no votes in foreign affairs?

'It's not just that, Minister. The Government has to be nice to foreigners but the electorate want you to be nasty to them. For instance, they resent foreign aid to less developed countries while there is unemployment in the Midlands.'

My constituency's in the Midlands! [*The fact that Bernard Woolley gave this example was hardly coincidental – Ed.*] And, once I started to think about it, there are a variety of reasons for avoiding the FO. The Secretary of State for Foreign Affairs has to go gadding about the world, while all the rest of the Cabinet are involved in the nuts and bolts of government policy. The unemployed would see pictures of me on the news eating fancy meals in our Paris Embassy while their hospitals are being closed.

And in terms of world politics, the Foreign Office is virtually irrelevant. We have no real power, we're just a sort of American missile base, that's all.

Bernard commented that the Prime Minister would send the Foreign Secretary out on all the tricky foreign missions – but would go abroad personally and take the limelight if there was any glory to be had.

Nothing new in that. It's the same for the Chancellor. Everyone thinks that Chancellors lose elections but that the Prime Minister wins them. Chancellors never get the credit, only the blame.

I sighed deeply. 'It's a choice between the devil and the deep blue sea,' I told Bernard.

He had an unusual twinkle in his eye. 'Unless . . .' he replied hesitantly . . . 'um, there is, of course, one other option.'

I couldn't think what.

'Do the middle job.'

'No, Bernard,' I said. 'Home Secretary? Don't be daft. Be responsible for all the muggings, jailbreaks and race riots? Thanks a lot.'

'No, Minister, be the one who takes all the credit.'

At first I didn't see what he meant. Then I saw! *Prime Minister!* Bernard is even more ambitious for me than I am for myself! It was more than I had dared hope for, or even think of. But now that Bernard has suggested it to me, I can't get it out of my mind.

I asked him modestly if he was serious. He confirmed that he was. 'Why not, Minister? Now that you've considered the various possibilities, it does all seem to be pointing in one direction.'

The major problem is that I'm literally up to my neck in the Euro-sausage. [*Not literally, we presume – Ed.*] But if that problem could be solved . . .

Anyway, I thanked Bernard. I told him that it had been a most useful conversation and that I would have to consider whether or not my candidature was a serious possibility.

Bernard said that, of course, it was not for him to say, being a mere civil servant. But he suggested that I should consider asking my Parliamentary Under-Secretary[1] to stand in for me at tomorrow's Guildhall ceremony. It seems that there is likely to be an anti-government protest in the street on arrival, and he suggested that this might not be the time to be seen in a controversial context or hostile environment.

He's absolutely right, and I followed his advice. I told him that he was getting more like Sir Humphrey every day.

'Thank you, Minister, I see that as a compliment.'

'You must have very good eyesight,' I joked. But he was right. It was.

[*While Bernard Woolley, acting on Sir Humphrey's instructions, was planting the seed of Prime Ministerial ambitions in the fertile and plentiful soil inside Hacker's head, and ensuring that Hacker avoided all controversy, Sir Humphrey himself was not idle. He telephoned Jeffrey Pearson, the Chief Whip, and invited him to a secret meeting at the Cabinet Office. There is no record of this conversation in Sir Humphrey's private papers, perhaps because of its sensitive nature and security implications. Jeffrey Pearson, being a politician, had no such scruples, and the conversation is reported in his elegant memoirs* Suck It And See *– Ed.*]

I got a phone call from Sir Humphrey Appleby, the Cabinet Secretary, asking how the race for the leadership looked from the Whips' Office.

He knew the grim prospect only too well. If Eric got Number Ten there would have been a split in the party in three months. If Duncan, there would have been a split in three weeks.

He gave me some startling information. He revealed that there were security question marks over both candidates. I pressed him for details but he said that he could say no more. The only person he could disclose this to,

[1] Hacker's junior minister.

in the PM's absence,[1] and since it was essentially a party matter, was the Chairman of the Party. [*Jim Hacker – Ed.*]

He had invited Hacker to a meeting in the Cabinet Office, and wanted me to be there also. Naturally I accepted. He also asked me to suggest a compromise candidate. My first thought was that it could be any one of half a dozen.

Sir Humphrey asked if I'd considered the Party Chairman himself. The idea of Jim Hacker as Prime Minister, though it struck me as ludicrous at first, rapidly became an idea that was really no worse than any other. After all, who *is* fit for the job? You never know, till you suck it and see.

Sir Humphrey pointed out that there have been less likely Prime Ministers. I wonder who. [*Extensive research suggests that Sir Humphrey must have been referring to the Marquis of Bute – Ed.*]

[*Hacker's diary continues – Ed.*]

January 4th

I got a message to see Sir Humphrey urgently, in his office. To my surprise Jeffrey Pearson, the Chief Whip, was also there. A big burly man, with twinkling eyes just visible behind huge heavy-framed glasses topped by a shiny bald head which reflected the overhead chandelier. I felt I should have brought my sunglasses.

Humphrey was at his most courteous. 'So good of you to call, Minister. I have a problem. I need your help.'

'Can't you run the country on your own?' I asked.

He was not amused. 'Yes, it *is* rather a grave matter, I'm afraid.'

I became grave at once.

'It's about the leadership election. The PM felt that he had no alternative but to call you in.'

So it was *that* bad. I nodded, and waited. Then he said something that I couldn't quite get the hang of – perhaps I wasn't concentrating properly.

[*Sir Humphrey's remarks that Hacker couldn't follow are recorded in a minute, reproduced opposite, which Sir Humphrey sent to the Prime Minister shortly after the meeting with Hacker – Ed.*]

---

[1] The Prime Minister, having announced his resignation, went abroad on what were ostensibly goodwill visits to friendly countries. In reality he was setting up a lucrative lecture tour and some profitable consultancies.

70 WHITEHALL, LONDON SW1A 2AS

Memorandum
To: The Prime Minister
From: The Secretary of the Cabinet

> I informed Mr Hacker that there are certain items
> of confidential information which while they are
> in theory susceptible of innocent interpretation do
> nevertheless contain a sufficient element of ambiguity,
> so that, should they be presented in a less than
> generous manner to an uncharitable mind, they might
> be a source of considerable embarrassment, and even -
> conceivably - hazard, were they to impinge upon the
> deliberations of an office of more than usual
> sensitivity.

[*Hacker's diary continues – Ed.*]

Jeffrey Pearson explained that Humphrey was talking about security.

'Security?' I repeated, puzzled. 'What do you mean?'

'Secrets,' he said.

I tried to conceal my impatience. Obviously I know what security *means*. But what did Humphrey mean? Exactly.

'I'm not allowed to know,' said Jeffrey.

'Why not?' I asked.

'Security,' he replied.

I turned to Humphrey for clarification. For once, he obliged. He explained to me that, as in the Prime Minister's absence I was deputising on party matters, he needed me to look at the Security file on the Chancellor of the Exchequer. He was not allowed to give me the whole file, but only to show me the relevant items.

He then showed me some astonishing pieces of paper. Reports on Eric from the Security officers, from the Special Branch, an interview with his driver, and a confidential memo from the PM himself.

I really can't go into the details here. This information is dynamite, and if the wrong person were to get their hands on this cassette [*Hacker always dictated his diaries into a cassette recorder – Ed.*] it would be disastrous for Eric. Suffice to say that Eric had never struck me as a sex maniac or a dirty old man, and I simply can't imagine how a workaholic like him finds the time for everything that I read about today.

Sir Humphrey has an explanation. 'My experience is that people who are highly active in one area of life tend to be equally active in all the other areas.'

'I mean, to look at him you couldn't think that he went in for . . .' I was stuck for a sufficiently delicate phrase.

Sir Humphrey supplied it. 'I believe the current expression is horizontal jogging, Minister.'

I pointed out that all of this horizontal jogging had happened a while ago, and none of it proved conclusively that Eric had breached security.

Humphrey readily agreed. 'That's why the PM thought it all right for him to be Chancellor. But in view of the Yugoslav one . . . and the South Africans . . . not to mention the shady lady from Argentina . . . and it's thought that she's just a cover, by the way.'

This was even more mind-boggling. A cover? What on earth *for*? If these 'ladies' are a cover story, I can't imagine what his real requirements are.

Nor can Humphrey, apparently. But it is clear that Defence or the Foreign Office might be a little too delicate for such a minister. And if Eric became PM he'd be head of the Security Services as well. I could see why old Humphrey was worried. It would be unthinkable.

'So,' I said, 'what you're saying is, it's got to be Duncan.'

Sir Humphrey hesitated. Then he reached across his desk for another Top Secret file. 'I was coming to that,' he replied carefully. 'This is the Foreign Secretary's file.'

Another staggering pile of paper! More from the Special Branch. And from the Fraud Squad, and the Inland Revenue. Secret auditors' reports. Letters from the Bank of England Foreign Exchange Division.

It took longer to read and grasp the essentials of this file. I wondered if everything revealed in it could be technically legal.

Sir Humphrey nodded judiciously. '*Technically*, maybe. But it certainly ruled him out of consideration for the Treasury.'

I suddenly got a little paranoid. I wonder if there were reports like this on me in the Cabinet Office. [*Definitely – Ed.*] Not that anyone could suspect me of this sort of impropriety. [*This is almost certainly true. Hacker's private life was fairly dull – Ed.*] I asked Humphrey how they found out so much about Duncan's finances.

He evaded the question. 'Let's just say it's all been gone into quite enough.' Like the shady lady, I suppose.

I suppose that MI5 is behind all these investigations. Though Sir Humphrey's line on MI5 is that it doesn't exist. 'We do not admit that it exists. But if it did exist, which of course it does not, its title would actually be DI5. Which, since it does not in any case exist, is never used.'

I don't believe a word of that. I'm sure MI5 exists. [*Hacker was right. Sir Humphrey was giving Hacker the official disinformation, which is devised to try to confuse MI5 watchers – Ed.*]

I must admit that I was totally amazed by everything I'd read about my colleagues Eric and Duncan. I turned to the Chief Whip. 'Isn't this amazing?' I said.

He was now looking irritable as well as shiny. 'I don't know,' he snapped. 'I haven't seen it.'

I apologised and turned back to Humphrey. 'Humphrey,' I said, 'I don't want you to think me stupid . . .'

'Perish the thought, Minister,' he replied, a little slow on cue, I thought.

'But,' I went on, 'why is the Chief Whip here if he's not allowed to see these classified files?'

Jeffrey gave me the answer himself. 'We, the Party, dare not risk these scandals coming to light – if they are as embarrassing as you both seem to think. It could be a deep embarrassment to both the country and the Party if either of them were Head of Government. We don't want to be caught with our trousers down.'

Not like Eric. I didn't say that though, it was all far too serious. I simply remarked that the situation was serious.

'Very serious,' agreed Jeffrey.

'Very serious,' echoed Sir Humphrey.

We gazed thoughtfully at each other. 'So,' I asked, 'what *could* happen if either of them were elected PM?'

'Something very serious indeed,' replied Sir Humphrey carefully.

'Very serious,' agreed Jeffrey.

'I see,' I said, and waited.

'Serious repercussions,' mumbled the Chief Whip.

Sir Humphrey nodded. '*Serious* repercussions,' he emphasised.

'Of the utmost seriousness,' added Jeffrey, clarifying the situation.

'In fact,' said Sir Humphrey seriously, 'I would go so far as to say that it could hardly be *more* serious.'

We all fell silent. So I decided to sum it up. 'I think we're all agreed then,' I said. 'This is serious.'

They nodded. We were all in agreement.

The question was, what should happen next? Jeffrey had an answer. 'We've got to have another candidate. Quick.'

'The Chief Whip,' murmured Humphrey, 'wondered if you had any ideas.'

'As you're the Party Chairman,' explained Jeffrey.

Naturally Bernard's words were ringing in my ears. Why not go for the top job? Be the one who gets all the credit. But I couldn't suggest myself right away. They might think that I had delusions of grandeur. So I assumed a look of studied thought.

'It's pretty difficult,' I said. 'We're looking for someone pretty remarkable – a potential Prime Minister. Someone's who's sound.'

'Flexible,' added Sir Humphrey.

'Yes,' I agreed. 'And normal,' I remarked, bearing Eric's pre-dilections in mind, and knowing that I was unassailable on that score.

'And,' Jeffrey reminded us forcefully, wearing his Chief Whip's hat, 'someone who's acceptable to both wings of the Party.'

'And someone who understands how to take advice, Minister,' concluded Humphrey.

The Cabinet Secretary and the Chief Whip looked at me politely, waiting for my suggestion. But I was not willing to suggest myself, just in case I'd misread the signs.

Finally Jeffrey spoke. 'Have you considered doing the job yourself?'

I pretended to be completely astonished. '*Me*?'

'Why not?' enquired Sir Humphrey.

'Wouldn't you want to be Prime Minister?' asked Jeffrey.

I decided to be modest. I explained that I'd love it, but that I was not sure that I actually could do it.

Humphrey seemed to accept this *far* too easily. 'Perhaps this was not a good idea after all,' he said, turning to Jeffrey.

I was forced to ask Humphrey what he meant. 'Perhaps you do not feel, Minister, that you are absolutely Prime Ministerial calibre.'

I told Humphrey, very firmly, that I think that there is no doubt about *that*. Modesty forbids, but I have absolutely no doubt about my ability to do the job.

But Jeffrey said there was a fly in the ointment. 'You are a bit of an outsider. Unless you can stage-manage some sort of public success in the next few days.'

I suggested that I merely start campaigning, and let people know I want the job.

'Quite the reverse, I think,' said Jeffrey. 'Better to let people know you don't want it.'

I wondered if that would be enough. Jeffrey and Sir Humphrey were quite sure it would be provided that I let *everybody* know that I don't want it. Jeffrey offered to manage my campaign. If anyone asks me, I am simply to say that I have no ambitions in that direction.

And if anyone tries to trap me by asking if I'd *refuse* to stand, Humphrey advised me that on previous occasions a generally acceptable answer has been that, while one does not seek the office, one has pledged oneself to the service of one's country and if one's colleagues persuaded one that that was the best way one could serve, one might reluctantly have to accept the responsibility, whatever one's own private wishes might be. (I wrote it down at the time.)

Finally, we got to the question of the election. It seemed to me that it would inevitably be a three-way election. But the Chief Whip thinks differently. He wants an unopposed election. Unity always goes down well with the public, and the Party would welcome a little unity too.

But there are two more flies in the ointment, namely Eric and Duncan. I suddenly realised the relevance of the Security files – my two opponents have to be persuaded to withdraw. I asked Jeffrey if he was planning to have a word with them both.

'I can't.' He was insistent. 'I haven't seen the files.'

I asked Humphrey.

'No, Minister. It is an internal party matter. It would be most improper.'

The full horror of it now dawned upon me. They wanted *me* to force Eric and Duncan to withdraw. They want me to tell one of my colleagues that he's a swindler and the other that he's a pervert. I refused.

Humphrey said that I needn't say that at all, not in so many words. 'You can just let them know you know something.'

43

It seemed hopeless. 'They'll tell me to mind my own bloody business.'

Jeffrey intervened. 'If they do, you must say that as Party Chairman it's your duty to see that, if they stand, this information reaches those who need to know. The Party executive, its major contributors and elder statesmen. The Palace, perhaps. You must tell each of them that he has no alternative but to pull out and support someone who will . . . protect him.'

I could hardly believe my ears. Jeffrey wanted me to *protect* them?

Humphrey concurred, remarking that their private lives are nobody else's business as long as security is not involved.

I didn't quite have the stomach for this talk. Regretfully I told Humphrey and Jeffrey that I wouldn't . . . *couldn't* do this. But Humphrey wasn't prepared to listen. He told me that, now that I know about them, I have no choice.

'As no one else knows that I know,' I said firmly, 'I intend to forget all about it.'

Then Humphrey dropped his bombshell. 'That would be very courageous of you, Minister.'

I was appalled! Courageous? I don't want to do anything *courageous*! That's the kind of thing that finishes careers.

Sir Humphrey remained calm. 'If something were to happen and later it were to emerge that you had had the information and suppressed it . . .'

I interrupted. 'Do you mean you'd leak it?' I was aghast!

Humphrey did not answer my question. 'It would be seen as covering up for your chums. Greater love hath no man than this, that he should lay down his career . . .'

I told him to stop threatening me.

He tried to soothe me. 'No, Minister, I'm helping you.'

Jeffrey mopped his shining forehead and blotted the top of his head. 'You see, Jim, there is one other quality that Prime Ministers need. The killer instinct.'

He's right. The killer instinct. But do I have it? We'll see. Now that I know about Eric and Duncan, I have no choice but to stab them in the back.

Or the front.

Oh my God!

January 5th

Believing that there is no time like the present I rang Duncan this morning. I told him that I had something urgent to discuss with him about the contest for the Premiership. I refused to be drawn on the phone. Indeed, I could hardly have said what I had to say over the phone. But I tried to sound cheerful so that he'd think I had good news.

He cancelled some appointments and showed up here at the flat after dinner. I poured him a small Scotch and me a large Scotch, and we sat in front of the fire. I'd warned Annie and Lucy[1] to make themselves scarce.

Duncan was unusually cheerful. He raised his glass. 'Here's to Number Ten, eh?'

'Thanks,' I said, without thinking. He gave me a funny look. I corrected myself somehow, drank up my Scotch and poured myself another biggie. I turned from the sideboard to see Duncan eyeing me with suspicion.

'What's up, Jim?'

'Duncan, I have a . . . a problem.'

'You're not going to support me?'

The conversation was getting out of control and it had only just begun. I drank my next large Scotch, and told him that some information had come my way. Serious information. To do with his personal financial operations.

Of course he pretended he didn't know what I meant. So I referred to the collapse of Continental and General, which he said was just bad luck, and I mentioned earlier transfers of funds to Directors' nominee companies, to which he replied that there was nothing wrong with that.

I replied that technically there wasn't, but if you looked at it in conjunction with a similar case at Offshore Securities . . .

I let that remark hang in the air, unfinished.

Duncan swallowed. 'Where did you get all this?'

I didn't answer. But I indicated that, if he stayed in the running for PM, I would be obliged to share my knowledge with senior members of the party, the Revenue, the Fraud Squad, and so forth. 'Not that it would matter if it's all above board,' I added innocently, 'and I'm sure it is if you say it is. But the Americans would also have to know. And Her Majesty . . .'

He took a drink and considered his position. 'There was nothing improper,' he said. Not a very convincing denial.

'Fine,' I said cheerfully. 'If that's what you say, I'll feel free to talk

[1] Hacker's daughter.

about it to them all. Bring it all out in the open.'

He panicked. 'Hang on! Financial matters can be misinterpreted. People get hold of the wrong end of the stick.'

I sipped my drink and waited. It didn't take long. It transpired that, according to Duncan, he didn't really want Number Ten at all. He said he'd never wanted it really. He felt the Foreign Office was a much better job in many ways. He wanted to assure me that he had only wanted Number Ten to keep Eric out. 'I just want to make one thing clear – I won't support Eric!' he insisted hotly.

I suggested that Eric might not get it. 'How would it be if you transferred all your support to someone else?'

Duncan looked blank. 'Who?'

'It would be a question of finding someone who recognised your qualities. Someone who'd want you to stay on as Foreign Secretary. Someone who would be discreet about Continental and General. Someone you trust. An old friend.'

I thought for a moment I'd overplayed it. I'm an old acquaintance of Duncan's but scarcely an old friend. And clearly there's no one he trusts. No one at all.

But he sat there, staring at me, and I smiled back at him, and gradually I saw it dawning upon him.

'Do you mean – you?' he asked.

I pretended surprise. 'Me? I have absolutely no ambitions in that direction.'

'You do mean you,' he observed quietly. He knows the code.

Perhaps I do have the killer instinct.

January 6th

Today I dispatched my other colleague and rival. It's all proving much easier than I thought.

Eric came for a drink at the House.[1] This time I found I was able to come to the point much more quickly. I have tasted blood now. I certainly believe that, having killed once, it's much easier for a murderer to kill again.

Anyway, I told him what I knew, roughly. He went pale and downed his Scotch. I offered him another.

'Yes please,' he said quietly. 'I need a stiff one.' Actually, that doesn't seem to be his problem. I asked him if he realised that his position was . . . serious.

---

[1] of Commons.

Grimly, he said that he saw that only too well. 'And,' he said, eyeing me bitterly, 'you're not going to help me, right?'

'Yes,' I said.

He was confused. 'Yes you are or yes you're not?'

'Yes,' I said, and hastily added: 'Yes I'm going to help you. But not to get elected Prime Minister.'

'You said you were.'

Really, how could he not see that things are quite different now? I patiently pointed out that my offer to help him predated my knowledge of the shady lady from Argentina. And others.

'Look, Eric, as Party Chairman I have my duty. It would be a disaster for the party if you were PM and it came out.' I realised that there was an unintentional innuendo there, so I hurried on. 'I mean, I wouldn't care to explain your private life to Her Majesty, would you?'

'I'll withdraw,' he muttered.

About time too, I thought. If he practised withdrawal a little more often he wouldn't be in this predicament now. But I told him reassuringly that we would say no more about it. To anyone.

He thanked me nastily and snarled that he supposed that bloody Duncan would now get Number Ten.

'Not if I can help it,' I told him.

'Who then?'

I raised my glass to him, smiled and said, 'Cheers.'

The penny dropped. And so did his lower jaw. He was staggered! 'You don't mean – you?' he gasped.

Again I put on my surprised face. 'Me?' I said innocently. 'Our children are approaching the age when Annie and I are thinking of spending much more time with each other.'

He understood perfectly. 'You *do* mean you.'

This *is* fun!

January 9th

Events are moving fast. Although Eric and Duncan are both out of the running, no one knows that but me, Humphrey and Bernard. The trouble is, although they're out of the running, I'm not yet *in* the running. I do need some sort of public success to swing the party *my* way at the crucial moment, so that the others can plausibly drop out.

My big problem remained. I was stuck with the awful Eurosausage hot potato, and somehow I've got to pull something rather good out of the hat. Or out of the delicatessen.

47

But we took a big step along that path today and, I must say, to give credit where credit is due, old Humphrey was quite a help.

Apparently Maurice, the European Commissioner who landed me with this mess, was in London yesterday. And Humphrey found out that his flight was delayed and managed to fix a brief meeting with him.

I was summoned to an urgent meeting in Humphrey's inner sanctum at the Cabinet Office. The only problem was that it was all arranged at such short notice that I only got there moments before Maurice himself arrived. So I had no idea what Humphrey's strategy was, or what I was to say or anything. Humphrey simply whispered to me that he hoped to persuade Maurice to solve our little sausage problem, that I was to leave the talking to Humphrey but give him support when he asked for it.

Maurice arrived all smiles. 'Jeem, to what do I owe zis pleasure?'

Of course, I didn't know the answer to that. But Humphrey rescued me at once.

Sitting us all down in his conversation area, Humphrey began by explaining (wholly untruthfully) that I had asked him to arrange the meeting to see if he could help us with a problem. Of course, it wasn't a *real* lie, more a white lie really – the whole convention of our government is that when Civil Servants think of a good idea they give the credit to the Minister. Quite right too – we take the blame for all their mistakes, we certainly deserve the credit for their occasional good ideas!

Anyway, I nodded, and echoed that we had a problem. Maurice said of course he'd help.

'The problem is,' said Humphrey smoothly, 'that the EEC is becoming very unpopular over here.' He turned to me. 'Isn't that so, Minister?'

No problem there. 'Yes,' I said.

Maurice knows this already. 'And you want to restore its image?' he asked.

'Yes,' I said, jumping the gun.

'No,' said Humphrey firmly.

'No,' I corrected myself hastily, resolving not to speak again until it was quite clear what Humphrey wanted me to say.

Humphrey continued. 'The problem is that the Minister feels there would be more votes – that is, he would be better expressing the views of the British people – by joining the attack on the EEC rather than leaping to its defence.'

He looked at me. I was happy to agree with that. Furthermore, it was actually true!

I was surprised how much this threat upset Maurice. It can't have been news to him. But he seemed quite appalled. 'But . . . your government is committed to support us,' he expostulated, glaring at me.

I wasn't quite sure how to answer this, as I hadn't yet got Humphrey's drift. But Humphrey came to the rescue again.

'The Minister's point, as I understand it, is that the government's commitment is to the concept and the treaty.'

'Treaty,' I repeated firmly.

'But it is not committed,' Humphrey was quite adamant here, 'to the institutions. Or to the practices. Or to individual policies. You were giving me an instance, just now, weren't you, Minister?'

He looked at me. This was my cue. But I couldn't imagine what he wanted me to say. He must have seen the panic in my eyes. 'About food production,' he hinted.

I suddenly saw the plan! 'Yes.' I fixed Maurice with my tough gimlet-eyed gaze. 'I discovered recently that one of your staff spends all his time paying people to produce food, and the man in the next office spends all his time paying people to destroy it.'

Maurice was outraged. 'That's not true.'

Humphrey and I were surprised. A barefaced denial? How could this be, we'd had the story from the horses' mouths.

'Not true?' queried Humphrey.

'No,' said Maurice. 'He's not in the next office. Not even on the same floor.'

'The Minister has hundreds of similar examples of the EEC's nonsensical behaviour,' continued Humphrey inexorably.

'Hundreds,' I agreed, trying to remember another.

'And the nub of the problem, Maurice, is that the Minister is beginning to think that some member of the Cabinet ought to start telling the British people about them.'

Maurice was angry now. 'But that would be intolerable,' he cried. 'Even the Italians would not stoop so low.'

I saw my chance, and went for the jugular. 'The Italians are not being asked to redesignate salami as Emulsified High-Fat Offal Tube.'

Our cards were on the table. Was Maurice going to pick up the ball and run with it? Yes, he grasped the nettle with both hands. [*Yet again Hacker's mixed metaphors give us a special insight into the*

49

quality of intellectual coherence in the mind of one of our great national leaders – Ed.]

'What', enquired Maurice carefully, 'are you proposing? After all, we are committed to harmonisation. We cannot call it the sausage. What do you suggest?'

I had no idea at all. What do you call a sausage if you can't call it a sausage? The whole point was that we *should* be able to call it a sausage. But I should have realised – Humphrey had thought ahead.

'Politics is about presentation. Can't we call it the British Sausage?' he murmured.

A brilliant idea. Maurice tried it out in a few of the EEC languages. 'Saucisson anglais . . . Salsicce inglese . . . Britischerwurst.' Dreadful show-offs, these Continentals. 'Mmm, yes, I think we could recommend that to the Commission.'

Of course he could. It was an offer he couldn't refuse.

We wrapped up the meeting, all agreeing furiously that the EEC is an absolutely splendid institution. I even kissed Maurice on both cheeks.

After he left, I had a long think. Humphrey and Bernard suggested that I call a press conference of all the European correspondents, to tell them that I've solved the Eurosausage problem.

But I have a much better idea. Solved problems aren't news stories. For the press, bad news is good news. So why should I give them such a non-story? A solved Eurosausage problem is not going to catapult one into the leadership of the Party – the public doesn't even know the problem exists, so why should they care if I solve it? No, I've decided that tomorrow I shall give them news of a disaster. They'll love that. Then when I give them a triumph a few days later I'll be a hero.

January 10th
Today I held an off-the-record, non-attributable briefing with the European correspondents.

The lobby system really is invaluable. The hacks are keen to get a story, yet lazy enough to accept almost anything that we feed them. I told them that we had a big problem coming up with Brussels. Since they'd be hearing about it anyway some day soon, I told them I'd level with them now and give them the whole embarrassing story. They lapped it up!

'Brussels', I said, 'is going to make the British sausage illegal under EEC regulations.'

Bernard looked very worried, and passed me a hurried note reminding me that the EEC plan was not to illegalise the British sausage, but merely to prevent us *calling* it a sausage.

I crumpled up his note decisively. Bernard just doesn't understand politics. [*Though he did understand the difference between truth and falsehood – Ed.*]

I threw the meeting open to questions. The first question picked up the same point. 'What do you mean, *illegal*?'

I qualified my answer. 'Effectively illegal,' I replied. 'Pork sausages will have to be seventy-five per cent lean pork, and beef sausages too.'

Somebody from *The Sun* asked if beef sausages will have to be seventy-five per cent lean pork, too. Typical lobby correspondent. If he was the sole entrant in an intelligence contest, he'd come third.

I explained that insisting that sausages contained seventy-five per cent lean meat would put them in the luxury foods bracket. The implications for the average wage-earner were all too clear.

One of them asked when this was to be promulgated. I told him: next month. Then, cunningly, I added that the EEC will probably deny it at the moment. In fact, they will probably try to tell the British press that they are only discussing changing the name of the sausage.

Finally, one of the reporters asked me what the government is going to do about it. I looked despairing, pathetic and helpless, and told him that I had no idea, that it is a big problem, and that I wouldn't pretend that we have an answer.

Then I sent them all out into the waiting room so that the Press Office could ply them with drinks. As they left, Bernard cornered me. 'Minister! You realise the press will be printing something that isn't true?'

'Really?' I smiled at him. 'How frightful!'

January 12th

It all went like clockwork. The story about the outlawed sausage has been all over the front pages for the last two days. It's caused a major political storm. All the commentators and pundits have been saying that, with the government and the party leaderless, the sausage could be a banana skin.

Everyone's been saying that the succession is also unclear. Jeffrey has been quoted all week as an Unofficial Spokesman, an Informed Source, Feelings in the Party, Sources Close to the Leadership, and as a Growing Body of Opinion. His fingerprints are all over the stories in the press saying that the party is increasingly troubled by the fact that the two obvious candidates for the leadership represent the extreme wings of the party.

I've been leaking a little myself, to the effect that pressure is mounting for both Eric and Duncan to withdraw in favour of a compromise candidate. Unfortunately, the lobby correspondents to whom I've been chatting have not had the sense to name me as the aforesaid compromise, but have foolishly added their own comments to the effect that none of the contenders has so far caught the public imagination. It is astonishing how you have to spell *everything* out to journalists. And not only can't they draw the simplest conclusions, they can't even quote me correctly: I actually said 'moderate' not 'compromise'.

I've planned a big press turnout for my constituency speech tomorrow night. BBC News and ITN are going to be there. Bernard asked me why they were so interested in fire and safety policy in government.

I didn't answer. But I'm sure he will not be surprised if I talk about other issues as well.

[*Hacker's big speech did indeed attract a full press, radio and TV turnout. 'Sources Close to the Minister' had hinted that he was going to make a major policy speech, and it was clear to all in Fleet Street that this meant that he was mounting a bid for the leadership. Much was to hang on how well Hacker's speech went that night. The result was exactly as Hacker had hoped and planned, as can be detected from the triumphant tone of his diary – Ed.*]

January 13th

I have a feeling that tonight I clinched the leadership of the Party and, if I did, it's only a matter of time before I'm in Number Ten. Today was Friday the thirteenth, and thirteen is my lucky number. [*But perhaps not the United Kingdom's – Ed.*]

There were several bursts of applause during my speech, some lasting for up to half a minute, and at the end I sat down to cheers and a standing ovation. The last part of the speech really got them going. I think I might have a future as a major demagogue.

[*The original typescript of the speech has been lost, so we cannot publish it in full. However, we can reproduce a transcript of the last section of it – taken from the BBC Nine O'Clock News recording. Audience reaction is marked – Ed.*]

THE ATTACHED TRANSCRIPT WAS TYPED FROM A RECORDING AND NOT
COPIED FROM AN ORIGINAL SCRIPT. BECAUSE OF THE RISK OF
MISHEARING THE BBC CANNOT VOUCH FOR ITS COMPLETE ACCURACY.

'NINE O'CLOCK NEWS' 'NEWSNIGHT'

TRANSMISSION: JANUARY 13th

ACTUALITY:

THE RT HON. JAMES HACKER MP: I'm a good European.
I believe in Europe. I believe in the European ideal!
Never again shall we repeat the bloodshed of two World Wars.
Europe is here to stay.
        But, this does not mean that we have to bow the knee
to every directive from every bureaucratic Bonaparte in
Brussels. We are a sovereign nation still and proud of it.
(APPLAUSE)
        We have made enough concessions to the European
Commissar for agriculture. And when I say Commissar, I use
the word advisedly. We have swallowed the wine lake, we
have swallowed the butter mountain, we have watched our
French 'friends' beating up British lorry drivers carrying
good British lamb to the French public.
We have bowed and scraped, doffed our caps, tugged our
forelocks and turned the other cheek. But I say enough is
enough! (PROLONGED APPLAUSE)

- 1 -

53

BRITISH BROADCASTING CORPORATION

(CONT) The Europeans have gone too far. They are now threatening the British sausage. They want to standardise it - by which they mean they'll force the British people to eat salami and bratwurst and other garlic-ridden greasy foods that are TOTALLY ALIEN to the British way of life. (CRIES OF 'HEAR HEAR', 'RIGHT ON', AND 'YOU TELL 'EM, JIM')

Do you want to eat salami for breakfast with your egg and bacon? I don't. And I won't! (MASSIVE APPLAUSE)

They've turned our pints into litres and our yards into metres, we gave up the tanner and the threepenny bit, the two bob and half crown. But they cannot and will not destroy the British sausage! (APPLAUSE AND CHEERS)

Not while I'm here. (TUMULTUOUS APPLAUSE)

In the words of Martin Luther: 'Here I stand. I can do no other' (HACKER SITS DOWN. SHOT OF LARGE CROWD RISING TO ITS FEET IN APPRECIATION).

[*The following day Hacker was interviewed by Ludovic Kennedy, the well-known television interviewer. We have been fortunate in obtaining the complete transcript from BBC Television, and reproduce it below – Ed.*]

[1] Sixpenny piece.
[2] Threepenny piece
[3] Two shilling piece.
[4] Two shillings and sixpenny piece.

THE ATTACHED TRANSCRIPT WAS TYPED FROM A RECORDING AND NOT
COPIED FROM AN ORIGINAL SCRIPT. BECAUSE OF THE RISK OF
MISHEARING THE BBC CANNOT VOUCH FOR ITS COMPLETE ACCURACY.

TRANSMISSION: JANUARY 14th

ACTUALITY:

KENNEDY: Your speech was strong stuff, Mr Hacker.

HACKER: Well, it's something I feel very strongly
about. In fact, I sometimes wonder whether you media people
really appreciate how strongly the rest of us feel about our
country and our way of life. We love it and we're proud of it.

KENNEDY: So you're at odds with Government policy
over the EEC?

HACKER: I'm very happy with Government policy,
Sir Ludovic. Sorry. Mr Kennedy. It has never been Government
policy to abolish the British sausage. Sausages are not just
good to eat, you know. They're full of top-quality nourishment.

KENNEDY: Brussels has denied ever wanting to
abolish the British sausage.

HACKER: Well, they would, wouldn't they? They
know what they're up against. They know the strength of British
public opinion.

KENNEDY: Minister, your speech certainly got a
lot of coverage and a lot of praise. Was there any significance
in its timing?

- 1 -

BRITISH BROADCASTING CORPORATION

```
HACKER:              (CONT) What do you mean?

KENNEDY:             With your Party looking for a new leader.
After all, your name has been mentioned by a few people.

HACKER:              Quite a lot of people, actually. But
no.  Absolutely not.  I have no ambitions in that direction.

KENNEDY:             You mean, you wouldn't let your name go
forward?

HACKER:              Well, Ludo ... all I've ever wanted to do
is serve my country.  I've never sought office.  But I suppose
that if my colleagues were to persuade me that the best place to
serve it from was Ten Downing Street, then I might reluctantly
have to accept the responsibility, whatever my own private
wishes might be.

KENNEDY:             So, if you're not in the running, who
will you be voting for?

HACKER:              Well, of course, it's too early to say.
But what I will say is that I see this as a time for healing.  A
time to stress what we agree about, not what we disagree about.
We need to see the good things in our opponents, not to keep
looking for their faults.  There's good in everyone, you know,
Ludo.

KENNEDY:             Except the French.

HACKER:              Except the Fre ... No, even the French.
```

[Hacker's diary continues – Ed.]

January 18th

I've been too anxious to do anything these last three days. Even making notes for the diary was too great a strain. But today I made it! I'm it! I'm in! I did it! I got it! I won!

I'll try to recount the last events of the leadership campaign in a coherent manner.

56

The committee held the annual meeting today. The ad hoc party leadership committee, that is. Eric and Duncan withdrew after the success of my speech put me unexpectedly at the front of the race. Of course, rather than vote for each other, they now both promised to put their weight behind me. As I've got them both by the balls, this was no surprise to me, though it impressed everyone else no end!

So today the only issue was whether or not the Parliamentary Party was going to put up another candidate to oppose me. If so, we would have had to have an election.

I called both Eric and Duncan this morning, to check that they were supporting me. They were both slightly equivocal. It was still possible for them to withdraw and support someone else. In which case I'd *probably* have won the election, but the agony would have been prolonged by another two or three weeks – and who knows what might have happened in that time? If a week is a long time in politics, three weeks is an eternity.

Then I went to Humphrey's office and we waited, all through lunch, Humphrey and me. Would the phone never ring? There were two phones on his desk. I asked him which one they'd ring on.

'This one, probably,' he replied. Then, after a moment's thought: 'Or this one. Either, really.'

I was none the wiser. Even that information was denied me. I told Humphrey that I'd just sit and relax. As I sat his intercom buzzed, sending me three feet into the air. Bernard had arrived.

'Minister,' he told me reverently, 'the Palace has been on the phone.'

'The Palace?'

'They're checking with all the possible candidates, to see if they'd be free to kiss hands[1] at five o'clock. That's only in the event of an unopposed recommendation, of course.'

I told Bernard that I thought I could probably make time for it.

We sat and waited. And then I made a spontaneous and generous suggestion which I think I regret already. I asked Bernard to be my Principal Private Secretary at Number Ten, should I become PM.

His reply was characteristically ambiguous. 'Oh Minister. Gosh!' But he smiled and went a little pink.

Pleased, I turned to Humphrey, whose face had turned to stone. I asked him if that would be all right.

'The Prime Minister's word is law,' he replied bleakly.

[1] The formal expression of allegiance to the Sovereign by a newly appointed Prime Minister.

Reprinted by kind permission of The Observer.

GO TO WORK ON A SAUSAGE !

Perhaps he's right. On second thoughts, I was hasty. I'm not actually sure that Bernard is up to it, he is so naïve. But I'm sure he'll manage somehow and he is very loyal and he never plots against me. [*Hacker's calling Bernard naïve in this context shows a remarkable lack of awareness of Bernard's true loyalties, divided as they were – equally – between Hacker, his political master, and Sir Humphrey Appleby, his Civil Service master – Ed.*]

I think I could have done better than Bernard [*Hacker was correct – Ed.*]. Still, I've done it now.

At that moment, with Bernard all dewy-eyed with gratitude, the phone rang. I grabbed it. Nobody there. Humphrey coolly picked up the other one. 'Yes?' he said. 'Yes . . . yes . . . yes he's here . . . I'll tell him.'

He rang off. I looked at him. I couldn't speak. But written all over my face was the question: was it me? Was I unopposed? Had I reached the top of the greasy pole at last?

'Yes – Prime Minister,' said Humphrey. And I fancy that he looked at me with new respect.

2

The Grand Design

January 23rd

The last few days have been overwhelmingly exciting. I went to the Palace and kissed hands. The next morning I moved into Number Ten. I'd read in the memoirs of past Prime Ministers that the staff line up in the front lobby, and in the long corridor inside it that leads down to the grand central staircase, and applaud the incoming Prime Minister. I wonder why they didn't applaud me. [*This accolade is only granted, traditionally, to a Prime Minister who had just won a general election – Ed.*] I hope this does not bode ill.

It took a day or two to move in. The PM lives in the flat 'above the shop', and the whole building is extremely confusing. From the outside it looks like an average size Georgian terrace house – but inside it is absolutely huge, a small stately home, a mini palace.

This is because it is, in reality, two houses. Not two houses side by side (the Chancellor of the Exchequer lives in Number Eleven), but two houses that almost back on to each other, joined by corridors, stairwells and courtyards. Each house has five or six floors, and the house at the back has large, elegant staterooms for entertaining my subjects. [*Hacker was plainly suffering from delusions of grandeur, and was confusing himself with the monarch – Ed.*]

The main problem in finding one's way around Number Ten is that, because it is two different houses, because of subsidence during the war,[1] and because the ground slopes away towards the back, it's almost impossible to know what floor you're on once you're upstairs.

But my confusion on moving in was like nothing compared to my state of mind today, my fifth day in office, on being taken into the top-secret operations room below the MOD.[2]

It looked just like you'd expect: maps of the five continents, girls at video terminals, officers at desks. I was shown around by the Chief of

[1] World War II.
[2] Ministry of Defence.

the General Staff, General Sir Geoffrey Howard, a tall dapper chap with sandy hair, bushy eyebrows and a brisk commanding voice. Sir Humphrey and Bernard were hovering about, as always.

Naturally, my first question was about the Hot Line. The General looked puzzled.

'Which one?'

'To Russia.'

'Ah. That's in Downing Street,' the General told me. I glanced at Bernard. Why hadn't I been shown it? He looked surprised – perhaps he hasn't been shown it, either.

I continued: 'So if there's an emergency, can I get straight through to the Soviet President?'

'Theoretically, yes,' General Howard replied cautiously.

'Does that mean no?'

'Well, it's what we tell journalists. In fact, we did once get through to the Kremlin, but only to a switchboard operator.'

'Couldn't the operator put you through?'

'We couldn't find out, she didn't seem to speak much English.'

'How often is it tested?'

The General looked blank. Testing had clearly not occurred to him.

'They try not to test it too often,' Humphrey intervened smoothly. 'It tends to create unnecessary panic at the other end. And panic is always a good thing to avoid where nuclear weapons are concerned, don't you think?' I certainly do.

The General walked me over to a telex machine.

'Now this –' he said meaningfully, '*is it!*'

'Is it?' I asked.

'Yes,' he said.

'Good,' I replied, encouragingly. Then I realised that I was going to get no further clue as to what he was talking about. 'Er . . . *what* is it, exactly?' I enquired casually, with what I hoped was a knowledgeable air.

'It's the trigger, Prime Minister,' Sir Humphrey murmured.

I felt a sudden chill. 'The trigger?'

'Yes. The nuclear trigger . . . the button.'

'This?' I couldn't believe it. I stared at the innocent-looking telex machine.

'Indirectly, yes.' The General could see my concern. 'It's simply a telex link to HMS Northwood. You would send a coded signal, you see. Then the telex operator at Northwood sends out an authentication signal.'

'So he knows it's from you, you see,' added Sir Humphrey softly.

'And when the instruction has been authenticated, and a target indication been made, Northwood would send the command to one of our Polaris submarines, and they'd actually press the button.' The General seemed quite satisfied with all this.

It all seemed so simple, so cut and dried. I give the order, they carry it out. My mouth felt all dry, but I had to find out more.

'They'd do it . . . just like that?'

'Just like that.' General Howard was visibly proud.

'When I say so?'

'When you say so.'

'But wouldn't anyone . . . *argue* with me?'

General Howard was shocked. 'Of course not. Serving officers obey orders without question, Prime Minister.'

I swallowed. 'But supposing I get drunk?' I asked, jokingly. Humphrey replied, rather too seriously: 'On the whole, it would be safer if you didn't get drunk.'

'Yes, but . . . seriously,' I asked 'what happens if I go off my rocker?'

'I think the Cabinet might notice.' Sir Humphrey was trying to sound reassuring.

I wasn't reassured. I don't think one can count on the Cabinet noticing that kind of thing. For a start, half of them, if not exactly off their rockers themselves, are not exactly what you'd call well-balanced.

I had to know more. 'Supposing I gave the order to press the button, and then changed my mind?'

'That's all right,' said the General with a chuckle, 'no one would ever know, would they?' Everyone else chuckled appreciatively.

I tried to chuckle too, but somehow I just couldn't. Instead, I asked how many actual bombs we have.

'Four Polaris submarines,' said the General. 'Sixteen missiles on each. Three warheads per missile.'

Mental arithmetic has never been my strong point and I didn't like to fish out my pocket calculator. Bernard saw my problem and spoke up. 'One hundred and ninety-two actual bombs, Prime Minister.' Obviously he'd been told before.

One hundred and ninety-two nuclear bombs! It doesn't bear thinking about! And Humphrey piled on the pressure, pointing out that each has at least five times the power of the Hiroshima bomb.

They all waited for me to speak. But I felt quite overwhelmed by the horror and the insanity of my new responsibilities.

The General looked at me with sympathy and understanding. 'I know what you're thinking,' he said. 'Not very many.'

That wasn't *at all* what I was thinking! I told him sharply that one hundred and ninety-two bombs seemed plenty to me. He didn't agree. 'Not with twelve hundred Soviet missiles trained on Britain, waiting to retaliate instantly.'

Twelve hundred? I felt I should assume a stiff upper lip. 'Ah well,' I remarked, 'Britain's always fought against the odds, haven't we? The Armada, the Battle of Britain . . .'

Even as I spoke I realised that the notion of fighting bravely against the odds is completely irrelevant in the context of nuclear war.

But General Howard saw this as an opportunity to put in a plug for Trident. He pointed out that we would have much more fire power at our disposal when it is delivered. And therefore we'd have a much greater deterrent.

'Meanwhile,' I said, 'thank God we've got our conventional forces.'

They all looked at me, slightly sceptically.

'Prime Minister,' said the General stiffly, 'our conventional forces could hold the Russians for seventy-two hours at most.'

'At most?'

'At most.'

The General was standing at attention. It looked most odd in his civilian suit. As a matter of fact, I thought irrelevantly, all these men around me were unmistakably soldiers, even though none of them were in uniform. Unless you call baggy blue pinstripe suits a uniform.

I forced myself to consider the ghastly implications of the latest piece of information that I'd just taken on board. 'So, in the event of a Russian attack, I would have to make an instant decision, would I?'

Generally Howard shook his head and smiled. 'No, Prime Minister. You'd probably have twelve hours.'

Twelve hours? That's what *I* call instant. I asked him if we shouldn't do something about that.

The General agreed emphatically. He thinks we certainly should do something about it. But, he informed me bitterly, the military has been told by the politicians for thirty years that this country can't afford the conventional forces to do the job.

Sir Humphrey, at my shoulder, nodded.

'Conventional forces are terribly expensive, Prime Minister,' he explained. 'Much cheaper just to press a button.'

January 24th

I had a sleepless night last night. My visit to the MOD had unsettled me quite profoundly. I couldn't get those figures out of my head. My powers of concentration are pretty remarkable [*we believe Hacker intended no irony here – Ed.*] but today I found it hard to keep my mind on my work.

'Seventy-two hours,' I found myself murmuring in the middle of a meeting with Bernard.

'Um, Prime Minister?' He was trying to bring me back to what we'd been discussing. 'Isn't seventy-two hours a bit generous for a meeting with the New Zealand High Commissioner?'

He was being facetious, I suppose. He could see I was thinking about the length of time that NATO forces could hold the Russians. I asked him if we could persuade the Americans to strengthen *their* conventional forces.

Bernard felt that it wouldn't really help. 'Apparently the American troops in Germany are all so drug-ridden that they don't know which side they're on anyway. And on the last NATO exercise the US troops dispersed and picnicked in the woods with lady soldiers.'

I asked him about the other NATO armies. He said they were all right on weekdays. I asked him to make himself clear.

'The Dutch, Danish and Belgian armies all go home for the weekend.'

This was the most extraordinary thing I'd heard yet. 'So,' I followed through with my usual relentless logic, 'if the Russians are going to invade we'd prefer them, on the whole, to do it between Monday and Friday.'

He nodded.

[*In fact, even if Warsaw Pact forces had invaded between Monday and Friday it would hardly have helped the NATO forces. The NATO barracks were so far behind their forward positions that the invaders would have, in any case, reached those positions first – Ed.*]

'Is this widely known?' I asked, amazed.

He could see I was thinking of the Russians. He explained that if he knew it, the Russians certainly do. 'The Kremlin usually gets NATO defence information before it filters through to us at Number Ten.'

I summed up. 'So it all comes back to Trident.'

'When it comes,' he agreed.

'When it comes,' I mused, wondering when that would really be.

'If it works,' Bernard added.

If it works? What did he mean?

Casually, he told me. 'Frequently, Prime Minister, when new weapons are delivered the warheads don't fit the ends of the rockets. That's what happened with Polaris. You know the sort of thing. It's all in the files.' He flipped through a file. 'Wiring faults, microchip failure. Ground-control transmitter on a different frequency from the receiver on the missile.' He looked up at me apologetically. 'We didn't have the means of delivering Polaris for some years. Cruise is probably the same. Trident might be too.'

I told him that I considered this absolutely intolerable, that we should take the manufacturers to court.

Bernard shook his head sadly, and explained that it is impossible for us to risk the publicity. And he's right of course. Security makes it impossible. And the manufacturers know it.

I asked him about changing manufacturers.

'Oh we do.' He sighed. 'All the time. But the trouble is that all the manufacturers know it too. That's why that torpedo landed on Sandwich Golf Course.'

I thought I'd misheard him. A torpedo on Sandwich Golf Course? Why hadn't we seen that in the papers?

Bernard knew all about it. 'There was a cover-up. The members just found a new bunker on the seventh fairway the next morning.'

I didn't know whether I was more concerned about the cover-up or the malfunctioning torpedoes. I asked Bernard why even our torpedoes don't work. He reassured me. Apparently it's only the *new* ones that don't work. All the others are working fine – the ones that were designed during World War II.

But these are forty years old. Why, I wanted to know, do they work better than our latest weapons? The answer was so obvious that I should have thought of it myself: the old torpedoes had lots of testing. We can't afford to test modern weapons properly – partly because it's too expensive and partly because if there *is* a nuclear war it won't last long enough for weapons tests.

I wondered what other revelations lay in store, now that I was entitled to know all our military secrets. I decided I'd better find out. 'What else don't I know about the defence of the United Kingdom?' I asked Bernard.

'I don't know, Prime Minister. I don't know what you don't know.'

I don't think he was being insolent because he went on to give me some useful advice. If I want another view, I might find it valuable to have a word with the Government's Chief Scientific Adviser. Apparently he sees the problem rather differently from the MOD.

I told Bernard to get him in at once. Bernard was hesitant. 'A late drink may be better,' he advised. 'Better not to let the Cabinet Office know. Sir Humphrey gets rather upset – he doesn't regard the Chief Scientific Adviser as one of us.'

I looked up the Chief Scientific Adviser in *Who's Who*. Professor Isaac Rosenblum. DSO at Arnhem. How could Humphrey not trust a man who fought on our side at Arnhem, and who was decorated by His Majesty for bravery?

'I'm afraid that it doesn't make up for his speaking with an Austrian accent,' Bernard remarked. 'And he certainly didn't go to Oxford or Cambridge. He didn't even go to the LSE.'

One of Bernard's little jokes. I think.

January 25th

Tonight I asked Professor Issac Rosenblum up to my flat for a late drink. And now my mind is reeling. It's not very often in politics that you meet, and talk to, a genuine intellectual. I used to be a poly-technic lecturer, and you don't get very many intelligent conversa-tions in academic life either. [*Hacker, it seems, regarded polytechnics as part of academic life – Ed.*] There are a *few* intellectuals in both walks of life, of course, but politicians never dare own up to it and academics prefer gossip anyway.

Professor Rosenblum is a small wiry elderly man. He is in his mid-seventies, lean, bright-eyed, and with a mind like a steel trap. I felt like an undergraduate at a tutorial. But I certainly learned a thing or two, and I believe that tonight's discussion will have a decisive effect on the future of my government and of this country. There will be changes made. [*Hacker was so excited when dictating this entry into his diary that he completely forgot about the Civil Service – Ed.*]

He popped in to Number Ten this evening, long after Humphrey had gone home.[1] I arranged with the security people that he should be allowed in through the back door, as there's always press watching the front.

He began by asking me if I believed in the nuclear deterrent.

'Yes,' I said.

'Why?' he asked.

I didn't quite know what to say. I mean, everyone believes in the nuclear deterrent. I asked him to repeat his question.

'Why?' he asked again.

[1] 6 pm.

'Because . . . it deters,' I replied, weakly.

'Whom?'

I'd never before met anyone who spoke in such short sentences. You never find *them* in politics, nor in academic life either. But I couldn't see quite what he was driving at.

'I beg your pardon?' I asked.

'Whom?' he asked again. He could see I didn't understand. He clarified his question. '*Whom* does it deter?'

It seemed obvious to me. 'The Russians. From attacking us.'

'Why?' There it was again, that irritating little word. Why *what*? I played for time. 'I beg your pardon?' I asked.

'Why?'

Why does the deterrent deter the Russians from attacking us, that's what he was asking. 'Because,' I replied firmly, 'they know that if they launch an attack I'd press the button.'

'You would?' He sounded surprised.

'Well . . .' I hesitated, 'wouldn't I?'

'Well . . . *would* you?'

'In the last resort, yes. Definitely.' I thought again. 'At least I *think* I definitely would.'

His questions continued relentlessly. I had to think carefully. [*Hacker was out of practice at this – Ed.*]

'And what is the last resort?'

'If the Russians invade Western Europe.' That at least seemed quite obvious.

Professor Rosenblum smiled. 'But you would only have twelve hours to decide. So the last resort is also the first response, is that what you're saying?'

Was that what I was saying? It seemed crazy.

The Chief Scientific Adviser stared at me critically. 'Well, you don't need to worry. Why should the Russians try to annex the whole of Europe? They can't even control Afghanistan.' He shook his head. 'No. If they try anything it will be salami tactics.'

[*Salami tactics was the description customarily given to 'slice by slice' manoeuvres, i.e. not a full scale invasion of the West, but the annexation of one small piece at a time. More often than not, the first steps would not be annexation of land but small treaty infringements, road closures, etc. – Ed.*]

Rosenblum stood up. He paced enthusiastically up and down my living-room, a glass of orange juice in hand, expounding an assortment of defence scenarios. First, he postulated riots in West Berlin, with buildings in flames, and the East German fire brigade crossing the border to help. He stopped pacing, stared at me, and asked me if I'd press the button in such circumstances.

Obviously the answer was no. Rosenblum nodded. He seemed to agree. Then he asked me if I'd press the button if the East German *police* came with the fire brigade. Again I shook my head. How could I start a nuclear war because of such a small territorial infringement?

Rosenblum started pacing again. A little smile was now visible around the corners of his mouth. 'Suppose the East Germans send some *troops*. Then more troops – just for riot control, they say. And then the East German troops are replaced by Russian troops. You press the button?'

Russian troops replacing East German troops in West Berlin? Would I start a nuclear war? I don't see how I could. I shook my head again.

The Chief Scientific Adviser smiled, and suggested cheerfully that the next 'slice' would be that the Russian troops don't go. They would be 'invited' to stay, to support the civilian administration. Then the civilian administration might close the roads and Tempelhof Airport. West Berlin would now be cut off. [*West Berlin was an island of the West German Federal Republic, sixty miles inside the border of the German Democratic Republic. 'Democratic', in this context, naturally means communist – Ed.*] Would I *now* press the button? he enquired.

I didn't know. I told him I needed time to think.

'You have twelve hours!' he barked.

I felt totally panicked. Then I reminded myself, and him, that he was inventing all this, and I relaxed.

He shrugged. 'You are Prime Minister today. The phone might ring now, from NATO Headquarters.'

The phone rang! It shook me to the core. Bernard hurried across my study and answered it. 'Hello. Yes?' He turned to me. 'NATO Headquarters, Prime Minister.'

Was a nightmare coming true? Then Bernard went on. 'Are you willing to address NATO's annual conference in April?'

I *thought* I was – but by then I was no longer sure of anything. I couldn't reply.

'Yes,' said Bernard into the phone, and rang off.

Professor Rosenblum turned to me again. 'Right,' he began. 'Scenario Two. Russian army manoeuvres take them "accidentally" on purpose across the West German frontier . . . is *that* the last resort?'

'No,' I replied. It didn't seem to be.

'All right,' he continued with great enthusiasm. 'Scenario Three. Suppose the Russians *have* invaded and occupied West Germany, Belgium, Holland and France. Suppose their tanks and troops have reached the English Channel. Suppose they are poised for an invasion, is *that* the last resort?'

I stonewalled. 'No.'

'Why not?' he demanded. *'Why not?'*

My mind was a fog. I was trying to see sense in all this. 'Because,' I fumbled, 'because . . . we would only fight a war to defend ourselves. And how can we defend ourselves by committing suicide?'

'So what *is* the last resort?' smiled the little old Professor. He shrugged, sat down and settled back into the overstuffed chintz armchair by the fire. 'Piccadilly? Watford Gap Service Station? The Reform Club?'

I stared at him, trying to put my thoughts in order. 'If you put it like that,' I said to him, 'the nuclear deterrent makes no sense. Is that what you're saying?'

Professor Rosenblum shook his head. 'No – I'm not saying that. If either the Russians or the Americans have the bomb, the other side must have it too. And we might as well keep Polaris, just in case.'

I didn't yet understand what exactly he was proposing.

He spelt it out to me. 'Cancel Trident. Spend the £15 billion you will save on conventional forces. Because you wouldn't really press the button, would you?'

'I might,' I said carefully, 'if I had no choice.'

He sighed. 'But we've been through this. They'll never put you into a situation where you have no choice. They'll stick to their salami tactics, remember?'

'So,' I took a deep breath, 'what happens if we divert £15 billion from Trident. What do we spend it on – tanks?'

'No. We spend it on ET.'

What on earth could he mean? Extra-terrestrials?

He saw what I was thinking, and smiled. 'ET stands for Emergent Technology. Smart missiles. Target finding. Infra-Red. The ET needs to be operated by a large conventional army.'

And then I got my inspiration! I suddenly saw what to do. Everything fell into place. It is ridiculously simple, but *completely workable*. First, we cancel Trident. We don't buy Cruise either. Then we introduce conscription, which will not only solve our defence problems by giving us a large conventional army, it also solves our unemployment problem! Excited, I explained my thoughts and Bernard raised a worry. 'Isn't conscription a rather courageous policy, Prime Minister?'

Bernard was quite wrong. Conscription would certainly be a courageous policy in times of full employment – but nowadays it would give young people something to do.

In fact, there are other definite plusses. Conscripted young people would be learning trades and skills. They'd even learn to read – the army never discharged anyone who was illiterate. In fact, we will be able to give our young people a comprehensive education, to make up for their Comprehensive Education.

We shall call the whole thing National Service, just like they used to – to remind everyone that the young people will be out in the country, serving the community and the nation.

It's a great policy. A new deal for Britain. I shall call it my Grand Design. Hacker's Grand Design. I already have notes for my House of Commons speech in which I shall outline the whole concept: 'From time to time, in our great island story, it falls to one man to lead his people out of the valley of the shadows and into the broad sunlit uplands of peace and prosperity.'

I wonder why I never thought of all this till tonight.

[*One reason, perhaps, was that Hacker and Professor Rosenblum had only just met – Ed.*]

January 26th

Things have really got to change round here, and I'm the man to see that those changes happen. [*After only a week in office Hacker appears to have slightly lost touch with reality – Ed.*]

A very busy morning was spent in Cabinet Committee and in appointing the remaining members of my government including some junior ministers. Then I went upstairs to the flat for lunch.

But there was none. As I came in Annie was putting on her raincoat. And she wasn't in too good a mood. When I asked her in a tone of only mild surprise if she was going off somewhere she reminded me that she was late for her Voluntary Services Committee. Whatever that is.

I asked her if there was any chance of some scrambled eggs or something. *Anything* really. She told me that there were eggs in the fridge.

I couldn't believe it. She wanted me to make lunch. I mean, it's not that I'm a male chauvinist or anything, but I am the Prime Minister and I do have plenty of other things to do. And as a politician I'm not really eligible to eat with all the Downing Street civil servants in the Cabinet mess.[1]

I can see her point. We did agree that she could carry on with her work if I became PM and we moved to Number Ten. She had been very opposed to the move here anyway, and I begin to see why. There's not much privacy. We were just discussing the eggs and I was fairly unhappy at finding myself cast as Mother Hubbard when there was a knock on the open door and a young woman messenger marched in with a Foreign Office Green Box.

'Foreign Office telegrams, Prime Minister,' she explained.

Annie was absolutely fed up. 'See what I mean?' she complained. 'It's bad enough living in this goldfish bowl anyway. I've got to be able to get out and live my own life. Every time I want to step out for some cigarettes I have to walk past a dozen journalists, a TV film crew, a bunch of messengers, housekeepers and policemen in the lobby, and fifty gawping tourists at the bottom of the street. There's no privacy *anywhere*!'

I pointed out that there is a back door. She thinks it makes virtually no difference which door we use. And there's total privacy up here in the flat. Or nearly total privacy. Well, *some* privacy, anyway.

'Our life's not our own any more.' She hammered home the point. 'What about the President ringing you in bed from the White house at two o'clock this morning?'

Rather foolishly I replied that it was only nine p.m. in Washington, which, I agree, hardly makes it any better from her point of view. I was about to explain that it was an important call to discuss my forthcoming visit to Washington when there was another knock on the door and in burst two sniffer dogs with tongues hanging out dragging a couple of police dog-handlers behind them. Apparently there was a bomb scare, and they had to search the place.

Annie looked at me and asked, 'Privacy?'

She wasn't being very reasonable, in my opinion. Surely she'd rather have security checks than be blown up. I told her that she could always have privacy if she went for a walk in the garden. I've never seen anyone out there at all.

'I've tried that,' she answered with defiance. 'About sixty people stare at you from the windows of Number Ten, Number Eleven, Number Twelve *and* the Cabinet Office. It's like exercising in a prison yard and being watched by the inmates and the warders. To think we

[1] Attached to the Cabinet Office.

actually have to pay rent for this place. They should pay us to live here.'

I must admit I share her resentment about the rent. I should have thought – I *did* think – that we would be given the place to live in, in view of the great personal sacrifice one makes for one's service to the nation. [*Many non-politicians do not see the acquisition of the greatest political power and patronage in the land solely in terms of 'great personal sacrifice'. And many others may wonder why Hacker imagined that, on attaining power, he should be entitled to live rent-free – Ed.*]

The dogs and dog-handlers left. I said to Annie: 'Look, it's actually a pretty nice place to live, at least it's quiet.' It was an idiotic thing to say – no sooner had I uttered it than the bloody brass band started playing on Horse Guards Parade, right outside the window.

She snarled at me. 'That's been going on since seven o'clock this morning.' True, but it *is* Horse Guards Parade out there, and they are the Horse Guards – they have to rehearse somewhere. Of course, I'm lucky, because I'm always up by 7 a.m. in any case.

I tried to calm her down. 'Be reasonable, Annie. A career of public service inevitably involves some sacrifice.'

She buttoned her coat up. 'Fine. I sacrifice my sleep. You sacrifice your lunch.' And off she went.

I ran after her. 'What did *you* have for lunch?' I called down the staircase.

'Half a Yorkie bar.'

Seething, I returned to the flat to look for the other half. I couldn't even find it. There were indeed some eggs in the fridge but I just couldn't face cooking. So I meandered gloomily down the stairs and mooched into my study. Hungrily I stood at the window, watching the military band marching up and down. I left a message in the private office that Bernard should pop up to see me as soon as he returned from lunch.

Forty-five minutes later he bounced in, cheerful and well-fed. I turned and asked him if he'd had a good lunch.

He was slightly surprised. 'Quite good, yes.'

'Where did you have it?'

'In the Cabinet mess.'

'Three courses?'

'Yes.'

'Wine?'

'A glass of claret, yes.' He paused, trying to understand what I was driving at. 'Um . . . if you're interested, Prime Minister, I had mulligatawny soup, followed by a veal chop with sauté potatoes and . . .'

71

'I'm not interested, Bernard,' I snapped. 'Do you want to know what *I* had for lunch?'

He sensed that I was upset, but still couldn't quite see why. 'Um . . . do you want to tell me?' he asked.

I smiled unpleasantly. 'Yes,' I snapped. 'Nothing.'

'Are you dieting, Prime Minister?'

I explained succinctly that I was not dieting. I expressed my total astonishment that there are facilities at Number Ten for feeding Bernard, and all the private secretaries, the whole of the Cabinet office, the press office, the garden-room girls,[1] the messengers . . . but not me. And I bloody live here!

Bernard asked if Mrs Hacker could cook for me. I reminded him that she has her own job. Then he offered to get me a cook. It looked a good offer – until closer examination revealed that I would have to pay for it. And, according to Bernard, the cost of a full-time cook would be between eight and ten thousands a year. I can't afford that. Trying to get himself off the hook, he suggested that I talk to the Cabinet Secretary – obviously he didn't want to get involved in a discussion when it wasn't in his power to change the system.

But I was very irritated. Still am, come to that. I turned back to the window and fumed silently.

Bernard cleared his throat. 'I think the Cabinet Secretary's due here in a few moments anyway. So shall we get on with the affairs of the nation?'

'Stuff the affairs of the nation,' I replied. 'I want a cook.'

Bernard promised that the matter would be looked into, and ushered in Malcolm Warren, the Number Ten press officer. He's a big bluff Yorkshireman, a career civil servant but with a sense of the way things are done in the real world. He was appointed by my predecessor in Number Ten, but I've kept him on because he has an iron grip on the lobby correspondents and the whole Whitehall public relations machine.

I asked him to be brief, as I was due to meet the Cabinet Secretary any moment.

'Certainly, Prime Minister. Two things. First, and most important, we should discuss your first TV appearance as Prime Minister.'

This is such a big and important subject that I asked him to postpone discussion of it for a day or two, until we have time to go into it thoroughly.

[1] The name given to the very high-class ladies of the registry and typing pool at Number Ten, who worked in a basement room that leads out on to the garden.

The other thing he wanted to discuss was my official Washington visit. Of course, that's much less important than my first TV appearance.

The one urgent point he wanted to raise was that an awful lot of press want to come with us to Washington. I think that's good. Malcolm was worried about the expense. But I explained to him that this would be a terribly important occasion. I shall be standing there, on the White House lawn, side by side with the President of the United States. There will be national anthems. Photographs of two world leaders together. He will tell the world about our happy relationship, our unity and resolve. He'll probably say a word or two about my own courage and wisdom and statesmanship. And it is essential that, if so, it is fully reported back here in Britain. This sort of publicity is vital to Britain. [*Hacker meant that it was vital to him – Ed.*] Vital to our prestige. [*His prestige – Ed.*] Our place in the world. [*His place in the history books – Ed.*]

Malcolm readily agreed, especially when I told him that, as a matter of policy, I intended that we should have no secrets from the press about this country's successes. I told him that we must be absolutely frank about my government's achievements. I want fearless honesty about every government triumph.

He understood. He raised the nit-picking point that, as I have only been in office for seven days, there aren't all that many triumphs yet. Perfectly true. But there will be.

I also gave him an idea for a good press story: I told him that I had had to make my own lunch today. I asked him if he knew. It appeared that he hadn't been informed of this. So I told him all about it. How there's no cook or housekeeper for the flat upstairs, how Annie has her own job, we can't afford staff, and that it looked as though I'd be washing the dishes and washing my socks.

He was a bit slow on the uptake. He couldn't see that there was a good press story in all this. I explained that he could do one along the lines of 'Jim Hacker's not stuck up. He can identify with the problems of ordinary people.' That sort of thing.

Malcolm wanted to think about it. 'We don't want you to seem *too* ordinary, Prime Minister, even though you are.'

Did he mean that the way it sounded? I don't think so, because he continued: 'What I mean is, that sort of publicity can be counter-productive. You remember when Jimmy Carter was attacked by a rabbit?'

I did vaguely remember. He looked a bit of a fool. Also there was that photo of him out jogging, looking as though he was on the point of total collapse. He probably thought it was a good idea to be photographed taking exercise – but it made the voters think that he was not long for this world. Lost him a lot of support. Maybe Malcolm's right to be cautious.

Malcolm amplified his point of view. 'Perhaps it's better that we build you up a bit – photos of you doing the washing might make you look a bit wet.'

I sent him out and Bernard brought Humphrey in. I told him I'd been thinking.

'Good,' he said encouragingly.

'I've been Prime Minister for a week now,' I said.

'And a very good Prime Minister you are too, if I may so.'

I was pleased. It's always nice to have the approval of one's colleagues, especially if they are as hard-bitten as Humphrey. I told him that I wasn't fishing for compliments. But it *has* been going well, and I'm glad he recognised it.

However, we immediately uncovered our first mistake, or rather *their* first mistake, and a pretty serious mistake it is too. I remarked, casually, that it's nice to be able to reward one's old allies. 'Was Ron Jones pleased about his peerage?' I enquired.

'Oh yes,' said Bernard. 'He said his members would be delighted.'

I couldn't think what Bernard meant. 'Members?'

'The Members of his Union. The National Federation of . . .'

I suddenly saw what had happened. I was livid. 'Not *him*!' I yelled. 'I meant our backbencher. I wanted to offer the peerage to Ron Jones, not *Ron Jones.*'

'Ah,' said Bernard. A rather inadequate response, I thought.

We all sat and stared at each other. There was no going back on it now. Bernard tried to make the best of it. 'If it's any consolation to you, Prime Minister, I gather he was awfully pleased.'

I bet he was! Pleased – and amazed! I asked Humphrey what we could do about *Ron Jones's* peerage – could we give him one too? Humphrey thought not. 'With respect, Prime Minister, we can't send *two* Lord Ron Jones to the Upper House – it'll look like a job lot.'

But I've promised him an honour of some sort. We scratched our heads for a bit. Then Humphrey had an idea. As Ron isn't remotely interested in television, hasn't even got a TV set, we're going to make him a Governor of the BBC.

Then we passed on to important matters. I explained to Humphrey that we need a cook–housekeeper in the flat upstairs.

He suggested that I advertise. He was missing the point. I explained that we need a *government* cook–housekeeper.

Humphrey, as I expected after my talk with Bernard, was not entirely helpful. He said that it could be difficult to get a government cook–housekeeper as Number Ten is a private home which just happens to be in a government building.

I pointed out that I happen to live in it. And therefore – surprise, surprise! – happen to eat in it too. 'It is not unreasonable to want someone to cook my lunch.'

'No. But it's not possible,' said Humphrey categorically.

I've never heard anything so ridiculous. Humphrey was asking me to accept that I have the power to blow up the world but not to ask for scrambled eggs. [*It was not in dispute that Hacker had the power to* ask *for scrambled eggs – Ed.*]

I explored this nonsense a little further, taking it to its logical conclusion. 'Suppose I invited the German Ambassador to lunch?' I asked.

'That would be all right,' reflected Humphrey. 'Official engagement. Government hospitality will gladly provide five courses, with three wines and brandy. No problem.'

So what Humphrey was saying was that the German Ambassador's lunch is government business, but my lunch isn't. And not just the German Ambassador's, of course – *any* ambassador's.

So, there and then I told Bernard to get the diary out. Then I ordered him to arrange for me to have lunch with the German Ambassador on Monday, with the French Ambassador on Tuesday, and on Wednesday the American Ambassador. Then, not forgetting the Commonwealth, on Thursday I would lunch with the New Zealand High Commissioner. 'Bernard, how many countries are there in the United Nations?'

He knew the answer, of course. 'One hundred and fifty-eight.'

'Good,' I beamed at Humphrey. 'That'll keep me in lunches for about six months. Then we'll go round again.'

Bernard was hurriedly leafing through the diary. 'Prime Minister, you're not free for lunches with ambassadors every day. Sometimes you will have other official lunches.'

'Good news,' I replied. 'So much the better. We can just use ambassadors to fill up the blank spaces.'

Humphrey was looking worried, and remarked that the Foreign and Commonwealth Office might have views on this matter. [*This would undoubtedly have been the case. It has always been said that one*

Prime Minister's lunch with an ambassador destroys two years of patient diplomacy. The Foreign Office would have been unlikely to react favourably to such lunches – Ed.]

I didn't much care what the Foreign Office would say. 'It's quite absurd that there's no one to cater for me and my family.'

Humphrey couldn't see why. But then he wouldn't, would he? He gets his lunch in the Cabinet mess too. 'Prime Minister, it's the way things have been done for two and a half centuries.'

'Is that the clinching argument?' I demanded.

'It has been for two and a half centuries.'

Bernard, bless his heart, intervened in his usual pedantic and obsessive fashion. 'Um . . . with respect, Sir Humphrey,' he began disrespectfully, 'it can't have been the clinching argument for two and a half centuries, because half a century ago it had only been the clinching argument for two centuries, and a century ago only for one and a half centuries, and one and a half . . .' Humphrey was staring malevolently at him and he ground to a halt. But Bernard's logic was both as impeccable and irrelevant as always.

I stepped in hurriedly, to distract Humphrey and direct his wrath away from my loyal Private Secretary. 'Humphrey, I am not convinced. I want a cook and I want you to see that it's paid for.'

Humphrey was stony-faced. Stubbornly he turned to me. 'Then let me put it like this. How would you like the press to announce that your first act as Prime Minister was to give yourself an effective salary increase of eight to ten thousand pounds a year?'

I hadn't thought of that. But I couldn't see why we should tell them. Nobody would ever know.

Humphrey read my thoughts. 'We must tell them, by the way. We have no alternative. The Prime Minister's salary and expenses have to be published.'

'Isn't there any way we can . . . not refer to it?' I asked hopefully.

'Open Government, Prime Minister. Freedom of Information. We should always tell the press, freely and frankly, *anything* that they can easily find out some other way.'

I simply do not believe that there is no way to solve this problem. But I had to let it drop for today. Humphrey's position is that ever since Number Ten was first used as the PM's official residence, two hundred and fifty years ago, there has been no solution to this problem. And therefore, according to Civil Service reasoning, there never will be.

Humphrey changed the subject. 'Prime Minister, you said you had been thinking.'

'Yes, Humphrey,' I replied. 'We have agreed that things have been going well ever since I've been Prime Minister. So I have been asking myself: "How do I ensure that this run of success continues?"'

Humphrey gazed at me hopefully. 'Have you considered . . . masterly inactivity?'

Ridiculous. But I was patient with him. 'No, Humphrey, a Prime Minister should be firm.'

'Indeed!' he agreed. 'How about *firm* masterly inactivity?'

I could afford to be nice – after all, I'm in the driving seat now. 'No,' I smiled, 'but I *shall* be firm.'

'Good,' said Sir Humphrey.

'And decisive,' I went on.

'Absolutely,' agreed Sir Humphrey.

'And imaginative,' I added provocatively.

'I'm not so sure about imaginative.' I *bet* he's not!

'And above all,' I finished up, 'I must offer leadership.'

'Leadership.' He was at his most encouraging. 'Leadership, above all.'

'And as I'm the Prime Minister I have the power to do so, don't I?'

'Indeed, Prime Minister, you are the Prime Minister, and wherever you lead we shall obediently follow.'

So I told him my new policy. My Grand Design. 'I've decided to cancel Trident, spend the £15 billion on conventional forces and the ET,[1] bringing in conscription, and thus solve our defence, balance of payments, education and unemployment problems at a stroke.'

He gaped at me. I glanced at Bernard, who was watching his old boss with considerable interest.

I waited for Humphrey's response. But answer came there none. Not at first, anyway. He seemed absolutely poleaxed. I gave him a few moments to pull himself together and then, as I was getting bored with waiting, I told him to say something.

'I . . . er . . . where did this idea come from?' Not a very flattering question. But I reminded him that I'd been thinking.

'You can't do that!' he said with desperation.

At first I thought he was telling me that I can't think. Or mustn't think. But he went on to say that what I was proposing was completely revolutionary, an unprecedented innovation.

---

[1] Emergent Technology.

So the gloves were off! He meant that I could not pursue my policy. Well, in my opinion it is not up to him to say.

He clearly thinks it is. 'Prime Minister, you can't simply reorganise the entire defence of the realm, just like that!'

My answer was simple. 'I'm the Prime Minister.' Besides, he had said he would follow me. He had agreed that I should be decisive. He had agreed that I should offer leadership. So what was he complaining about? [*Presumably Sir Humphrey wanted Hacker to be decisive only if he took decisions of which Sir Humphrey approved. And leadership was only welcome if it went in the approved direction – Ed.*] 'Furthermore,' I added, 'I have the power.'

He didn't like that one bit. 'Yes – but only within the law and the constitution and the constraints of administrative precedent, budgetary feasibility and Cabinet government. What about your Cabinet colleagues, what do they think?'

I was obliged to admit that I hadn't told them yet. But I know they'll love it. They'll love anything that cuts unemployment. Half of them would even welcome inflation on those grounds. And I know that the Cabinet will be only too happy to have an extra £15 billion of Trident cash available for other public spending. Anyway, I'm the Prime Minister, what does it matter what they think?

'I appoint the Cabinet,' I said simply.

Humphrey smiled coldly. 'I'm sure you don't want to *dis*appoint them.'

Very droll, as he used to say so patronisingly to me. I didn't laugh. I didn't say anything. I just waited for him to capitulate. Unfortunately he didn't say anything either.

'Humphrey, you're very silent.'

'You've given me a lot to be silent about.'

'You mean, *you* think we should keep Trident?'

He could only answer that one way. 'It is not for me to say, Prime Minister.' Quite right. He's only a civil servant.

'Fine,' I agreed magnanimously, 'that's agreed then.'

Humphrey couldn't let it go. 'But since you ask my opinion . . .'

I was enjoying myself. 'Go on then.'

'Yes,' he said grimly, 'I do think we should keep it.'

I told him I couldn't see the sense in it. Humphrey, groping for my reasoning, asked if I was therefore going to buy Cruise missiles instead.

I told him that I intended that the UK should buy no more nuclear weapons.

78

He blanched. 'But Prime Minister – you're not a secret unilateralist, are you?'

I explained that I was nothing of the sort, that we still have Polaris, and that I have no intention of getting rid of that.

He relaxed a little. At least (in his view) I was not a security risk, just a loony. He tried to tell me Polaris is not good enough, that it's a ramshackle old system, whereas Trident is superb – faster, more warheads, independently targeted. According to Humphrey, Trident is almost impossible to intercept whereas the Soviets might easily develop a multi-layered ballistic missile defence system that can intercept Polaris.

'By when?' I asked.

'In strategic terms, any day now.'

I can spot an evasive answer at fifty paces. [*The more so since Hacker was himself a master of the evasive answer – Ed.*] I asked him by what year, precisely, this might happen.

'Well . . . 2020.' I smiled. 'But that's sooner than you think,' he added hastily.

'And you're saying that such a missile defence system could intercept all 192 Polaris missiles?'

'Not *all*, no. But virtually all – ninety-seven per cent.'

I took out my pocket calculator and did a few quick sums. I looked up at him. 'That would still leave five Polaris bombs which could get through the defences.'

Humphrey was triumphant. 'Precisely – a mere five.'

'Enough,' I reminded him gently, 'to obliterate Moscow, Leningrad and Minsk.'

'Yes,' he sneered, 'but that's about all.'

I wasn't sure I was understanding him correctly. 'I would have thought that that's enough to make the Russians stop and think.'

Humphrey's enthusiasm for Trident knows no bounds. 'But don't you *see*, Prime Minister – with Trident we could obliterate the whole of Eastern Europe!'

I don't want to obliterate the whole of Eastern Europe. I told him so. He nodded impatiently. He knew that. He thought I was missing the point. 'It has to be an effective deterrent, Prime Minister.'

'But it's a bluff,' I told him, 'I probably wouldn't use it.'

'They don't *know* that you probably wouldn't use it,' he argued.

'They probably do,' I said.

He was forced to agree. 'Yes . . . they *probably* know that you probably wouldn't. But they can't *certainly* know.'

He's right about that. But they don't have to certainly know. 'They *probably* certainly know that I probably wouldn't,' I said.

'Yes,' he agreed, 'but even though they *probably* certainly know that you probably wouldn't, they don't *certainly* know that although you *probably* wouldn't, there is *no probability* that you certainly would.'

Bernard was taking careful minutes. It's lucky he does shorthand and was able to reconstruct this conversation for me in writing by the end of the day.

But Humphrey could see that he was making no headway with his deterrent argument. So he made one attempt to persuade me to keep Trident, this time by flattering me and playing on my vanity. I can't imagine why he thought that would have any effect!

'Look, Prime Minister, it all boils down to one simple issue. You are Prime Minister, Prime Minister of Great Britain. Don't you believe that Britain should have the best?'

'Of course.'

'Very well.' He took that as a cue to rhapsodise. 'If you walked into a nuclear-missile showroom you would buy Trident – it's lovely, it's elegant, it's beautiful, it is – quite simply – the best. And Britain should have the best. In the world of the nuclear missile it is the Savile Row suit, the Rolls-Royce Corniche, the Château Lafite 1945. It is the nuclear missile Harrods would sell you! What more can I say?'

'Only,' I replied calmly, 'that it costs £15 billion and we don't need it.'

Humphrey shook his head sadly. In his view I had completely missed the point. 'You could say that about anything at Harrods,' he replied reasonably.

January 30th

Tonight we had a reception at Number Ten. Six-thirty to eight. My first party since I became Prime Minister, though many of the guests were hangovers from the previous regime.[1] As we were members of the same party, it didn't matter much.

I wasn't looking forward to it much, after a long and trying day. But, as so often happens, something truly unexpected emerged from a chance conversation. Among the guests was General Howard, who had showed me over the MOD a week or so ago. I buttonholed him. I told him that I had to sound him out on something, and that he was not going to like it.

[1] And a few *had* hangovers from the previous regime.

'Tell me the worst, Prime Minister,' he said stiffly.

So I did. I said that even though it would doubtless come as a severe blow to the services and would be most unpopular, I intended to cancel Trident.

He muttered something that I only half heard. 'Now hold on,' I said, 'don't jump on it too quickly, it's no use arguing, I . . .' And I stopped. I realised what I'd half heard. 'What did you say?' I asked, in case I was fantasising.

'Good idea.' Terse and to the point, as always. I wasn't sure I understood him correctly.

'You mean, you're in favour? Of cancelling Trident?'

'Of course.'

For the second time in just over a week, all my preconceptions about defence were stood on their head.

I stood there, gazing up at this imposing, sandy-haired, beetle-browed, six-foot-four giant. 'Why are you in favour?'

'We don't need it,' he replied briefly. 'It's a complete waste of money. Totally unnecessary.'

I could hardly believe my ears. The most senior army officer in the country agrees with me that Trident is a complete waste of money. I told him that I hoped to keep Polaris, keep the American bases, and strengthen our conventional forces.

'You're right.'

I wondered if he were a tame eccentric. 'Does the whole Defence Staff agree?'

He shook his head. 'No. The Navy want to keep it. It's launched from their submarines. Take away Trident and they've hardly got a role left.'

'So they'll resist it?'

'Yes, but the Navy resist everything. They nearly lost us World War I by resisting convoys.'

'And the RAF?' I asked.

'Well,' he replied dismissively, 'you can ask them. If you're interested in the opinions of garage mechanics. But I'm afraid they'd want Trident. Only they want it in the form of a missile launched from the air, like an Exocet.'

Suddenly it was all making sense to me. Why had I ever thought the Services would have a joint view of the matter?

General Howard continued to explain the RAF mentality as he sees it. 'They want the Bomb to be carried around in an aeroplane, you see. All they're really interested in is flying around dropping

81

things on people. Not that they're any good at it – I mean, they couldn't even close the runway at Port Stanley. They'd probably never even find Moscow. If they did, they'd probably miss.'

The problem is clear. How do I get the policy past the MOD if only the army is in favour of it? I put this to the General and he had a ready-made solution. 'The Chief of Defence Staff job is shortly becoming vacant. Technically it's the Navy's turn. But it's your decision. If you appoint a soldier . . .'

Delicately, he let his sentence remain unfinished. I already knew that he is the most senior soldier. So if I appoint him, I'll have the Chief of Defence Staff on my side. I don't know whether that'll be enough, or how the Navy will respond if I overlook their man, but it's obviously something I have to consider in due course.

[*Sir Humphrey Appleby also had a few words with General Howard at the reception at 10 Downing Street that evening. And their conversation, unlike General Howard's conversation with the Prime Minister, apparently changed the course of events. Sir Humphrey's recollections of that conversation are to be found in his private papers – Ed.*]

The General seemed unusually relaxed after a short talk with the Prime Minister, which I had been observing. When in due course I spoke to him, he remarked that he was pleased to have come across a Prime Minister with a bit of sense.

I asked which country was so blessed with such a leader. I knew, of course, that he was referring to Hacker, and my guess was that Hacker had not put him fully in the picture.

I was right, of course. The PM had spoken to General Howard about cancelling Trident, but *not* about reintroducing conscription. When I mentioned all the details the General was horrified, as I knew he would be.

Hacker wants conscription because it helps unemployment and therefore wins votes. The army does *not* want conscription, and has never wanted it. They are very proud of their élite, professional army. It is tough, disciplined, possibly the best in the world. The Chiefs of Staff do not want a conscripted mob of punks, freaks, junkies and riff-raff, a quarter of a million hooligans on its hands with nothing to do except peel potatoes at Aldershot. The generals are afraid that this would turn it into an ordinary army. [*Like the one that won World Wars I and II – Ed.*]

They are also worried about the new equal-opportunity legislation. In America it is well known that the NATO commanders don't know if the troops being posted to them are men or women. Not until they arrive. Sometimes not even then.

In view of the potential conscription General Howard felt that it would be better to keep Trident, with all its faults. He urged me to find some method of 'stopping' the Prime Minister from pursuing this unfortunate policy.

I explained that, unfortunately, Prime Ministers cannot be 'stopped'. But they can be slowed down. In fact, they almost invariably are – after a few months most new Prime Ministers have more or less ground to a halt.

My idea is to have a quiet word with the American Ambassador. General Howard approved.

[*Hacker's diary continues – Ed.*]

January 31st

Today there was good news and bad news. The bad news came first.

In my morning meeting with Humphrey, Bernard and Malcolm we went over the final preparations for my American visit. Malcolm is to make sure that the BBC News and ITN get really good positions on the White House lawn, so that they can get a close two-shot of me and the President.

I've also told him to ensure that there are good photo opportunities inside the White House as well. Shots of me and the President alone together.

I've given him a list of all the photo ideas that I've had: coverage of the start of the talks on the second day, coverage of the President saying goodbye to me, hopefully grasping my elbow with his left hand, the way he did with the West German Chancellor, it looked frightfully chummy.

I wanted him to arrange all of this with our Embassy, but Malcolm felt that it could be difficult. I must say, I don't know what we have all these Embassies for. Any time we need anything important for Britain [*i.e. for Hacker – Ed.*] they always make trouble.

It's not that I'm concerned with political advantage or vote winning, or anything like that. It's good for Britain to be seen by the rest of the world as an equal partner of the United States, that's all.

Humphrey was unwilling to discuss the publicity aspects any further. I wondered why. Instead, he showed me the Cabinet agenda.

You didn't have to be Hercule Poirot to see that the agenda had been tampered with. The discussion of the cancellation of Trident was conspicuous by its absence. I questioned Humphrey about this – after all, as Cabinet Secretary it's his job to draw it up.

'We were indeed going to discuss Trident, Prime Minister, but I thought perhaps it might be wiser to leave it a little longer. Go into it thoroughly, closer scrutiny, think through the implications, produce some papers, have some inter-departmental discussions, make contingency plans. We are discussing the defence of the realm.'

I can't believe that he still thinks these old devices will fool me. I challenged him, and he protested innocence. 'No, indeed, Prime Minister, but the Cabinet must have all the facts.'

I grinned. 'That's a novel idea.'

He was not amused. 'Important decisions take time, Prime Minister.'

I could see immediately what he was playing at: delaying tactics, the oldest trick in the book. The longer you leave things, the harder it is to get them off the ground.

But then came the bad news. It was a real bombshell. Apparently Humphrey has learned from the American Ambassador – informally – that the Americans would be very unhappy if we cancelled Trident unless we ordered another of their nuclear missiles instead.

At first I was defiant about it. After all, I have to think of what's best for Britain. But it seems they claim to have two reasons for their disquiet: the first is that they feel that they need our partnership and do not want to carry the nuclear burden alone. This is perfectly reasonable, but as we would still have Polaris they wouldn't be doing so. So the second reason is the real one: the little matter of losing billions of dollars of business and tens of thousands of jobs in the American aerospace industry.

The question is what – if anything – I can do about this American opposition to my Grand Design. I told Humphrey that I have no intention of changing my policy. The Americans will have to learn to live with it.

'As you wish, Prime Minister,' he said, 'but I thought if we kept your Trident proposal secret until after your American visit, it might save some embarrassment.'

I replied sharply that I didn't agree. 'If there has to be some tough talking, I might as well have it out with the American President when we meet.'

He shook his head sadly. 'Ah, well, that's the point. As you know, the agenda of your meeting must be agreed in advance. You can't just go all the way there for a chat.'

'Why not?'

'Well . . . you might not think of anything to say. And, if your Trident proposal were put to the Americans in advance, I understand there would be a slight change of plan.'

'What change of plan?'

'You would not be met by the President. You would be entertained by the Vice-President.'

I was thunderstruck. The Vice-President? I could hardly believe my ears. I thought he wasn't serious. But he *was*!

It's absurd. It's ludicrous. It's a total insult. Even Botswana was met by the President. [*Botswana had not just cancelled an order for Trident – Ed.*]

Humphrey tried to put it as nicely as he could. 'I'm sure they'd do it gracefully, Prime Minister. He'd have a diplomatic toothache, like Krushchev's. Or they'd explain that the President had catarrh, or bruised his thumb or something. Fallen asleep, perhaps.'

Humphrey knew as well as I that the whole point of the visit to the States was the PR value of being seen meeting the President. I asked him what choices we had. He advised me that in practice I have no choice at all. And that if I want to be entertained by the President I must leave Trident off the agenda.

This is a terrible blow. I have to raise it with the United States sometime. When better than while I'm there? But what must be, must be.

There remained the question of whether or not I should raise the Trident question in Cabinet. Humphrey advised me to leave it until my return, in case the discussion leaked to the US Ambassador. He could be right. Clearly someone has been leaking to him already on this subject. I wonder who.

'Anyway, Humphrey,' I said miserably, 'a new Prime Minister must show that he has arrived, show that there's a new mind and a firm hand in Number Ten. I must make my mark.'

And then Humphrey revealed the good news. It seems that I have accomplished something that none of my predecessors ever accomplished. A cook, no less! Seconded from the Cabinet Office canteen, to do our lunch in the flat when required. Except for weekends and bank holidays, of course.

This was gratifying. A place in the history books. I think that this shows that I have started the way I mean to go on. I am in charge, and the Civil Service can clearly see that there is a new mind and a firm hand in Number Ten.

I told Humphrey that, as far as Trident's concerned, I am not changing my policy and I am not changing my mind. In due course I shall lose it. [*Hacker presumably meant that he would lose Trident, not his mind – Ed.*] But in the meantime I see no harm in postponing the Trident discussion till I return from America, and I gave Humphrey my firm decision to leave Trident off the agenda for tomorrow.

He took it like a lamb. 'Yes Prime Minister,' he replied deferentially.

3

The Ministerial Broadcast

February 6th

I don't remember much about today. I got back from America last night and was in my study first thing this morning after a fairly sleepless night. But I needn't have hurried. I wanted to speak to Humphrey about something but he didn't seem to be around today. Bernard told me there wasn't much happening, and there were no appointments in the diary, so we spent some time reviewing what the papers had said about my American trip, and congratulating ourselves on the success of it. That's about it, really.

SIR BERNARD WOOLLEY RECALLS:[1]

The Prime Minister's recollection of his return from the United States is somewhat clouded by jet-lag, I fear. He was frightfully tired.

He lurched down the stairs from his flat and into his study, looking very white – except for his eyes, which were very red. He claimed that he was not jet-lagged, though he was concerned that he could not remember anything that the President said to him at the White House. Actually, this was not due to jet-lag – the President hadn't really said very much. Perhaps this was because the President was frightfully tired too.

Hacker yawned a lot and sent for Sir Humphrey Appleby, who had not been to Washington and was consequently very fresh and alert. Hacker, aware of his exhaustion, expressed concern that statesmen [*the word that politicians use to describe themselves – Ed.*] nowadays spend so much time jetting around the world, taking part in major negotiations that could affect the future of mankind when they are 'zonked', as he described it.

Sir Humphrey explained that this is the reason why such negotiations are nearly always completed in advance by humble servants such as himself. They could hardly be left in the hands of the 'zonked'.

Fortunately Sir Humphrey's comment passed unnoticed by the Prime Minister, who gently nodded off while he spoke. Perhaps this accounts for the Prime Minister's mistaken recollection that Sir Humphrey was absent that day.

[1] In conversation with the Editors.

We attempted to wake the Prime Minister. After some moments we succeeded. He opened his eyes, sat up slightly startled and said: 'Ah, Humphrey, good morning.'

Unfortunately Hacker had no recollection of sending for Sir Humphrey, nor could he remember why he had done so. I didn't know why either, because Hacker had fallen asleep before he told me. So Sir Humphrey left us. As he did so the Prime Minister nodded off again, and I left him to snooze in peace.

Much later in the day he buzzed down to me in the Private Office, and asked me to review with him the large backlog of work which he assumed – incorrectly – would have built up in his absence.

I was obliged to explain to him that there was no backlog, and that – contrary to public belief – he would have much less work to do now that he is Prime Minister and no longer has a department of his own.

The fact is that everything that one reads in the newspapers about how hard the Prime Minister has to work is rather a myth, generally put out by the Press Office. I listed the jobs for the Prime Minister that he actually has to do:

1. *Chair the Cabinet*   Two and a half hours per week.
2. *Chair two or three Cabinet Committees*   Four hours per week.
3. *Answers questions in the House*   Half an hour per week.
4. *Audience with the Queen*   One hour maximum (if she doesn't get bored before that).

This is a total of eight hours per week. Apart from that the Prime Minister has to read all the briefs, minutes, submissions, Foreign Office telegrams, and so forth. And the Private Office arranges to rush the Prime Minister from place to place, shaking hands with people. But in fact, although there are lots of things people want the Prime Minister to do, lots of things he should do, and any number of things he *can* do, there are very few things he *has* to do. After all, the Prime Minister is the boss.

[*In fact, there is much to be said for the system adopted by a United States President in the mid-1980s, of doing virtually nothing. This left time to think, if he felt up to it, or to sleep if he didn't – Ed.*]

In the absence of the expected backlog of work, the Prime Minister wanted to look at his press clippings.

He was delighted with the report sent to him by Malcolm Warren, the Number Ten Press Officer. Apparently in our absence the PM had been on all the TV news bulletins for three successive nights. There had been a special feature on *Panorama*. There were 1269 column inches in the nationals, and thirty-one photos. There were also sixteen radio reports.

I asked the Prime Minister if he regarded the Washington visit as a success. He did not understand my question – in his view, it was by definition a success if it achieved all this publicity.

My question related to possible agreements with the Americans. However, it seems that little progress was made on that front.

[*Later that day Bernard Woolley had a meeting with Sir Humphrey*

Appleby in his office. Sir Humphrey records the meeting in detail in his own diary – Ed.]

BW came to give me a report on the PM's Washington visit and confirmed that he had not mentioned his new defence policy to the President. This was a relief.

Nonetheless, we still have a considerable problem. By 'we' I mean all of us in the Cabinet Office, the Treasury, the MOD, the FCO and sundry lesser departments. The Prime Minister still wishes to cancel Trident and Cruise, continue with Polaris and bring back conscription to achieve a large conventional army.

BW, very properly in his role as Principal Private Secretary, defended the Prime Minister's ideas. He argued that to save money, reduce unemployment and make our defence credible is a worthy aim. I give him alpha plus for loyalty but nought out of ten for common sense.

He appears to believe that the purpose of our defence policy is to defend Britain. Clearly in this modern world this is an impossibility. Therefore, the only purpose of our defence policy is to make people *believe* that Britain is defended.

Some advocates of the deterrent theory understand this, but they assume that our defence policy is designed to make the Russians believe that we are defended. This is absurd. Our policy exists to make the *British* believe Britain is defended – the Russians know it's not.

Our defence policy is therefore designed to impress all those simple ignorant British citizens who shuffle in and out of houses, buses, pubs, factories and the Cabinet Room. We are trying to make them feel secure.

BW and the PM are seeking a better way, which is doubtless thoroughly laudable. But the very words 'better way' imply change, always a most dangerous notion.

At the moment we have a magic wand. It is called Trident. No one understands anything about it except that it will cost £15 billion, which means that it must be wonderful. Magical. We just have to write the cheque, and then we can all relax. But if people in the government start talking about it, eventually they will start *thinking* about it. Then they will realise the problems, the flaws in the reasoning. Result: the nation gets anxious.

BW was quite clear about these dangers after I had explained them to him. But he raised the question of the PM's impending television broadcast. He was concerned that the PM might want to use it to announce his new policy, immediately after discussing it in Cabinet and announcing it to the House. He might seek to use a TV appearance to open a national debate. This would be a bad precedent – one should not open a national debate until the government has privately made up its mind.

BW thinks that the PM has indeed made up his mind. If so, he must unmake it. I instructed him to see to it immediately.

BW was not sure that he could oblige, and loyally he pointed out that the PM is the PM, and, as such, he has certain rights and powers.

The PM's rights are obvious and generous. He gets his own car and driver, a nice house in London, a place in the country, endless publicity and a pension for life. I asked BW what more the PM wants.

'I think he wants to govern Britain,' he replied.

This must be stopped! He is not qualified.

[*Appleby Papers WB/CAA/400*]

[*Hacker's diary continues – Ed.*]

February 7th

I felt much more energetic today, and I also saw Humphrey for the first time since I'd been back, which was very pleasant.

But we began the day with a big meeting with Malcolm, to discuss my first broadcast on TV since I became Prime Minister. It raised a whole lot of interesting questions and problems that, as a mere Cabinet Minister, had never before confronted me.

The first question he raised was whether the broadcast should be an interview or to camera. I didn't understand the difference at first so I just said yes. But he explained that it had to be one or the other.

At first I suggested an interview, because I felt it might be less like hard work. But Malcolm immediately asked who I should like to be interviewed by. It seemed that the choice was between Robin Day, Brian Walden, Terry Wogan or Jimmy Young [*all well-known media people during Hacker's first term as Prime Minister although now, alas, forgotten – Ed.*].

'It depends, Prime Minister, whether you wish to be seen as a thinker, a man of power, the people's friend or just a good fellow.'

'All of them, really,' I said, but he misunderstood this and said that they wouldn't all interview me at once. I hadn't meant all of *them*, I'd meant that I wish to be seen to have all those qualities. Since I have them I couldn't see a problem.

Malcolm shook his head knowledgeably. 'An image is automatically created by the choice of interviewer. How do you wish to place the emphasis?'

I suggested that I should be seen primarily as a thinker. This, apparently, meant Brian Walden would talk to me. But Malcolm said there were problems associated with Brian Walden. 'He knows rather too much. He was an MP himself, don't forget.'

'Isn't that a help?' I wondered.

'No. Because if you don't answer the question, he asks it again. If you don't answer it a second time, he asks it a third time. Then, if you don't answer it three times, he tells the viewers you haven't answered it, and that you had three opportunities.'

On reflection, it seemed that Walden might not necessarily be the best choice. And perhaps, I thought, it would be good if my image were more the Man of Power rather than the Thinker.

Apparently this meant that I'd have to talk to Robin Day. But Malcolm said I would have to dominate him to get away with it. Dominating Day seemed a tall order, but clearly Malcolm felt that otherwise he might look more like a Prime Minister than I do.

Bernard Woolley felt that Robin Day was a little easier to handle since he got his K.[1] Be that as it may, I felt it would be better to take no chances. 'How would it be,' I asked, 'if I just opt for being a good fellow.'

'That means Wogan,' replied Malcolm. 'But you'd have to bandy words with him.'

I couldn't think what Malcolm meant. 'Bandy words?'

Bernard explained. 'You'd have to be witty.'

I could see no problem there. I've always been very witty. But Malcolm and Bernard were looking excessively gloomy. I couldn't see why, till Bernard suddenly said: 'Well . . . the trouble is, he rather goes in for insult humour.'

'Would he insult the Prime Minister?' I couldn't believe it.

'He insults everybody, if he feels so inclined.'

I had an idea. 'Perhaps *he'd* like a knighthood.'

Bernard didn't think much of that idea. 'Sir Terence Wogan? I hardly think so, Prime Minister.'

I was forced to agree that it would be a bit much, although a CBE would be okay and might ensure that he wasn't insulting.

Bernard was still unimpressed with the idea. 'Well . . . he's Irish. I'm not sure they really understand about honours. Also, being a Commander of the British Empire mightn't go down awfully well in Ireland. Especially in the peat bogs from which he emanates.'

It seemed to me that Bernard had a point. So it just left one option: I'd have to appear as the People's Friend, on the Jimmy Young show.

'There are problems with him too,' remarked Malcolm. 'You rather get shoved in between the record requests, the traffic news and the shopping basket.'

Bernard agreed. 'He's awfully chummy, but it can all look a bit lightweight. Furthermore, he's only on the radio.' [*How something can look anything on radio Bernard did not explain – Ed.*]

By this time I'd rather gone off the whole idea of an interview. It seems to me that it's much better for me to talk to the camera – then

[1] Knighthood.

I'll be in charge, not those failed MPs and jumped-up disc jockeys.

Malcolm suggested a party political. I thought that was a really crummy idea. Party politicals spell instant boredom. My whole idea is that it should be a Prime Minister addressing his People.

Bernard intervened. 'If you do that it will be a ministerial broadcast, and the Leader of the Opposition will want the right of reply.'

On the face of it, that is absurd. I said I wouldn't give a right of reply. Reply to what? I am Prime Minister, and I wish to speak to the people of my country.

Bernard was insistent that, constitutionally, we do have to give a right of reply. I asked him whose side he was on.

He was at his most punctilious and prissy. 'I am simply thinking ahead, Prime Minister. When you are the Leader of the Opposition, you will want the right of reply.'

I have no intention of being the Leader of the Opposition, at least not in the remotely foreseeable future. But I could see that I had to concede the point. So I told Bernard that I'd do it into the camera, like a party political.

'But you said they were boring,' he said.

I was getting fed up with him. 'I didn't say *I* would be boring, did I?' Silence. 'Do *you* think I'd be boring?' He made no reply. I should think not! It is highly unlikely that I would ever make a boring speech or broadcast, as he knows only too well!

Malcolm asked me if I'd done much talking to cameras. As I haven't, he offered to fix a rehearsal – an excellent idea.

Then he raised one final question. 'What is the broadcast to be about?'

I couldn't think what he meant for a moment. Obviously the broadcast is to be about me. I explained this to him, and he saw the point entirely. However, he wanted further clarification on one small matter of detail: what exactly was I going to say?

I couldn't see that this mattered much, but he wanted to know which policies I'd be referring to. I explained that it would be the usual: go forward together, a better tomorrow, tighten our belts, all pull together, healing the wounds, that sort of thing.

He was happy with that, but urged me to consider what I'd say *specifically*. My first thought was that I'd talk about specifically tightening our belts, healing specific wounds in our society.

But Malcolm pressured me to consider saying something *new*. I'd never considered that. Then, suddenly, I realised what an opportunity I have here: I shall talk about my Grand Design. I told

Malcolm that I'd let him have the text in due course. Meanwhile, he is going to find a suitable producer for the broadcast and set up a rehearsal. It all looks very promising.

February 8th

Tense meeting with Humphrey today. He had requested it for the earliest available moment today.

As soon as I was settled in my study I sent for him. He arrived almost at once. He must have been waiting downstairs for me.

'Ah, Humphrey,' I said. 'Here already?'

'Yes. I gather you want to discuss a television appearance.'

I was surprised that this was what he wanted to talk about. 'It's not that desperately urgent, is it?' I asked.

'Absolutely not,' he agreed. 'Not remotely important.'

I wasn't awfully pleased that my first TV broadcast should be described by Humphrey as not remotely important. He must have seen the expression on my face, because he hastily added that it was terribly important, but not a worry or a crisis.

It was quite clear that he wasn't worried about the broadcast *per se*, but about my Grand Design. He doesn't want me to mention it on the air.

I told him that I proposed to do just that and I asked him for his opinion.

'I think it is a mistake, Prime Minister.'

'The policy?' I asked. I was enjoying myself.

'No, no, announcing it on television. Precipitate. Premature. Perilous.'

He has an undoubted talent for alliteration when under pressure. I continued my little game. 'So . . . you do approve of the policy?'

He was trapped. He couldn't say he disapproved of both the policy and the TV announcement. It's not up to Civil Servants to approve policy. He hesitated. I waited. But of course, he was not lost for words for very long. 'I . . . er . . . I think the policy, is, er, interesting . . . imaginative . . . stimulating. A *most* stimulating approach. *Tremendously* refreshing to have a new mind on the old problem, challenging old ideas, questioning the whole basis of government thinking for the past thirty years.'

The implication was clear. If I was about to overturn all government thinking for the past thirty years, I must be an moronic idiot.

So I gave him the opportunity to express his opinion. 'You don't approve of the policy?'

As usual, he was less than frank. 'That's not true, Prime Minister. It's just that there are implications. Repercussions. Reverberations. Knock-on effects. We need time to sift and weigh the evidence. Examine the options. Test the arguments. Review. Research. Consult.'

I couldn't have been more helpful. I told Humphrey that he should press on with all those tasks, and, meanwhile, I would announce the policy in the broadcast.

'No!' he yelped. 'You can't. Not yet.'

'Why?' I wanted to know. He still hadn't come up with a reason.

'Well . . . we have to tell the Americans.'

Now I was angry. Suddenly I'd had enough. Only last week, before I went to America, he advised me *not* to tell the Americans. That's why I didn't do it while I was there. I faced him with this.

'Ah . . .' he replied carefully, 'yes, but that was before your visit. It was the wrong moment to talk to them.'

'And after I've got back,' I enquired with heavy irony, 'is the right moment to talk to them?'

He was defiant. 'Yes. But they will have grave objections. It will take many months of patient diplomacy. Delicate issues need sensitive handling.'

I decided it was time to remind Humphrey who was boss. 'Humphrey, who has the last word about the government of Britain? The British Cabinet or the American President?'

He sat back, crossed his legs, and considered the matter for a moment. 'That's a fascinating question, Prime Minister. We often discuss it.'

'And what conclusion do you come to?'

'Well,' he replied, 'I have to admit I'm a bit of a heretic. I think it's the British Cabinet. But I know I'm in a minority.'

I told Humphrey that I had news for him. From now on he is in the majority.

He was surprised. 'But you got on so well with the President.' He's right. I did. In fact, when we started our talks I read him my brief and he read me his, and then we decided it would be much quicker if we just swapped briefs and read them to ourselves. So we spent nearly all the time rubbishing the French. Terrific.

But now the honeymoon's over. I told Humphrey in no uncertain terms that from now on Britain will be governed in the interests of the British and not the Americans.

Humphrey wouldn't accept this. 'Prime Minister, are you sure you can make that change without the approval of the Americans?'

I brushed his objections aside. I told him we would start to assert our independence with my Grand Design.

'Good, good,' he said. He was very unhappy. 'Excellent – but . . . not yet! It is my duty to speak up for the legitimate constitutional interests of the Cabinet. I'm their Secretary.'

A ridiculous ploy. 'You don't have to do that,' I pointed out. 'I appointed them. They are my government.'

'With respect, Prime Minister, they are Her Majesty's Government.' Now he was splitting hairs.

'With all due respect, Humphrey,' I said, putting him firmly in his place. 'I shall raise the policy formally with OPD[1] and then put it to Cabinet. I've sounded most of them out privately. They think it's a major contribution to the defence of this country, and, as such, very popular [*i.e. a vote-winner – Ed.*].'

'With *great respect*, Prime Minister,' he was pulling no punches, 'it's not just a matter for the Cabinet. You know it must be announced to the House first. You are still a House of Commons man.'

I didn't need to be reminded of this. 'With the *greatest* respect, Humphrey,' I replied nastily, 'I'm announcing the Grand Design in the evening broadcast. I'll tell the House that same afternoon.'

'With the *greatest possible* respect, Prime Minister . . .'

I won't put up with that sort of insolence. 'You may regret that remark,' I informed him abruptly.

February 10th

Today we did the rehearsal for my television appearance. A very difficult and slightly embarrassing day.

We started with me sitting at a desk, talking to the camera. The script was on one of those autocue things.

We got off to a fairly bad start. I started the speech. It was the usual drivel. 'So let us be abundantly clear about this. We cannot go on paying ourselves more than we earn. The rest of the world does not owe us a living. We must be prepared to make sacrifices.' And so on. Cliché after cliché.

I demanded to be told who wrote this rubbish, and Bernard told me, in front of everybody, that I did. I couldn't believe it at first, but it turned out to be a rather old speech written when I was much less experienced.

Nonetheless, I had to explain that it wasn't drivel exactly (which

[1] The Overseas Policy and Defence Committee of the Cabinet.

I'm afraid it was) but that I felt we should be rehearsing with the draft of my actual broadcast.

Bernard seemed reluctant, because it was only a draft. I couldn't see that it mattered, since we were only doing a practice. Bernard said that it was highly confidential as it referred to my Grand Design, cancelling Trident, reintroducing conscription and so forth. I still couldn't see a problem – everyone in the room had been cleared.

So I insisted that they put the actual draft speech up on the autocue. I couldn't see why Bernard was being so unhelpful about it all.

Malcolm has found an ex-BBC producer called Godfrey Essex to advise me on the art of television. Very nice chap, I thought. Tall, slim, slightly grey, distinguished-looking with glasses – very experienced, with a gentle intelligent manner and a bow tie. While they changed the autocue I asked him how I was doing. He was extremely encouraging and said that I was pretty good.

But he raised an interesting point. The first of many, actually. He asked me if I'd be wearing my glasses.

I asked for his opinion.

'It's up to you,' he replied carefully. 'With them on you look authoritative and commanding. With them off you look honest and open. Which do you want?'

This was the first of many imponderables upon which I had to decide. I hadn't known this sort of thing mattered. I told Godfrey that I'd really like to look authoritative *and* honest.

'It's one or the other, really,' he said.

'Suppose . . .' I thought for a moment, 'suppose I sort of put them on and take them off while I talk?'

'That just looks indecisive.'

Well, I certainly don't want to look indecisive. That would be a travesty of the truth. I weighed up the pros and cons, unable to decide.

'What about a monocle?' suggested Bernard. I suppose it was one of his jokes.

I have left the decision about the glasses until the day of the recording.

The autocue was fixed, the new script in, and I began. Godfrey, Bernard, and Fiona – a charming make-up lady – all clustered around a monitor, watching me carefully. I felt as though I were a specimen under a microscope. It is a strange feeling, being watched so minutely.

I was pleased with the speech as it began. 'The Trident programme is too expensive. By cancelling it we shall release billions of pounds to fund an imaginative and radical attack on the nation's problems.'

Godfrey interrupted me. He told me it was *very* good, but he clearly had something on his mind. Bernard tried to talk to me as well, but I told him to wait.

Godfrey said that I was leaning forward too much, and that this made me look as though I was selling insurance. Trying to urge the customers to sign.

I tried a variety of ways of sitting, leaning and looking. I could tell that Godfrey didn't totally approve of any of them. Bernard and Malcolm had been off in a corner, and came back with a slightly different version of the speech: *We shall of course be reviewing a wide range of options over the whole field of government expenditure.*

'Bernard,' I exclaimed, slightly exasperated. 'That doesn't say anything.'

'Thank you, Prime Minister.'

He'd missed the point. 'Totally devoid of impact,' I explained.

'You're too kind,' he replied with a modest blush.

'No Bernard – *I don't like it!*'

He was surprised, and looked at it again to see how it could be given more impact. 'How about *urgently* reviewing?'

I scowled at him. He was a little edgy but stuck to his guns. 'I do really feel, Prime Minister, that it should be toned down a bit.'

I turned to Malcolm for his thoughts or guidance. He suggested: *The Trident programme is a heavy burden on your tax bill. £15 billion is a lot of money and we shall be looking at it very carefully to see if it merits the amount it costs.*

It obviously watered down the content somewhat but I accepted the compromise. I checked with Godfrey if it was okay to mention figures.

'Yes.' He was quite enthusiastic about figures. 'I mean, practically no one takes them in and those who do don't believe them. But it makes people think you've got the facts at your fingertips. Don't forget, people don't know you're reading them off the teleprompter.'

Good point. Apart from that his only criticism was that I was going a bit slowly. This was true – but I was going slowly because the teleprompter thing was going slowly. But I needn't have worried. He explained that it follows your speed – if you go fast, or slow, it just goes with you.

I tried it. Very slowly I said: 'The . . . Tri . . . dent . . . pro . . . gra . . . mme . . . is . . . aaa . . .' And then I speeded up abruptly:

'very-heavy-burden-on-your-tax-bill-Fifteen-billion-pounds-is . . . a . . . lot . . . of . . . mo . . . ney . . . and . . . we . . .' I was going dead slow again. And it worked. Very freeing, but quite difficult to make it look natural, spoken rather than read. Still, I think I got the hang of it pretty fast.

Godfrey picked up on another detail in that paragraph. 'I wonder if you'd mind not saying "*your*" tax bill? It makes you sound as if you're not one of the people. The ruler talking to the ruled. Them and us.'

Another good point. I should say *our* tax bill. I pay tax too!

Bernard was still worrying that this part of the speech was too direct. I couldn't see any problem with that, till Bernard reminded me that a lot of people's jobs in this country depend on Trident. He felt that until there had been some consultation we shouldn't exactly spell this out.

On reflection, I felt he might be right. Malcolm came up with an alternative: *Defence expenditure is one of the areas which this government will be examining closely to see if we can achieve the same level of defence at lower cost.*

It seemed okay to me. But Godfrey said it was too long, and should be said in two sentences. 'We find that if any sentence takes more than two lines, when it gets to the end most people have forgotten how it began. Including the person speaking it.'

So we split that bit into two sentences.

Godfrey was still worried about my position at the desk. Clearly I had not yet arranged myself to his satisfaction. He told me that I was starting to lean forward again.

I couldn't really help it. 'That's what I do,' I explained to him, 'when I want to look sincere.'

'The trouble is,' he replied, 'it makes you look like someone who wants to look sincere. If you lean back, you look relaxed and in control.'

I leaned right back. 'Not *too* far,' Godfrey said, 'it makes you look as though you had a liquid lunch.'

We certainly don't want that! I sat bolt upright, wondering what to do about looking sincere if I couldn't lean forward.

Godfrey had a solution. 'We'll underline the bits of the script where you want to sound sincere. When you come to them you frown, and say them a bit more slowly.'

So far so good. But then he started giving me acting lessons. He told me my face was a bit wooden! Nobody's ever said that to me before. I didn't quite know how to take it.

He explained that in normal speech people move their head and eyebrows and cheek muscles and so on. The teleprompter was apparently turning me into a zombie.

So I tried it again. My efforts to move my face seemed to provoke sniggers in the far corner of the room where the technicians were lurking. Godfrey told me I'd been doing it a little too much that time.

Bernard was still worrying about the relevant paragraph of the speech, which still read: *Defence expenditure is one of those areas which this government will be examining closely.* He still felt it was dangerously explicit. 'If you specify defence cuts it causes a lot of anxiety in places like Devonport, Portsmouth, Rosyth, Aldershot and Bristol.'

I suddenly saw his point. All those towns have marginal constituencies. I told him to tone it down a little. So we went on with another bit of the speech in the meantime.

It went like this. *You'll have heard a lot of nonsense from the Opposition. They say we waste money. They say we are selling out to the United States. I say, look at the mess they made when they were in power. Look at the damage they did to the economy.*

This time it was Godfrey who objected to the content of the speech. 'Prime Minister, if I might suggest – don't attack the Opposition.'

This was a very disappointing response. After all, those are the bits that the Party likes best.

But Godfrey's attitude was most interesting. His argument is that the Party will vote for me anyway. Attacking the Opposition will simply make the floating voters see me as an angry and divisive figure.

If he's right, we certainly don't want that. Godfrey also advised me never to repeat charges people make against me. It just gives more publicity to the criticisms. He also feels that people will think I'm really worried about the Opposition if I go out of my way to attack them.

So I couldn't see what I *could* say about them. His answer was simple. 'Don't mention them at all. Everything you say has to make you sound warm and friendly. Authoritative, of course, but loving. Father of the Nation. Try lowering the pitch of your voice.'

I found it enormously difficult to speak in a deeper voice. It sounded completely false, like a Paul Robeson impression. I'm told that I must take voice lessons from someone at the RSC[1] if I want to get it really right.

Anyway, in as deep a voice as I could muster I started on the next

[1] Royal Shakespeare Company, a theatrical production company which was highly regarded primarily for diction and voice production.

paragraph. *They reduced our gold resources, they destroyed our export trade, they concluded contemptible and infamous agreements* . . . I realised that all of this excellent knocking copy had to go as well. What a pity!

But Godfrey had a word with Malcolm and they slipped in an optimistic, positive piece about me and the future. I think he could be right that this is an improvement on saying negative things about the past: *We want to build a bright future for our children. We want to build a peaceful and prosperous Britain. A Britain that can hold her head high in the fellowship of nations.*

I thought it was rather good. I asked them where they had got it. It turned out they'd taken it from the last Party Political by the Leader of the Opposition. We'll have to paraphrase it.

Godfrey wanted to get back to the subject of my appearance. I prepared myself for more personal criticisms, but he wanted to discuss my clothes initially.

'What will you be wearing?'

'What do you suggest?'

'A dark suit represents traditional values.'

I said I'd wear a dark suit.

'On the other hand, a light suit looks businesslike.'

Another dilemma. To look traditional or businesslike. Again I wanted to look both. 'Could I have a sort of lightish jacket with a darkish waistcoat?'

'No, Prime Minister, that would just look as if you had an identity problem. Of course, you could try a tweed suit, which suggests the British countryside. Environment, conservation and so on.'

This sounded good too. But Godfrey had still more choices to offer. 'A sports jacket can be good – it looks informal and approachable.'

I explained to Godfrey that I am all of these things and have all of these qualities.

He was very good. He told me that I didn't have to make an instant decision, and gave me a list of pointers for when I had time to think about it. 'If you are all these things, then you should emphasise the one you're not. Or the one people are in danger of thinking you're not. So, if you're changing a lot of things, you want to look reassuring and traditional. Therefore you should have a dark suit and an oak-panelled background and leather books. But if you're not doing anything new, you'd want a light modern suit and a modern high-tech setting with abstract paintings.'

Fiona took Godfrey aside for a little word about my make-up. I had mixed feelings about it all. I must say, it is lovely to be fussed over and pampered, but I could hear the whole whispered conversation between them – which I think was not meant for my ears.

'Godfrey, are you happy about the grey hair or shall we darken it?'

'No, it's fine.'

'And the receding hairline?'

'Receding what?' I said, to indicate that I could hear them perfectly clearly.

Godfrey swung round. 'High forehead,' he said.

'Fine,' she said.

The next bit didn't please me all that much either, but Godfrey had warned me when he took on the job that he would have to be absolutely frank and honest with me or he wouldn't be of any help. He and Fiona stared at me in person, then at me on the monitor, then back at me again. 'Um, Fiona . . . can you do something about the eyes? Make them look less close-set?'

'Sure.' She could see no problem. Nor could I. 'And shall I lighten the bags underneath, and darken the pallid cheeks?' He nodded. 'The biggest problem is the nose.'

I intervened. 'The nose?'

Godfrey reassured me that there was no problem with my nose *per se*. It was just a lighting problem. There was a large shadow from somewhere, apparently.

I'd had enough of all this. I told them I wanted to get on with the rehearsal. But Godfrey asked Fiona if she had any other problems, reassuring me that all of this was in my interest: the better I look on television, the better chance I have of winning the next election. He's right, of course.

'There's just the teeth, of course,' said Fiona, and turned to me. 'Would you smile, Prime Minister?'

I smiled. They stared at me, gloomily. Then Godfrey sighed. 'Yes,' he said, in a tone of deep melancholy. And he strolled over to my desk. 'Prime Minister, how would you feel about a little dental work?'

I didn't feel very good about it at all.

But Godfrey was rather insistent. 'Just a little tooth straightening. People do pick on these things. And it did wonders for Harold Wilson. Look.' Fiona handed me two photos of Wilson, before and after his dental work.

I'll make an appointment for next week.

[*We have been fortunate to find the two photographs amongst Hacker's private papers, stored with the original cassette of this section of his diary. We reproduce them below – Ed.*]

So we began again. I sat back, but not too far back. I spoke in a deep voice, moved my face and eyebrows a little, and read at a variable speed: *We shall of course be reviewing a wide range of options over the whole field of government expenditure* . . . and I realised that this was exactly what I'd started out with!

I was getting irritated. I told Bernard that we seemed to be going round in circles.

'Prime Minister,' he said, 'I do think that this is the most suitable, most appropriate . . .'

'Most meaningless,' I interjected.

He begged leave to differ. 'Not exactly meaningless, Prime Minister. More non-committal.'

I was beginning to despair of ever getting it together. I asked Godfrey for his opinion on the material.

He wouldn't give it, of course. I don't blame him. It's not his problem. 'It's up to you, of course, Prime Minister,' he said, returning the ball firmly to my court. 'All I can say is that, if that's what you want to say, I suggest a very modern suit. And a high-tech background and a high-energy yellow wallpaper with abstract paintings. Everything to disguise the absence of anything new in the actual speech.'

I told him that I might go back to the original speech.

'Then,' said Godfrey obligingly, 'it's the dark suit and the oak panelling.'

Bernard was quite extraordinarily upset at my suggestion that I might go back to the old version. 'Prime Minister, I do earnestly beg you to reconsider.'

I decided that the moment had come to make my position plain. I told him, told them all, that as this is my first broadcast as PM it is imperative that it deals with an important subject. I can't just go on the air and waffle. My speech must have impact.

Bernard said that he agreed wholeheartedly (which he didn't, by the way) but couldn't I make a speech on a less controversial subject. I explained that, by definition, less controversial subjects have less impact than more controversial subjects.

'Surely some less controversial subjects have impact?'

'Such as?' I waited for his suggestions with interest.

'Well . . . litter!' Was he being serious? 'A stinging attack on people who drop litter. Or safer driving. Or saving energy. Lots of subjects.'

I made my own suggestion. I told him to save some energy himself.

Godfrey raised one final matter. The opening music. The same rules apply apparently: Bach for new ideas, Stravinsky for no change.

I suggested to Godfrey that it might be appropriate if we used music by British composers. Something that reflects my image. He seemed to like that idea. 'Elgar, perhaps?'

'Yes,' I said, 'but not *Land of Hope and Glory*.'

'How about the *Enigma Variations*?' said Bernard. I silenced him with a look.

[Three days later Bernard Woolley sent a note to Sir Humphrey Appleby, about the content of Hacker's television speech. Fortunately this came to light amongst the documents released under the Thirty Year Rule. We reproduce the original below – Ed.]

10 DOWNING STREET

From the Principal Private Secretary

February 13

Dear Humphrey,

I'm afraid the TV appearance looks unpromising. The Prime Minister has ordered a dark suit and oak panelling. This means that he is planning to say something new and radical on the air, hence the need for a traditional, conventional, reassuring image.

I know that this will cause you some concern, but he is very keen on it.

Yours ever,

B.W.

[Bernard Woolley received this reply on the following day – Ed.]

70 WHITEHALL, LONDON SW1A 2AS

From the Secretary of the Cabinet and Head of the Home Civil Service

February 14

Dear Bernard,

The Prime Minister's intention to discuss his so-called Grand Design on television is a matter of the utmost concern.

The fact that he is very keen on it is neither here nor there. Things don't happen just because Prime Ministers are keen on them. Neville Chamberlain was very keen on peace.

This is precisely what we had hoped you would avoid.

Why has this happened?

Yours ever

AH.

[Bernard Woolley immediately sent a brief note in reply – Ed.]

1O DOWNING STREET

From the Principal Private Secretary

February 14

Dear Humphrey,

The explanation is that the Prime Minister thinks that his Grand Design is a vote-winner.

The party has had an opinion poll done. It seems that the voters are in favour of bringing back National Service.

Yours ever,
B. W.

SIR BERNARD WOOLLEY RECALLS:[1]

Yes, I remember that exchange of notes. Humphrey Appleby was not at all pleased that I had failed to have Hacker's speech watered down, in spite of my best efforts.

He asked me to drop in on him in the Cabinet Office, to discuss the situation. He was most interested in the party opinion poll, which I had seen as an insuperable obstacle to changing the Prime Minister's mind.

His solution was simple: have another opinion poll done, one that would show that the voters were *against* bringing back National Service.

I was somewhat *naif* in those days. I did not understand how the voters could be both for it and against it. Dear old Humphrey showed me how it's done.

The secret is that when the Man In The Street is approached by a nice attractive young lady with a clipboard he is asked a *series* of questions. Naturally the Man In The Street wants to make a good impression and doesn't want to make a fool of himself. So the market researcher asks questions designed to elicit *consistent* answers.

Humphrey demonstrated the system on me. 'Mr Woolley, are you worried about the rise in crime among teenagers?'

'Yes,' I said.

'Do you think there is a lack of discipline and vigorous training in our Comprehensive Schools?'

'Yes.'

'Do you think young people welcome some structure and leadership in their lives?'

'Yes.'

'Do they respond to a challenge?'

'Yes.'

'Might you be in favour of reintroducing National Service?'

'Yes.'

Well, naturally I said yes. One could hardly have said anything else without looking inconsistent. Then what happens is that the Opinion Poll publishes only the last question and answer.

Of course, the reputable polls didn't conduct themselves like that. But there weren't too many of those. Humphrey suggested that we commission a new survey, not for the Party but for the Ministry of Defence. We did so. He invented the questions there and then:

'Mr Woolley, are you worried about the danger of war?'

'Yes,' I said, quite honestly.

'Are you unhappy about the growth of armaments?'

'Yes.'

'Do you think there's a danger in giving young people guns and teaching them how to kill?'

'Yes.'

'Do you think it wrong to force people to take up arms against their will?'

'Yes.'

'Would you oppose the reintroduction of National Service?'

[1] In conversation with the Editors.

I'd said 'Yes' before I'd even realised it, d'you see?

Humphrey was crowing with delight. 'You see, Bernard,' he said to me, 'you're the perfect Balanced Sample.'

Humphrey really had a very fertile mind. It was a pleasure to work closely with him.

He had more suggestions to make. The Prime Minister was planning to make his broadcast in three or four weeks' time. The Cabinet Secretary urged me to tell Hacker that he should make the broadcast within the next eleven days.

I thought the Prime Minister might refuse. It was rather soon. Humphrey had foreseen this. He advised me to tell Hacker that I had just learned from the Joint Broadcasting Committee that the Opposition would have a Party Political in eighteen days' time, that Hacker was entitled to do his Ministerial first, but that if he didn't the first political broadcast of his Premiership would be given by the Opposition.

I wondered if Humphrey was telling me the truth. I challenged him on it. 'It will be,' he said with a smile, 'if you don't tell him till tomorrow morning.'

The reason for bringing Hacker's broadcast forward was to outflank him. He would not be able to use it to announce his new policy because within the ensuing eleven days he would have been able to squeeze in only one meeting of the Overseas and Defence Policy Committee – not enough to clear such a radical change of direction with his Cabinet colleagues.

His colleagues were largely in favour of the policy at that time. But only personally. Only politically. Not *officially*!

As responsible departmental Ministers their official reaction had to depend on the advice that they received.

[*Meetings at Whitehall were invariably minuted. Inter-departmental meetings were no exception. Everything had to be recorded on paper, as a record of what was decided and how it was to be acted upon. There was a wide measure of agreement that this was essential for the continuity of government. One meeting, however, was never minuted: this was the weekly meeting of Permanent Secretaries, which took place in the Cabinet Secretary's office every Wednesday, the day before Cabinet met. This was an informal 'keeping in touch' meeting, with no agenda.*

Fortunately for historians, Sir Humphrey did make private notes about some of these meetings, for his own purposes. He guarded them jealously throughout his lifetime. Lady Appleby has been good enough to make these notes available to us, and they include a record of the Permanent Secretaries' meeting on the morning of Wednesday 15 February – Ed.]

Very useful chin-wag this morning. Among those present were Dick, Norman, Giles and David. [*Sir Richard Wharton, Permanent Under-Secretary of the Foreign and Commonwealth Office; Sir Norman Coppitt, Permanent*

Under-Secretary of the Ministry of Defence; Sir Giles Bretherton, Permanent Under-Secretary of the Department of Education and Science; and Sir David Smith, Permanent Under-Secretary of the Department of Employment – Ed.]

We discussed the Prime Minister's so-called Grand Design. We agreed at the outset that the idea of abandoning Trident and Cruise missiles and of increasing conventional forces by means of conscription was both a novel and an imaginative proposal. [*From these two adjectives can be seen the depth of the contempt and animosity which those Civil Servants present at the meeting felt for Hacker's policy – Ed.*]

We agreed that as loyal Permanent Secretaries we have a duty to do everything in our power to assist its implementation.

Nonetheless, we suspected that our political masters may perhaps not have thought through all the implications. In view of this we discussed them at length, in order to be able to brief them when the PM raises the question tomorrow in Cabinet Committee.

Dick said that there were problems from the FCO point of view. The Americans simply won't stand for it. Not that British policy is determined by the Americans – Heaven forbid! – but, in practice, we do know that it is sensible to clear all new initiatives with Washington. Last time we failed to do so the results were unfortunate.[1]

I warned Dick that the Prime Minister might be somewhat hazy about the events at Suez, and therefore this argument might not worry him. Nor will he wish to look as though he is kow-towing to the Americans.

Dick raised one further point: cancelling Trident so early in his Premiership might look like weakness. Appeasement of the Soviets. Lack of courage and resolve. We agreed that this should form the basis of the Foreign Office view. The Prime Minister admires courage, from a safe distance. I enquired if Dick had been stating the views of the Secretary of State for Foreign Affairs. Dick was confident that these would be his views by tomorrow.

Norman was particularly concerned about the new policy, since it affects him most closely at the MOD. The Secretary of State for Defence is fairly confused at the moment – his special problem is that the advice from the Navy, Army and RAF is not always identical. There is underlying harmony, of course, but they have no one on whom to vent their warlike instincts except each other. However, the one thing that unifies the three Services is their implacable opposition to conscription. They have nothing against the young people of this country, but they do not want their skilled professional élite armed forces diluted by riff-raff. British officers are the best leaders of men in NATO. It is true that there are hardly any men to lead, which might be the reason why they lead so well.

I indicated to Norman that the Prime Minister might not take the opposition of the Service Chiefs as the clinching argument.

Norman felt that the argument should be kept simple: Trident is the best and Britain must have the best. This is an argument that could well appeal to the Defence Secretary. He is very simple himself and he will be able to follow it. We agreed that Norman would give him a little coaching.

[1] The Suez crisis, 1956.

The discussion turned to the DES. Giles felt that there could be problems with conscription from the educational point of view. Our educational system has been a triumphant success in turning out socially integrated and creatively aware children who are fully trained in the arts and techniques of self-expression. The DES has a proud record in this, and has done a first-class job. However, Giles felt that conscription would inevitably give publicity to the fact that many school-leavers cannot actually read, write or do sums. So the NUT[1] will be violently against its introduction.

Furthermore, there is a slight incidental risk that the Services might take over most of the Colleges of Further Education and use them for *teaching* purposes. We all agreed that such unnecessary interference would be rather shocking – a total distortion of their function.

I was concerned that, as conscription is not really an educational issue, it would be hard for Giles's Secretary of State to involve the NUT veto. Giles felt that, on the contrary, the NUT might veto his Secretary of State, making his life impossible.

I asked Giles what advice he proposed to give his political master. Giles remarked that although conscription is not what the DES call education, it would work very well in terms of actually teaching people things. So it's hard to oppose. Not that any of us want want to oppose it.

Norman wondered if the issue could not be raised that there has been a lack of reasonable time for deliberation. Fatal to rush things.

I suggested that there might be educational question marks about the credentials of the man putting the idea forward: Professor Rosenblum.[2]

Giles agreed enthusiastically. He felt it could be argued that Rosenblum's figures have come under severe critical scrutiny, or perhaps that he is academically suspect. He felt that this would be his Secretary of State's view, once the Secretary of State heard the facts. Indeed, Giles recalled that there is a paper coming out that criticises the whole basis of Professor Rosenblum's thinking. It will be coming out tomorrow morning. [*This technique is known in the Civil Service, as it is in football, as Playing the Man Not the Ball – Ed.*]

It so happens that this paper will be written [*Sir Humphrey made a slip here. He should have said* has been written – *Ed.*] by one of the Professors who was passed over for Chief Scientific Adviser. Not that he is jealous – he just feels that Rosenblum's influence may not be an entirely good thing.

We agreed that, to avoid hurting his feelings, it would probably be best if Professor Rosenblum does not actually see the paper. It should be submitted by Giles as personal advice to the Secretary of State. [*It is essential, if you play the man and not the ball, that you do not let the man know you are doing so – Ed.*]

We turned finally to the employment implications. It is a significant part of this scheme that National Service might involve young people in doing useful jobs in the community.

David felt that this was a jolly good idea, on the face of it. But it does create grave problems with the Unions. Once you start giving jobs to non-

[1] National Union of Teachers.
[2] See Chapter 2, page 65.

members of Trade Unions you are on a very slippery slope. Once you let a couple of kids do up the old folks' houses, you will have an uproar from all the bricklayers, plasterers, painters, plumbers, electricians and carpenters who ought to be doing it instead.

We agreed that community service can be very damaging to the community. However, it is likely that the Prime Minister will argue that if the kids were earning a living and the old people were pleased with the work, that would be all right. This argument is of course an over-simplification, but the Prime Minister never seems too worried about over-simplification.

David had an excellent idea. He felt that the Secretary of State for Employment might argue that the unemployed young people are now unfit, unorganised, undisciplined and untrained. They are a problem – but not a threat! Conscription would mean eventually releasing on to the streets an army of fit young people all trained to kill.

We unanimously agreed that this is a far-sighted and responsible attitude, and we encouraged David to ensure that his Secretary of State had taken the idea on board by tomorrow.

In my summing up we all agreed that there was no question of our trying to oppose the Prime Minister's policy, which we believe to be novel and imaginative. We are only opposed to precipitate haste.

[*Appleby Papers PA/121/LAX*]

[*Hacker's diary continues – Ed.*]

February 16th

Cabinet Committee this afternoon, and my colleagues responded to the Grand Design in a way that I did not predict.

It was last on the agenda. I told them that I intended to announce my Grand Design in my TV broadcast on Friday, and – if the Committee agreed – I would put it to full Cabinet on Thursday morning and tell the House the same afternoon.

There was a bit of a silence. I took it as general assent. So I was about to pass on to the next item when Duncan[1] spoke up.

'Prime Minister, I think it is an excellent plan,' he began.

'Good,' I said.

'The only thing is . . . cancelling Trident so early in your premiership could look like weakness to the Soviets.'

Humphrey grunted an impressed grunt, nodded thoughtfully, and turned to me with an enquiring expression.

I was a little taken aback. When last I spoke to Duncan he had been completely in favour. 'I thought you were in favour of the idea. It would surely enable us to *strengthen* NATO through credible conventional forces.'

[1] Secretary of State for Foreign Affairs.

Duncan nodded, but he didn't agree. 'Yes . . . But it could *look* like lack of courage. It might smack of appeasement.'

I told Duncan that I would record his view, even though he was in a minority of one.

I had spoken too soon. Hugh[1] piped up.

'Well, actually, Prime Minister, although I think it's an excellent plan too, the fact is that Trident is the best and Britain should have the best.'

I was astonished. 'But, Hugh,' I said, 'I thought you wanted to get rid of Trident. Pointless waste of money, you said.'

Hugh looked a little uncomfortable. 'Well, yes, I did say that, but now I'm not sure. I've been reviewing the papers. There's more to it than I thought.' I stared at him coldly. 'Um . . . I'm simply against making an early announcement, that's all.'

'I'm against making an early announcement too, Prime Minister.' Now Patrick[2] was lining up with Duncan and Hugh. I was speechless, so I asked him why.

'Because the whole plan is based on Professor Rosenblum's figures. And my information is that he is academically suspect. I've just received a high-powered paper that severely criticises the whole basis of his argument.'

'But, Patrick,' I said, with rising anxiety, 'you agreed that conscription will solve the whole youth unemployment problem, as well as give us meaningful defence forces.'

Tom[3] replied instead of Patrick. 'Yes, but it has since occurred to me that it will also create an army of fit, disciplined, organised young people who will be released from the forces after two years, unemployed again but now trained to kill.'

I stared at him in disbelief. 'So you're against it *too*?'

He didn't answer directly. 'I'm against an early announcement. I think we need time to consider it all more fully.'

This entire conversation baffled me. Only a week ago they were all agreed that the policy was a real vote-winner. I shall have to think very hard about my next step.

Humphrey said that he'd minute the Committee meeting so as to leave the door open. Jolly helpful of him.

---

[1] Secretary of State for Defence.
[2] Secretary of State for Education.
[3] Secretary of State for Employment.

February 20th

Today I got a memo from Hugh at the MOD. They had an opinion poll done. It says that 73% of the public are against conscription. This is deeply confusing. The Party's poll said 64% in favour! And then the minutes arrived.

[*Sir Humphrey Appleby's minutes have survived the ravages of time, and are shown below – Ed.*]

Item 7, Grand Design   4.

          It is clear that Cabinet Committee is agreed
that the new policy is an excellent plan, in
principle. But in view of the doubts being
expressed, it was decided to record that,
after careful consideration, the considered
view of the committee was that while
they considered the proposal met
with broad approval in principle, it
was felt that some of the principles
were sufficiently fundamental in principle,
and some of the considerations so complex
and finely balanced in practice that
in principle it was proposed that the
sensible and prudent practice would
be to subject the proposal to more detailed
consideration with and across the relevant
departments with a view to preparing
and proposing a more thorough and wide-ranging
proposal, laying stress on the less controversial
elements and giving consideration to the
essential continuity of the new proposal with
existing principles, to be presented for
parliamentary consideration and public discussion
on some more propitious occasion when the
climate of opinion is deemed to be more
amenable for consideration of the approach
and the principle of the principal arguments
which the proposal proposes and propounds
for approval.

[Hacker's diary continues – Ed.]

I read this passage over a few times. I think it simply means that the Committee didn't want me to refer to the Grand Design on TV on Friday.

I have no intention of abandoning my policy. But I'll have a fight on my hands, I can see that.

Meanwhile, I have instructed Bernard that on TV I'd better have a light suit, high-tech furniture, a yellow high-energy wallpaper background, abstract painting – and Stravinsky.

4
The Key

February 27th
Dorothy Wainwright, my Chief Political Adviser, came to see me in the Cabinet Room this morning. She's a very attractive blonde of about forty, slim, efficient, and very hard-nosed.

When I say *my* Chief Political Adviser, it's hardly true. In fact she held that post for my predecessor, the previous Prime Minister, and it seemed a good idea to keep her on.

Humphrey Appleby had hinted that she wasn't awfully helpful – so it seemed an even better idea to keep her on! After all, I do need people who are not strictly within Humphrey's control. But since my first day here, when I asked her to stay, I've hardly seen her. So I was thoroughly surprised not only when she strode purposefully into the Cabinet Room, where I was sitting doing my paperwork, but also by her brisk opening remark.

'Look, Jim, if you don't want me as Political Adviser, I'd much rather you just said so.'

I was amazed. Why did she think I'd asked her to stay on? She was the only person that stopped my predecessor from losing all contact with the real world. But it seems that she has been given the impression that I've arranged for her to be kicked out of her office and banished to the servants' quarters.

'I used to be in the office next door to this room, didn't I?' Was it a rhetorical question or did it demand an answer?

I played safe. 'Yes.'

'And you asked for me to be moved to the front of the building, up three floors, along the corridor, down two steps, round the corner, and four doors along to the right. Next to the photocopier.'

This was news to me. I'd no idea where she'd been. 'I thought you were on holiday or something,' I explained. Actually, the job has been keeping me so busy that, to tell the truth, I'd hardly noticed she wasn't much in evidence. [*This was no coincidence – Ed.*]

'I might as well be on holiday,' she said sharply. 'I came back after your first weekend and found my office turned into a waiting room for Cabinet Ministers, officials and so on. All my things had been moved upstairs to the attic. Humphrey said it was on your instructions. Was it?'

I tried to think. Had I given such instructions? No, I hadn't. And yet . . . I *had*! 'You see, Dorothy, Humphrey came to me with a plan to rationalise things. Make better use of the space.'

She shook her head in silent wonderment. 'Don't you realise that the Civil Service has been trying to get me out of my office for three years?'

How could I have realised that? 'Why?'

'Because geographically it's in the key strategic position. It's the best-placed room in the house.'

'I don't see what difference that makes,' I said. 'You're still in Number Ten.'

'Just,' she said, tight-lipped.

'You get all the documents.'

'Some,' she acknowledged.

'We can talk on the phone,' I reminded her.

'When they put me through,' she said bitterly.

I thought she was being a bit paranoid and I told her so. Then she started talking about Albania and Cuba. She said Albania has very little influence on United States policy, whereas Cuba has a lot of influence. Why? Because Albania is remote and Cuba is near. She argues that, in Number Ten just as in the outside world, influence diminishes with distance. 'And I'm distant,' she finished balefully.

'You're not in Albania,' I said.

'No, I'm in the bloody attic,' she snapped. 'Look!' And she started to move things around on my desk. 'This desk is a plan of Number Ten. This file is the Cabinet Room, where we are now. Through the doors here' – she placed a book at one end of the file – 'is your private office. This ruler is the corridor from the front door – here. *This* corridor' – and she grabbed a paper knife and put it down alongside the file and the book – 'runs from the Cabinet Room and connects up to the locked green-baize door, on the other side of which is the Cabinet Office, which is this blotter, where Sir Humphrey works. This coffee cup is the staircase up to your study. And this saucer is the gents' loo – here. And *this* is – was – my office.' She put an ashtray down beside the file that represented the Cabinet Room. 'Now, my desk faced out into the lobby and I always kept my door open. What could I see?'

I stared at it all. 'You could see,' I said slowly, 'everyone who came in from the front door, or the Cabinet Office, or in and out of the Cabinet Room, or the Private Office, or up and down the stairs.'

She remained silent while I pondered this. Then, pressing home her advantage, she picked up the saucer and put it down again. 'And I was opposite the gents' loo. I *have* to be opposite the loo.'

I asked her if she'd seen a doctor about this, but apparently I was missing the point. 'The *gents'* loo,' she reminded me. 'Almost everyone in the Cabinet is a man. I could hear everything they said to each other, privately, when they popped out of Cabinet meetings for a pee. I was able to keep the last Prime Minister fully informed about all their little foibles.'

'Was that any of his business?' I asked.

'When they were plotting against him, yes!'

She's brilliant! No wonder Humphrey turned her office into a waiting room and banished her to the attic.

I buzzed Bernard. He appeared through the large white double doors from the Private Office, immediately.

'Ah, Bernard,' I said, 'I want you to put Dorothy back in her office.'

'You mean, take her there?' He pointed atticwards.

'No,' I said. 'I mean, take her to the waiting room, just outside here.'

Bernard was puzzled. '*Before* she goes back to her office, you mean?'

I was patient. 'No, Bernard. I mean the waiting room, which used to be her office, will again be her office.'

'But what about the waiting room?' he asked.

I told him to concentrate, listen carefully, and watch my lips move. 'The–waiting–room–' I said slowly and clearly, 'will–become–Dorothy's–office.'

He seemed to understand, but was still arguing. 'Yes, Prime Minister, but what about waiting?'

I lost my temper and shouted at him. '*No, Bernard, right away!*'

It *still* wasn't clear to him. Desperately he stood his ground. 'Yes, Prime Minister, I realise you mean at once, no waiting, but what *I* mean is, where will people wait if there is no waiting room to wait in?'

I saw what he meant. It was just a simple misunderstanding, that's all. But his question was still pretty daft. 'The whole building is full of waiting rooms,' I pointed out. 'All the state rooms upstairs, hardly ever used. And then there's the lobby, here!' I indicated my desk.

Bernard looked blank. 'Where?'

'There,' I said. 'Look. Between the ashtray, the cup and the saucer.'

He looked at the desk, then back to me, wide-eyed with confusion. 'Between the coffee cup and the saucer?'

He's so *dense* sometimes. 'The saucer is the gents' loo, Bernard,' I told him. 'Wake up!'

I sometimes wonder if Bernard's mind is agile enough for this job.

SIR BERNARD WOOLLEY RECALLS:[1]
Naturally I immediately acted upon the Prime Minister's instructions. I had no axe to grind, it was Sir Humphrey who had insisted that Mrs Wainwright was moved away from her strategic position overlooking the lobby outside the Cabinet Room.

The following day Humphrey phoned me and instructed me to explain myself or withdraw the instructions. I told him that there was nothing to explain – it seemed a matter of minor significance.

An hour later a note arrived from him, written in his own hand.

[Sir Bernard was kind enough to lend us the note from Sir Humphrey. We print it below – Ed.]

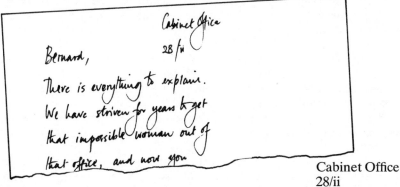

Cabinet Office
28/ii

Bernard,

There is everything to explain. We have striven for years to get that impossible woman out of that office, and now you snatch defeat from the jaws of victory.

The fact that the PM requested it is neither here nor there. You do not have to grant every little request from the Prime Minister. You have to explain that some of them are not in his own best interests. Most of them, in fact.

Our job is to see that the PM is not confused. Politicians are simple people. They like simple choices, and clear guidance. They do not like doubt and conflict. And that woman makes him doubt everything we tell him.

H.A.

P.S. Please destroy this letter immediately.

[1] In conversation with the Editors.

[*Fortunately for historians Sir Bernard did not obey Sir Humphrey's instruction to destroy the letter. Nor did he immediately withdraw the instructions to change Mrs Wainwright's office – Ed.*]

SIR BERNARD WOOLLEY RECALLS:[1]

No, indeed I didn't. I felt it was my duty to argue the Prime Minister's case. So Humphrey popped over to the Private Office to discuss it further. He wasn't pleased that I was taking an independent view.

I told him, quite simply, that Mr Hacker liked Mrs Wainwright. This argument did not impress him. 'Samson liked Delilah,' he commented. Fortunately, the Private Office was deserted. Humphrey had wisely chosen to come to talk to me at the end of the day when all the others had gone home.

I took a strong line with him. I told him that she was not dangerous, in my opinion. For a start, she didn't know very much of what was going on; we had always been careful to keep most of the important documents away from her.

This did not satisfy Humphrey. He reminded me, quite accurately, that we in the Civil Service were duty-bound to ensure the sound government of Britain. Whereas Mrs Wainwright's sole duty was to see that Mr Hacker was re-elected.

I rather felt that if Hacker governed Britain well he *would* be re-elected, and that this was the nub of the disagreement. Appleby maintained, to the end of his days, that good decisions and popular decisions were not only not necessarily the same, but that they hardly ever coincided. His belief was that if Hacker took 'right' or necessary decisions he would lose by a landslide. Therefore, every time we moved Hacker towards a 'right' decision, she would inevitably respond by warning him of potential loss of votes, making our job impossible.

Briefly, therefore, Appleby's thesis was that it was necessary to keep politics out of government. And, by extension, to keep Dorothy Wainwright in the attic.

As he explained this last point the double doors behind him opened and Dorothy Wainwright stepped out of the Cabinet Room. Sir Humphrey handled it with his usual aplomb.

'Ah, good evening, dear lady,' he said as he swung around. 'This is indeed a pleasure.'

She was unimpressed. 'Hullo, Humphrey. Waiting to see the Prime Minister?'

'Indeed I am, dear lady.'

'Why aren't you in the waiting room?'

He had no answer. I thought it was extremely funny but, as always, I had to hide my amusement.

Humphrey turned on me, determined to exert his authority some other way. He informed me that 'an alien' had been admitted to Number Ten the day before. The 'alien' turned out to be the Prime Minister's constituency agent, who had been allowed in without a security pass.

[1] In conversation with the Editors.

He was simply being petty. The policemen outside all knew the man. There was no risk. Nonetheless, Humphrey reminded me – in a slightly humiliating manner – that it was my duty to ensure that everyone who came to the front door must either show their Number Ten pass or have an appointment.

Mrs Wainwright was listening to this conversation, and it did nothing to improve her opinion of Sir Humphrey. 'Excuse me butting in, Bernard,' she said, 'but the Prime Minister asked me to make the necessary arrangements with you for moving my room back.'

I was embarrassed. Humphrey gave me a penetrating stare and waited for me to refuse her. I couldn't see how I could refuse, if the PM had made the request.

I tried to prevaricate, and told her that I just had to deal with Sir Humphrey's request concerning security passes. She said Humphrey's request could wait. He said that it couldn't. She said that it could!

Humphrey turned his back on her and walked into the Cabinet Room to see the PM.

I must say that in all my years in Whitehall I have never seen such direct rudeness as I saw when Sir Humphrey was faced with Mrs Wainwright. I wonder if it was because she was so forthright herself – she certainly didn't pull her punches, as Hacker's diaries reveal. Humphrey obviously disliked her very much indeed – and, if he didn't have cause to initially, he certainly had eventually.

[*Hacker's diary continues – Ed.*]

February 28th

I was dictating letters in the Cabinet Room today after a meeting with Dorothy. She was a little fed up that her office had not been moved back downstairs yet, but it was only yesterday that I gave the go-ahead for it. She felt sure there was opposition from the Civil Service and *I* felt she was being paranoid again.

No sooner had she left than I heard slightly raised voices in the private office. Then Humphrey appeared. 'I understand you are having second thoughts about our office reorganisation,' he said.

'No,' I replied. 'I've simply decided to put Dorothy back in her old office.'

'That, alas, is impossible.'

'Nonsense,' I retorted, and switched on my dictating machine preparatory to writing a letter.

But he didn't drop it. 'No Prime Minister, the whole reorganisation hinges on her moving out.'

I couldn't see why. I told him it was only a waiting room.

'Not *only* a waiting room,' he disagreed firmly, and strolled down the room towards me. 'A vital square on the board.'

'People can wait in the lobby,' I said, unaware that my dictating machine was recording us. 'Or the state rooms.'

'Some people, perhaps,' replied Sir Humphrey. 'But some people must wait where other people cannot see the people who are waiting. And people who arrive before other people must wait where they cannot see the other people who arrive after them being admitted before them. And people who come in from outside must be kept where they cannot see the people from inside coming to tell you what the people from outside have come to see you about. And people who arrive when you are with people they are not supposed to know you have seen must be kept somewhere until the people who are not supposed to have seen you have seen you.'

I couldn't possibly have remembered all that, and I had great trouble later today trying to decipher it. But the implications were clear: 'You mean while I'm quietly working away in here, there's an entire Whitehall farce going on outside that door?'[1]

'Prime Minister, Number Ten is a railway junction. It cannot work without its proper component of sheds and sidings and timetables. Mrs Wainwright's office is a vital shed.'

I challenged him. 'You want her out of the way.'

'Good heavens no, Prime Minister!'

'You think she's a nuisance. Be honest.'

'No, no. Splendid woman, Mrs Wainwright. Upright. Downright. Forthright.'

Sometimes Humphrey has a certain natural poetry. 'But a nuisance?' I asked again.

'Well,' he acknowledged cautiously, 'there have been occasions when her criticisms of the service have been, er, refreshingly outspoken. And when her conversations with the press have been . . . breathtakingly frank and full. And sometimes her requests for information and assistance could have been a touch less abrasive and persistent. But most of my staff who had nervous breakdowns in the past three years would probably have had them anyway.'

'But I find her advice valuable,' I reminded him.

'Of course, Prime Minister.' Humphrey's tone was now full of understanding. 'And you shall have it. On paper.'

'Where you can all read it?' I challenged him.

---

[1] Whitehall farce was a term used to describe a series of theatrical farces produced over a period of about twenty years at the Whitehall Theatre. Whitehall was also, of course, the street that connects 10 Downing Street to Parliament Square, and on which can be found a number of major government departments.

Immediately I realised I'd led with my chin. 'And why not?' he enquired. 'Will it be secret from me?'

Of course I had no answer to that. So I reiterated the main point of the argument. 'She needs to be where things are happening.'

'Think for a moment, Prime Minister. Is it fair to her?'

I couldn't think what he was driving at. 'All the rest of us in this part of Number Ten are career civil servants. Loyal. Trusted. True. Our discretion proved over many years. If just one temporary civil servant is from the outside, then whenever there is a security breakdown the finger of suspicion will be pointed at her. It is too heavy a burden for one lady to bear. However gracious.'

Is there any truth in this argument? It sounds plausible. It's certainly true that they'd take it out on her if they could! But I explained to Humphrey that she is valuable because of her *political* advice.

'Prime Minister,' he replied, 'you have the whole Cabinet to give you political advice.'

'They only advise me to give more money to their own departments. I need someone, Humphrey, who's on *my* side.'

Humphrey was now positively sweetness and light. 'But I'm on your side. The whole Civil Service is on your side. Six hundred and eighty thousand of us. Surely that is enough to be going on with?'

He seemed to be winning the argument. I should never have got into it at all. I should have just held firm to my decision. But it was too late now. I'd been sucked in to an argument I could never win. 'You all give me the same advice,' I said hopelessly.

'Which proves,' replied Humphrey with triumph, 'that it must be correct! So now, please, can we revert to the original reorganisation plan?'

I know when I'm beaten. I nodded.

Humphrey tried to sweeten the pill with a compliment. 'It's such a pleasure to have a decisive Prime Minister who knows his own mind.'

I asked Bernard to send for Dorothy. To my surprise she was waiting next door in my private office. She came right in. I waited for Humphrey to leave. He didn't. So I explained that I wanted a private word with Dorothy.

He still didn't leave. 'You can speak freely in front of me,' he smiled.

Dorothy could see which way the wind was blowing. 'The Prime Minister may be able to,' she snapped. 'I can't.'

'I'm sure you can,' Humphrey replied patronisingly.

This was a terrible situation, thoroughly embarrassing, and it really was my fault for not standing up to Humphrey properly. Dorothy turned on her heel and walked out. 'Bernard, perhaps you'll let me know when the Prime Minister is free.'

I stopped her, told her to come right back, and asked Humphrey to leave.

He didn't budge. 'If you think it's necessary, Prime Minister. But I understand you have only a few brief words to say and we have many other matters of moment to discuss.'

I couldn't think what. It was clear that Humphrey was determined to see that I denied Dorothy the office outside the Cabinet Room. While I was wracked with indecision, Dorothy turned on Humphrey.

'I'm sorry, Humphrey,' she said with steel in her voice, 'I thought I heard the *Prime Minister* asking you to leave.'

I kept silent. Humphrey realised that he had no alternative, turned and walked from the room. I signalled to Bernard to follow him.

The doors closed. Dorothy sat opposite me. She knew the whole situation only too well. She came straight to the point.

'He has no right to behave like this, you know.'

Trying to save face a little, I asked her what she meant. She explained that she meant barging in and out without so much as a by-your-leave, and telling me I couldn't spend too long talking to her.

'He is Cabinet Secretary,' I reminded her.

'Precisely. He's a Secretary.'

Now I felt I had to save Humphrey's face. 'He's the most senior Civil Servant.'

She smiled a wry smile. 'It's remarkable how people continue to consider you a civil servant when you behave like an arrogant master.'

Now I had to save *my* face again. 'I'm the master here,' I said in my best no-nonsense voice.

'That's right!' she said emphatically.

Encouraged, I told her that I am the Prime Minister, and that I shall be firm and decisive. As always. I told her that I wished to talk about her office, and that I've changed my mind.

She asked, impertinently, if I had done so firmly and decisively.

This was infuriating. I asked her precisely what her question meant. Unfortunately, she told me. 'Have you changed your mind or has someone changed it for you?'

I told her we need the waiting room. She asked why.

'Well,' I began, and realised that I was unable to reproduce Humphrey's argument. I'm afraid my version came out rather

122

differently. 'Because, if people come to see people who people don't know people are coming to . . . that is, if people saw people before other people saw them seeing them . . . and *other* people see people . . . well, the whole ship goes off the rails.'

I ground to a halt, embarrassed. She gazed at me, her cool blue eyes appraising me. 'Did you work all that out for yourself?' she enquired.

'Look, be fair!' I defended myself as best I could. 'I can't go into everything. I have to rely on advice from my officials.'

She acknowledged the truth of this. But her view is that I have to rely on advice *not only* from officials. She believes that Humphrey is trying to shut off all my sources of information and advice except the Civil Service. And, furthermore, she insists he wishes to make himself the only channel for Civil Service advice.

This sounds a little fanciful to me. But she has more experience of Number Ten than I have, and I do know that she's on my side – or at least she's not on Humphrey's side, which may not be the same thing.

But how can Humphrey make himself the only channel for advice when I have the whole Cabinet every Thursday, and lots of Cabinet committees?

That's a question that I can answer for myself. My Cabinet mostly argue their Civil Service briefs. That's what I always found I was doing. And Humphrey meets their Permanent Secretaries informally the day before Cabinet – presumably they agree on their briefs. That's why I'm having such trouble with my Grand Design – the Civil Service is against it.

However, there is also the Think Tank.[1] I reminded Dorothy that they report to me.

She looked sceptical. 'I wouldn't be surprised if Humphrey suggests having them report to him instead. Then he'll ask for more space in Number Ten.'

'Why?' I asked. 'The Think Tank's supposed to be in the Cabinet Office.' [*The Cabinet Office was a separate building which adjoined 10 Downing Street. It was entered from Whitehall – Ed.*]

'He'll say,' predicted Dorothy, 'that they need more space. He'll gradually encroach on your territory here. Why? Because it will give him the right to treat Number Ten as his own, as well as the Cabinet Office. Then you know what he'll do? He'll start getting you out of the way.'

[1] The colloquial term for the Central Policy Review Staff, known for short as the CPRS.

I've begun to think that Dorothy is a little crazy. 'Are you suggesting,' I asked, 'that he wants to be Prime Minister?'

'No, no,' she said impatiently. 'He doesn't want the title or the responsibility. He only wants the power. So, having made himself the focus of all information and advice, he'll start encouraging you to go off on long overseas trips. Then he'll have to take a number of decisions in your absence – sorry, recommend them to Cabinet – and you'll have to follow his advice if you're not there. And Cabinet will follow his recommendations because they'll be getting the same recommendations from the Permanent Secretaries.'

This seems a hideous scenario. I really can't believe it. However, I think Humphrey has to be curbed a little and, on reflection, I think that tomorrow I'll give Dorothy her office back.

March 1st

Today I really was firm and decisive. What a feeling! I have established my authority well and truly.

First I summoned Dorothy. I told her, firmly and decisively, that I had changed my mind again! She was to get her office back.

Then I asked Dorothy for her advice about Humphrey. Not that I would necessarily have taken it! But I wanted to know if she was recommending that I sack him.

She shrank from such a response. But she wondered if I might want to clip his wings. And she had a very good suggestion as to how to do it. As well as being Cabinet Secretary, he is Joint Head of the Home Civil Service. He is responsible for the Personnel side – appointments and so on. Pay and Rations are in the hands of Sir Frank Gordon, Permanent Secretary of the Treasury. So the job of the Head of the Civil Service is effectively split between Sir Humphrey and Sir Frank.

Dorothy's suggestion, brilliantly simple, is to take Humphrey's half of the job away from him and give it all to Sir Frank!

The danger of such a move, of course, would be that it might make Sir Frank as powerful as Sir Humphrey is now. Would that be any better for me? Hard to tell. I don't know Sir Frank all that well. But I don't have to commit myself yet. All I had to do today was put the frighteners on Humphrey! And that I certainly achieved!

I sent for him. He arrived while Dorothy was still with me. I began by telling him that I had *definitely* decided to give her her old office.

He started to protest, but I wouldn't let him speak. He asked for a private word about it. Dorothy smiled unpleasantly and said he could speak freely in front of her.

He seemed reluctant. I asked him if he were about to dispute my decision.

'Not once it *is* a decision, no,' he replied carefully.

'Good,' I said, closing the matter. 'Now, I have another important matter to discuss with you.' And I indicated to Dorothy that she should now leave. She smiled sweetly at me, and departed in triumph.

Before I could mention my threat to give some of Humphrey's responsibilities to Sir Frank, he spoke up. And I could hardly believe my ears.

'I think we should think about the Think Tank,' he began. My God, had Dorothy *known* this was coming? Or was it an inspired guess, based on her knowledge of the man? In any event, I realised at that moment that I could no longer risk dismissing her fears as paranoia.

'Can't the Think Tank think about themselves?' I asked casually.

'I'm worried that their lines of communication are unclear,' he said.

I looked surprised. 'How can they be? They report to me.'

'Operationally, yes. But administratively they report to me.'

Humphrey was claiming that this was a serious anomaly. So I pretended to misunderstand him. 'I see,' I said. 'So you want them to report to my office administratively as well.'

He hadn't foreseen that interpretation. 'No, no!' he answered hastily. 'It would be quite wrong to burden your office with administration. No. I suggest they report to me operationally as well.'

I pretended to be open to this new plan. Inwardly I was seething. 'So they should deliver their reports to you?'

Humphrey clearly felt he'd won. 'Yes, well, just for checking and so on,' he replied, leaning back in his chair and relaxing a little. 'To see that you get them in an acceptable form.'

'Humphrey,' I said, smiling my most insincere smile, 'this is *very* generous of you. Won't it mean a lot of extra work?'

He assumed his brave, British, *Cruel Sea* look. 'One must do one's duty,' he grunted.

I decided to put Dorothy's theory to the test. 'But . . . gosh . . .' I said innocently, 'how will you manage for space?'

'I was just coming to that,' he said. 'We shan't be able to accommodate the extra staff in the Cabinet Office. But I think we can probably find a few rooms here in Number Ten.'

She was right again, damn it!

'Here?' I asked.

'Well, there is some space,' he explained.

'In that case,' I asked, 'why did we have to move Dorothy's office?'

He was only fazed for a moment. 'Well . . . if she's staying here we could move a couple of them into her new office. Her old office. Her old new office.'

'Go on,' I said, playing with him.

'Is that agreed?' he enquired.

'No, it's not agreed,' I replied pleasantly, 'but it's fascinating. Anything else you want to propose?'

'Just some overseas visits,' he said, producing some sheets of paper. I nearly fell off my chair. 'You ought to consider them.'

I read the list he gave me. It included a NATO conference, the United Nations Assembly, the EEC Parliament, negotiations in Hong Kong about the future of the colony, Commonwealth meetings in Ottawa, and summits in Peking and Moscow. I marvelled at Dorothy's knowledge of the system and the people who operate it.

But to Humphrey I said: 'If I'm away all this time, won't it mean an awful lot of extra work for you?'

'I think, Prime Minister, that it's very important for you to take your place on the world stage.'

'I agree,' I said enthusiastically. 'But it's asking too much of you. I really must try to lighten your load.'

He eyed me with much suspicion. 'Oh no, there's no need.'

I exuded crocodile sympathy at him. 'Oh, but there *is*, Humphrey, there *is*! I've been thinking too. On top of everything else, you're Head of the Civil Service, aren't you?'

He was evasive. 'Well, the Treasury handle pay and rations.'

'But you are responsible for promotion, appointments and so on. Isn't that a bit much for you?'

He laughed off the notion. 'No, no, not at all. Takes no time at all. A doddle.'

I was enjoying myself. 'The promotion and appointment of six hundred and eighty thousand people is a doddle?'

'Well, I mean, it's delegated,' he explained carefully.

I smiled cheerfully. 'Oh good,' I said. 'So if it's delegated anyway, there'd be no problem in moving it to the Treasury.'

He was getting rattled now. 'Quite impossible,' he replied firmly. 'The Treasury already has far too much power – er, work.'

I was relentless. 'You see,' I said, 'with you doing promotions and them doing pay and rations, the lines of authority are unclear. It's all rather unsatisfactory. A serious anomaly.'

Humphrey saw an opening. His eyes lit up. 'Well, in that case I could take over pay and rations too.'

Nice try, Humphrey, I thought. I shook my head sorrowfully. 'On top of all your other burdens? Plus these you plan to assume? No, Humphrey, I can't allow you to make that sort of sacrifice.'

He was getting desperate. 'It's no sacrifice. No trouble at all!'

For once in his life he was probably telling the truth. 'Humphrey, you are too noble,' I replied. 'But I can see through your arguments.'

He eyed me like a frightened ferret. 'You can?'

'You're trying to sacrifice yourself,' I said gently, 'to save me from worry, aren't you?'

He was nonplussed. He couldn't figure out the safe answer, the answer that would get him what he wanted. 'Oh,' he said. 'Er . . . yes. Um, no,' he went on. 'It's really *no* sacrifice,' he concluded.

I was now bored with my game. So I told him a final no.

But Humphrey needed to know the answers to his other proposals, chiefly those concerning the Think Tank.

'The more I think about it, Humphrey,' I said, 'the more I realise that you already have too much on your plate. In fact, I don't want to keep you here any longer when you must have so much to do in *your* office.'

He couldn't quite believe his ears. Had he been dismissed? I decided to clarify his position. 'You may now leave. If you're needed again in Number Ten, you'll be sent for.'

He stood up, then paused to correct me. 'You mean *when*.'

I smiled apologetically. 'I mean when,' I agreed. He turned towards the door. 'And if,' I added mischievously.

He froze for a moment, then walked to the doors. As he left the room I made sure that he heard me pick up the intercom and ask Bernard to get Sir Frank over to see me as soon as possible.

March 2nd

Sir Frank was tied up yesterday, so I spoke to him on the phone.

'Frank,' I said, 'I just want to sound you out about something. It's about Humphrey. I'm wondering if he's got too much on his plate.'

As I expected, Frank assured me that Humphrey could manage splendidly, is tremendously able, is not overstretched, and has everything perfectly under control with no problem at all.

Then I indicated that the reason I was asking was because of Humphrey's role as Head of the Civil Service. I wondered, I said, if Frank could do some of Humphrey's job.

It will come as no great surprise to any reader that Frank said not one single word more about Humphrey's great ability. Instead he remarked that such a proposal could make a lot of sense.

I asked him to come to meet me tomorrow and, meanwhile, would he note down on paper his precise thoughts as to whether or not Humphrey is overstretched and send them over to me.

An hour later his thoughts arrived, duty noted. These are they:

H M Treasury

Permanent Secretary

March 2

Dear Prime Minister,

When I said that HA was not overstretched, I was of course talking in the sense of total cumulative loading taken globally rather than in respect of certain individual and essentially anomalous responsibilities which are not, logically speaking, consonant or harmonious with the broad spectrum of intermeshing and inseparable functions and could indeed be said to place an excessive and supererogatory burden on the office when considered in relation to the comparatively exiguous advantages of their overall consideration.

Yours ever,

Frank

I read it carefully several times. My conclusion: he *could* do part of Humphrey's job.

March 3rd
Frank came to see me today. But we never had the meeting.

When he arrived. I instructed Bernard to see that Humphrey did not interrupt us. I wanted complete confidentiality.

Bernard said: 'I'll do my best.'

'Your best may not be good enough,' I told him. Oh, my prophetic soul!

I had seen Dorothy first thing this morning. She had reminded me that, technically, Sir Humphrey is supposed to phone us from the Cabinet Office before coming through the green-baize door to Number Ten.

I checked this with Bernard. He was hesitant. 'Perhaps that is right in theory, Prime Minister, but in reality it's just a formality.'

'Good,' I said. 'Humphrey likes formality.'

Bernard agreed, but with reluctance. 'Yes, Prime Minister, but as they say . . . it is a custom more honoured in the breach than in the observance.'

I really am fed up with Bernard, Humphrey, Frank, the lot of them. Why must they all express themselves in such a pompous and roundabout manner? All this rot about customs being honoured in the breach . . . Why do they distort and destroy the most beautiful language in the world, the language of Shakespeare? [*Hacker was apparently unaware that Bernard was quoting Shakespeare:* Hamlet, *Act I, Scene iv – Ed.*]

SIR BERNARD WOOLLEY RECALLS:[1]
That day was a turning-point in my life and my career. I had never realised that my new post as Principal Private Secretary to the Prime Minister gave me the opportunity to assert my strength and independence from my old boss. It came as a revelation, a blinding flash, the road to Damascus!

I had just shown Sir Frank Gordon into the Cabinet Room and returned to the Private Office.

I dialled Humphrey's number on the phone.

I heard Humphrey's voice, loud and clear. 'Yes?'

'Ah, Sir Humphrey,' I said.

'Yes,' he said again, and I realised that the reason his voice was so loud and clear was because it was right behind me. He had entered the room.

'Bernard here,' I said stupidly. Well, I was flustered.

'So I see,' he replied. I replaced the receiver.

'Just the person I wanted to talk to,' I said, still very worried by his close proximity to Mr Hacker's secret meeting.

'Well here I am, in person. Even better,' he said.

'Yes and no,' I said. I was chattering on meaninglessly, saying that I wanted to have a word with him, which was why I was telephoning him, why else? And finally I managed to say that the Prime Minister had asked me to

[1] In conversation with the Editors.

129

remind him that it might be more convenient if he were to phone through from the Cabinet Office before popping over to see us in Number Ten.

Humphrey assured me that it was not inconvenient.

'Yes it is,' I said.

'No it's not,' he said.

And, much too firmly, I said: 'Yes *it is*!'

He stared at me. Then, suddenly very cool, he asked if the PM was busy.

I had to say that he was. Humphrey wanted to know with what. I tried being vague, and muttered that he was doing his paperwork. Humphrey really frightened me, you know, in those days.

Humphrey said that if it was only paperwork he could pop in and have a word with the PM. I was forced to admit that the PM was doing his paperwork *with* somebody.

Sir Humphrey eyed me carefully. It was clear to him that I was being less than frank with him, and perhaps completely mendacious. 'You mean, he's having a meeting?' I nodded. '*With whom, Bernard*?' he rasped.

I think he knew already. It's been in the air for two days now. No sooner had I admitted that the PM was meeting the Permanent Secretary of the Treasury than Sir Humphrey was through the doors into the Cabinet Room like a ferret up a pair of trousers. I couldn't possibly have stopped him – my reflexes just weren't quick enough.

[*Hacker's diary continues – Ed.*]

However, immediately I started to talk seriously to Sir Frank Gordon, Humphrey barged in. I asked him what he wanted. I was not welcoming. He said he was checking to see if he could be of service. I asked him if Bernard had told him I was in a meeting. Bernard nodded vigorously in the open doorway. Humphrey admitted this was so.

'So what do you want?' I asked impatiently.

He clearly had nothing to say to me. He was just checking up on me. 'Well,' he said, 'since it was a meeting with one of my professional colleagues, I thought – *hello*, Frank – that I might have a contribution to make.'

He smiled effusively at Frank who, I noticed, hardly smiled back.

'I see,' I said. 'No, thank you.'

I waited for him to leave. He didn't move.

'Thank you,' I said, quite clearly.

'Thank *you*, Prime Minister,' he replied, and still didn't move a muscle. He just stood at the door, waiting, listening, defying us to divest him of any of his responsibilities.

'Humphrey,' I said, feeling the irritation rising in me, 'this is a private meeting.'

'Ah,' he said. 'Shall I shut the door?'

130

'Yes please,' I said. Imagine my amazement when he turned and shut the door from his side. 'No, Humphrey, from the *other side* please.'

He was angry and defiant. 'May I ask why?'

Meanwhile Frank was getting distinctly nervous. He rose and offered to leave. I told him to sit down, and Humphrey to leave.

Humphrey seemed prepared to pretend that he was the village idiot rather than leave. 'In what sense of the word do you mean leave?' he asked, as if it were a sensible question.

I shouted at him to get out. I told Frank to go as well – I was now too upset and angry to continue a rational conversation with him.

Bernard was creeping away. I shouted at him too, telling him to come back. We were alone together.

I asked him, 'Why did you allow Humphrey in when I explicitly told you not to?'

'I couldn't stop him,' he replied with a helpless shrug.

'Why not?'

'He's bigger than me.'

'Then,' I said with grim determination, 'he must be confined to the Cabinet Office.'

'How?' he asked.

It was obvious. 'Lock the connecting door,' I said.

'But he has a key,' whimpered Bernard.

'Then take his key away from him,' I said.

Bernard couldn't believe his ears. 'Take his key away from him?' he asked incredulously.

'Take his key away from him,' I repeated.

'*You* take his key away from him!' said Bernard.

I've never heard such impertinence and open defiance. '*What*?' I exclaimed.

Bernard took a deep breath, stopped, and tried again. 'I'm sorry, Prime Minister, but I don't think it's within my power.'

Bernard is very academic and well educated, but so inhibited and constricted and highly trained to do things the way they have always been done, that sometimes he can't see the wood for the trees.

'I'm giving you the power,' I explained. 'I'm authorising you.'

He appeared to be on the verge of a complete crack-up. 'But . . . I don't know if I . . . I mean . . . crikey. He'll go completely potty.'

I smiled at Bernard. And he smiled back at me. Then his smile faded and he licked his lips nervously. He still didn't quite have the courage, I could see. 'It's up to you, Bernard,' I said gently.

'Yes, but . . .'

'Freedom, Bernard,' I said softly.

'Yes, but . . .'

'I'm giving you the power, Bernard,' I reminded him gently.

'Yes, but . . .'

'You, alone, will have access to the Prime Minister,' I encouraged him cunningly.

But even that didn't quite convince him.

'But . . . but . . .' He was unable to formulate his objections. His whole world was being turned upside down.

'But me no buts, Bernard. Shakespeare.' I thought it was time for me to demonstrate a little learning.

But a little learning is a dangerous thing. Bernard immediately sought refuge in useless and irrelevant pedantry. 'No, Prime Minister, "but me no buts" is a nineteenth-century quotation, circa 1820. Mrs Centlivre used the phrase in 1708, I believe, but it was Scott's employment of it in *The Antiquary* which popularised it.'

I thanked Bernard, and asked if we could stick to the point. He misunderstood me – wilfully, I think – in a further attempt to evade the issue of Sir Humphrey's access.

'Yes – the point *is*, Prime Minister, that I think you are confusing Mrs Centlivre with Old Capulet in *Romeo and Juliet, Act III, Scene v* when *he* said, 'Thank me no thankings, nor proud me no prouds.'

I thanked Bernard again, and told him to say that to Sir Humphrey.

He looked blank. 'Say what?'

'Proud me no prouds, Sir Humphrey.'

'Yes, Prime Minister.' He was not looking at all happy. 'Um . . . there's only one problem: if I'm to deprive him of his key, what reason can I possibly give?'

I lost my temper. He's a born Civil Servant – the man can only see problems. But with every problem there's also an *opportunity*. 'For God's sake, Bernard,' I snapped. 'Find a reason!'

He retreated. 'Yes, Prime Minister. Thank you, Prime Minister.'

I beamed at him over the top of my glasses. 'Thank me no thankings, Bernard,' I said.

[*Dorothy Wainwright's memoirs,* The Prime Minister's Ear, *were a bestseller two or three years after the event described here. In this extract we see, from her point of view, what happened later that day when Bernard Woolley exercised the authority which Hacker had just given him – Ed.*]

I was just contemplating my hoped-for move back into my old office, when I heard Bernard's raised voice coming out of the Private Office on the other side of the lobby. 'I said *no*, Sir Humphrey,' he said – and then he said it again.

Intrigued, I popped in on the Private Office. Bernard was on the phone. His face was pink and he looked very agitated. 'I *did* say no,' he was saying. 'The Prime Minister is busy.'

Sir Humphrey, at the other end of the phone, must have offered to come to see Bernard because Bernard then said: 'I'm busy too.'

There seemed to be some abuse crackling down the line for a moment. Then Bernard drew himself up to his full five foot ten and a half, took a deep breath and said: 'Sir Humphrey, you may not come through. You do not have permission.'

Humphrey shouted, 'I'm coming anyway' – *that* could be heard across the room – and slammed down his phone. Bernard rang off and sank into his chair, half delighted, half appalled. He looked at me with a dazed smile. 'He couldn't believe his ears,' he said with delight.

'What did he say?'

'That he's coming anyway.'

'Are you feeling strong enough?' I asked with sympathy.

Bernard sat back and relaxed. 'It's all right, he can't come. I instructed Security to take the key from his office.'

At that moment the door flew open. Sir Humphrey strode in. He was angrier than I've ever seen him. There literally was steam coming out of his ears. [*Literally, there could not have been – Ed.*]

Bernard leapt to his feet. 'My God!'

'No, Bernard,' snarled Humphrey, 'it's just your boss.'

[*Technically this description may have been correrct, as Sir Humphrey Appleby was Head of the Home Civil Service. However, since moving to Number Ten Bernard Woolley no longer reported to Sir Humphrey. As the Principal Private Secretary to the Prime Minister he now had virtually as much power and influence as the Cabinet Secretary – hence the row – Ed.*]

'How did you get through a solid door?' asked Bernard.

'Where has my key gone?' asked Sir Humphrey.

'You must have a spare!' deduced Bernard.

'Where is my *key*?' snarled Sir Humphrey.

Bernard took his courage in both hands. 'I was instructed by the Prime Minister to have it removed.'

I thought I should come to Bernard's rescue. 'That's quite correct,' I added.

Humphrey turned viciously. 'Would you mind, *dear lady*?' he snarled. 'This has nothing to do with you.' He turned back to Bernard. 'The Prime Minister does not have it in his power to deprive me of my key.'

'It's his house,' said Bernard bravely.

'It's a government building,' said Sir Humphrey.

Bernard didn't panic or lose his nerve. 'I believe it is the PM's decision as to who comes into his house. After all, I don't give my mother-in-law the key to my house.'

I almost laughed out loud. The analogy caused Humphrey to look as though he might explode with rage.

'I'm not the PM's mother-in-law, Bernard.'

Bernard didn't reply. He didn't need to. He simply stood there in silence. After a moment Humphrey walked to the window and did some quiet slow deep breathing to calm himself down. Then he turned back to Bernard with a crocodile smile.

'Look, Bernard, I don't want us to fall out over this. It's so petty of the Prime Minister. You and I have to work together for some years yet. Prime Ministers come and go – whereas your career prospects depend on those who have power over promotions and appointments on a long-term basis.'

'Let's stick to the point,' I said abrasively, and Humphrey flashed another vicious look in my direction. If looks could kill!

Bernard, to his great credit, *did* stick to the point. 'I must insist that you tell me how you came in.'

Sir Humphrey immediately pursed his lips. It was his familiar *my lips are sealed* look.

'You must have a personal key,' said Bernard. Humphrey stayed silent. 'Are you telling me that you haven't?' Bernard asked.

Humphrey half-smiled. 'I'm not telling you that I haven't. I'm simply not telling you that I have.'

Bernard held out his hand. 'Hand it over!'

Humphrey stared at Bernard for a few moments, then turned on his heel and walked out. Bernard sat down abruptly and hyperventilated for a bit. I told him he'd done well.

He nodded. Then he reached for one of his phones. He called Security, told them to change the locks on the door connecting the Cabinet Office to the house, and told them to bring *all* the keys to him.

[*Later on the same day, 3 March, there took place the weekly meeting of the Permanent Secretaries in Sir Humphrey Appleby's office. A most instructive note was recently found in Sir Frank Gordon's private diary, relating to a brief conversational exchange that happened informally after the meeting – Ed.*]

On my way out Humphrey asked me about my meeting with the PM. Didn't tell him that it shuddered to a halt after Humphrey's unwelcome intrusion. Instead, told him it was v. successful.

He asked me if any particular subject came up. I asked him if there were any particular subjects he was interested in. H asked me if the PM raised the issue of Service appointments, or if the PM foreshadowed any redistribution of responsibility. Since nothing was discussed by the PM I merely hinted that the topics may have cropped up, and that we had had a wide-ranging discussion.

Interestingly, he asked if it had moved towards any conclusion. He must be v. worried. I said that there were arguments on both sides, perhaps tending slightly one way more than the other way, but certainly nothing for *me* to worry about.

[*Hacker's diary continues – Ed.*]

March 6th

My plan was a total success. Humphrey knows his place at last. As I suggested to Dorothy only a day or two ago, it was time to clip Humphrey's wings. [*Alert readers may recall that, in an earlier entry in this diary, Hacker acknowledged that the suggestion to clip Appleby's wings came from Dorothy Wainwright – Ed.*]

Apparently Bernard changed the locks on the door between Number Ten and the Cabinet Office, so that Humphrey *had* to seek permission. When Humphrey phoned for permission to come through this morning, Bernard denied it.

Shortly afterwards, he and Dorothy heard thumps and bangings on the other side, accompanied by shouts of suppressed frenzy: 'Open the door! Open the door!'

Humphrey then ran out of the front door of the Cabinet Office into Whitehall, round the corner, and up Downing Street to Number Ten. The two policemen wouldn't let him in because he had no appointment card and no Security pass – only a Cabinet Office Security pass.

Bernard had instituted new security rules last week, apparently on Humphrey's own instructions: *no one* may now be admitted unless they have the Number Ten pass or are on the daily list.

The policeman knows Humphrey well, of course, and apparently buzzed through to the Private Office for permission. But by then Bernard and Dorothy had come into the Cabinet Room for a meeting with me.

Humphrey must have run back into his office, jumped out of the window into the garden of Number Ten, run across the lawn and the flower beds and clambered up the wall cat-burglar style to the balcony outside the Cabinet Room.

Certainly the first I knew of all this was when I saw a muddy and dishevelled Sir Humphrey balanced precariously outside the French windows. I smiled and waved at him. He grasped the handle of the window and tried to open it – and immediately we were absolutely deafened by bells and sirens. A moment later uniformed police and dogs and plain-clothes detectives rushed into the Cabinet Room.

We all shouted above the din that we were okay, and that we didn't need protecting from the Cabinet Secretary, however angry he was or however hurt his feelings.

The sirens were switched off.

Sir Humphrey stepped forward and handed me a letter, in his own handwriting.

'Humphrey,' I said, 'what's this?'

He was speechless, fuming, fighting back tears, trying to retain his dignity. He couldn't speak – he just indicated the piece of paper. I read it.

Cabinet Office

Dear Prime Minister,

I must express in the strongest possible terms my profound opposition to the newly instituted practice which imposes severe and intolerable restrictions on the ingress and egress of senior members of the hierarchy and will, in all probability, should the current deplorable innovation be perpetuated, precipitate a progressive constriction of the channels of communication, culminating in a condition of organisational atrophy and administrative paralysis which will render effectively impossible the coherent and co-ordinated discharge of the functions of government within Her Majesty's United Kingdom of Great Britain and Northern Ireland.

Your obedient and humble servant,

Humphrey Appleby

I read it carefully. Then I looked up at Humphrey.

'You mean you've lost your key?' I asked.

'Prime Minister,' he said desperately, 'I must insist on having a new one.'

I'm ashamed to say I played games with him. 'In due course, Humphrey,' I replied. 'At the appropriate juncture. In the fullness of time. Meanwhile, we have another decision to take. A more urgent one. About Dorothy's office.'

'Quite!' said Dorothy, aggressively.

Humphrey tried to brush this aside, as he always does. But I wouldn't let him. 'No, Humphrey,' I explained with great patience, 'it has to be resolved now. One way or the other. Like the question of your key, really.'

I could see from his face that the penny had finally dropped. While he wrestled with himself, I tried to give him a face-saving opening. 'I was wondering what your views were. They are, in a sense, the key to our problem. What do you think?'

He gave me what he hoped would seem like a considered opinion and a dignified compromise. 'I think – on reflection – that Mrs Wainwright *does* need to be nearer this room,' he said.

We were all relieved. 'So we'll move her back, shall we?' He nodded. 'At once?' He nodded again.

I told Bernard to give him the new key, I thanked him for his help and co-operation, and dismissed them all.

Later today, Bernard tells me, Sir Humphrey rang to ask if he could see me privately. I said 'Of course!' Bernard magnanimously invited him over. Humphrey entered my study deferentially, and asked whether the other matter was resolved.

Other matter? I couldn't think what he meant.

He cleared his throat. 'May I, er, enquire who is to be the Head of the Home Civil Service?'

'You – perhaps,' I said. He smiled. 'Or, maybe, Sir Frank,' I added. His smile faded. 'Or maybe . . . share it like now. I haven't decided yet. But whatever happens, it's my decision, isn't it, Humphrey?'

'Yes Prime Minister,' he replied, a sadder but wiser man.

5
A Real
Partnership

March 9th

I staggered upstairs to the flat for lunch today. Fortunately Annie was home. She took one look at me and asked me if it had been a bad Cabinet.

'Got anything for getting blood off carpets?' I groaned as I slumped into my chintz flowered armchair with a deep sigh. [*We presume that it was not the armchair which was the possessor of the deep sigh – Ed.*]

'Whose blood?' asked Annie, as she picked up the decanter.

'Everyone's,' I told her miserably.

She asked me if I wanted a small scotch or a double. I settled for a triple.

The nub of my depression was a Treasury Paper that had just been presented to us. The financial crisis is much worse than any of us thought. No one saw it coming – least of all me – except one person: my predecessor, the last Prime Minister. No wonder he resigned unexpectedly!

Annie wasn't a bit surprised. 'I always thought,' she mused, 'that it was strange that he resigned to make way for an older man.'

I was slightly put out. 'I'm not older than him,' I said.

'Oh.' She gazed at me with sympathy. 'Maybe you just look it.'

I do *now*, I thought, that's for certain! I really don't know what I'm going to do about all the cuts that have got to be made in the Cabinet's spending plans. They weren't at all prepared for this. They all have ambitious development ideas, because I asked for them.

We heard the sound of leaden footsteps. Bernard appeared at the living-room door. Annie offered him a Scotch.

'Triple, please,' he replied bleakly.

Annie nodded sympathetically, and wisely kept silent.

'Bernard,' I said, 'Humphrey should have warned me this was coming.'

He sat on the sofa and sipped his drink. 'I don't think Sir Humphrey understands economics, Prime Minister – he did read classics, you know.'

'Well, what about Sir Frank? He's head of the Treasury.'

Bernard shook his head. 'I'm afraid he's at an even greater disadvantage in understanding economics, Prime Minister. He's an economist.'

Annie joined us, with a Perrier. 'Jim, if there's an economic crisis, can't the Cabinet see there've got to be cuts?'

'They can see that the other departments have got to make cuts. Not theirs.'

'That's rather selfish,' she remarked. Annie still seems to think that the Cabinet is full of team spirit. It's not. They're in a constant popularity contest against each other. And the quickest way to become popular is to spend money. Public money. This makes them popular with their Department, the Party, the House and the press. Cutting spending makes everyone unpopular. Annie didn't see why. Bernard tried to explain, but he rabbited on for ages in a totally incomprehensible way about hats, making everything as clear as mud.

SIR BERNARD WOOLLEY RECALLS:[1]
My explanation was crystal clear, as it happens. Mrs Hacker seemed to feel, as I remember, that the public would be *pleased* if spending were cut, because the public are the taxpayers. I explained that it was and is a question of hats. The voter, wearing his voter's hat, is always frightfully pleased when the Government pays for something because he thinks it's free! He doesn't realise that, wearing his taxpayer's hat, he's paying for what he's receiving in his voter's hat. And the Cabinet Ministers, wearing their Head-of-a-Department hats, are competing with themselves because, wearing their member-of-the-Government hats, they have to pull economic success out of the hat and yet allow the taxpayer, wearing his voter's hat, to think that the Government is spending someone else's money when it's *not*, it's spending *theirs*, and so they have to try and keep this under their hat.

[*Hacker's diary continues – Ed.*]

Annie asked me, 'Presumably you encouraged all those spending plans because you wanted to be popular?'

Yes and no was the only possible answer. Of course I want to be popular – nothing wrong with that, that's how you get elected, being popular is what democracy's all about. But I also thought we could afford it. I didn't know, and nobody had told me, of these looming

[1] In conversation with the editors.

139

problems with inflation, the sterling crisis and low productivity.

Annie asked what I was doing about it. 'Did you order a clamp-down this morning?'

'I can't order anything, Annie,' I explained miserably.

She didn't understand. 'He's only the Prime Minister, Mrs Hacker,' said Bernard. 'He doesn't even have a department of his own to clamp down on.'

Annie thought – still thinks, for all I know – that the Prime Minister is completely in charge. It's a fallacy. A leader can only lead by consent.

'So who is in charge, if you're not?' asked Annie, rather perplexed.

I was perplexed by her question. There didn't seem to be an answer. I thought for a bit. 'Nobody really,' I said finally.

'Is that good?' She was even more perplexed.

'It must be,' I replied hopelessly. 'That's what democracy is all about.'

'It's made Britain what she is today,' added Bernard with sincerity.

Annie contemplated what she'd just been told. 'So your Cabinet are in control, not you.'

She'd got completely the wrong end of the stick! 'No!' I said. 'Think back, Annie! I wasn't in control when I was a Minister, was I?'

'No,' she said, 'but I thought that was just you.'

Annie, like the press and the media, keeps harping on about 'control'. But the point about government is that no one has control. Lots of people have the power to stop something happening – but almost nobody has the power to *make* anything happen. We have a system of government with the engine of a lawn-mower and the brakes of a Rolls-Royce.

Of course I'd never say any of this in public. The electorate would interpret this as defeatism. It's not, though! It's the truth! And I am going to fight it. [*We do not believe that Hacker wanted his readers to believe that he intended to fight the truth – Ed.*]

We began talking about the further implications of this financial mess. Tomorrow I've got a deputation of backbench MPs coming to see me, about a pay rise I promised them. Naturally I'll have to tell them they can't have it now. They'll be furious. They'll say:

1. That I can't go back on a promise.
2. That they are shamefully underpaid.
3. That it's all very well for me because I get fifty thousand quid a year.
4. That it's not the money, it's the principle of the thing.

5. That it's not for them personally.
6. That I am striking a blow against the very foundations of Parliamentary democracy.

How do I know they'll say all that? Because that's what I said when I was a backbencher.

The only way to reply is to lie. I shall say:

1. That I sympathise deeply – which I don't!
2. That they certainly deserve the money – which isn't true!
3. That I shall make it my number one priority when the crisis has passed – which I shan't!
4. And that if MPs vote themselves a whacking great pay rise and then tell everyone else there's no money for pay rises, it doesn't do wonders for the dignity of Parliament – which it certainly doesn't!

I shall forbear to add that when anyone says, 'It's not the money, it's the principle,' they *mean* it's the money!

I explained this all to Annie. To my surprise she sympathised with them. 'Aren't MPs underpaid, in fact?'

I was astonished. Underpaid? Backbench MPs? I explained to Annie that being an MP is a vast, subsidised ego trip. It's a job that needs no qualifications, that has no compulsory hours of work, no performance standards, and provides a warm room, a telephone and subsidised meals to a bunch of self-important windbags and busybodies who suddenly find people taking them seriously because they've got the letters MP after their names. How *can* they be underpaid when there's about two hundred applicants for every vacancy? You could fill every seat twenty times over even if they had to pay to do the job.

'But you were a backbench MP only five years ago,' said Annie.

'I was an exception,' I explained. 'I was the cream. That's why I rose to the top.'

Annie wanted to know if I thought my answers would shut them up. I don't think so. They never shut me up. 'But,' I said to her with a shrug, 'there's no choice. The country just won't accept pay rises for MPs when we're cutting back on nurses and teachers.'

'Nurses and teachers?' Annie looked worried. 'That's much more serious, isn't it?'

Sometimes I think Annie has learned nothing about politics. 'No, Annie,' I said wearily, 'much *less* serious. Nurses and teachers can't vote against me till the next election – backbenchers can vote against me at ten o'clock tonight.'

March 10th

As I predicted, I had a very stormy meeting with my backbenchers. They said all the things I said they'd say and I said all the things I said I'd say, and they said that I should remember that I wouldn't be able to say anything to anyone if I lost the support of my own backbenchers.

I called Humphrey in afterwards. I told him that if I'd had some notice I might have softened them up a bit in advance.

He agreed that the lack of notice was regrettable.

Which meant that he hadn't taken my point. 'It's up to you, Humphrey,' I emphasised. 'You're Secretary of the Cabinet. You must insist we get papers circulated earlier.'

Humphrey hung his head. 'Alas! There are grave problems about circulating papers before they are written.'

So if the papers weren't written, *why* weren't they written? I scowled at Humphrey. 'Surely the Treasury must have seen this coming?'

'Prime Minister,' replied Sir Humphrey with a shrug, 'I am not Permanent Secretary of the Treasury. You must ask Sir Frank.'

'What would he say?' I asked.

Humphrey shrugged again. 'It is not for a humble mortal like me to guess at the complex and elevated deliberations of the mighty. But in general I think Sir Frank believes that if the Treasury knows something has to be done, the Cabinet should not have too much time to think about it.'

I was furious. 'But that's an outrageous view.'

'Yes,' he said with a smile, 'it's known as Treasury policy.'

'Suppose,' I asked, 'that the Cabinet have questions to ask?'

'I think that Sir Frank's view,' said Humphrey carefully, 'is that on the rare occasions when the Treasury understands the questions, the Cabinet does not understand the answers.'

I was getting furiouser and furiouser. 'Do you support this?' I asked bluntly.

Humphrey looked truly amazed. 'I, Prime Minister? I merely try to carry out the wishes of the Prime Minister and the Cabinet.'

I instructed Humphrey that it is my wish that, in future, all papers are circulated at least forty-eight hours before Cabinet meetings. I told him to tell Sir Frank.

Humphrey said he would do so with pleasure, and that he would seek an audience with him at once. He left.

The regal phraseology did not escape me. He clearly thinks Frank is getting too big for his boots. Unless . . . he is still worrying about my threat last week to make Sir Frank head of the Home Civil Service. Of course! That's why he's so disloyal to Frank at the moment.

I wonder if I should put him out of his misery. Do I gain anything by keeping them both in suspense? Yes, I gain an anxious and co-operative Cabinet Secretary.

[*Later that day Sir Humphrey Appleby met Sir Frank Gordon, Permanent Secretary of the Treasury, at the Reform Club in Pall Mall. Sir Humphrey made a note about the meeting in his private diary – Ed.*]

Frank and I discussed the late arrival of Treasury papers for Cabinet this week, and the short notice of the information concerning the economic crisis.

Frank expressed a hope that I had explained that the short notice was due to America's sudden change of policy over interest rates. I assured Frank that I defended him gallantly, leaving the Prime Minister in no doubt as to the real cause of the rush.

Frank was delighted with this reply. He is less subtle than I would have expected.

He was concerned that we do not lose the PM's goodwill at this time. With the financial crisis, we shall obviously have to bring in some form of pay restraint. Unfortunately, the MPs are being denied the pay rise they have been expecting just at the moment that Frank is due to bring forward the proposed Civil Service pay rise.

This is indeed awkward. Obviously one is not interested in the pay rise for oneself. The last thing Permanent Secretaries care about is the money. We could all have made a fortune if we'd gone into industry. Money is money, and service is service.

Nevertheless, Frank and I are both in full agreement that we owe it to our junior colleagues to do everything we can for them.

Ironically, trying to help them will involve raising our own salaries – about which we don't care at all – and then we get criticised for feathering our own nests. Still, that is just another cross we have to bear.

[*This passage from Sir Humphrey's diary is most intriguing. Was he really able to convince himself that in pushing for a large Civil Service pay rise, in which he and Sir Frank would get the largest cash sum, he was acting altruistically? Or was he so cautious that everything he wrote, even for his private diary, could withstand scrutiny if stolen and leaked? – Ed.*]

I urged Frank to put our pay proposal in fast, before any pay restraint begins. It is also clear that it must go in the night before next Thursday's Cabinet – if Ministers have two days to spend talking about it to back-benchers and political advisers they'll come up with all sorts of objections.

Frank was worried about bouncing Cabinet two weeks running. I assured him that there was no alternative.

Frank then suggested that it would be better if the proposal came from both of us. I can see why – there is safety in numbers. However, he gave as his reasons that we are effectively joint heads of the Civil Service.

Needless to say, this is not a view that I accept. The Cabinet Secretary is the *de jure* head of the Service. Frank chooses to believe that, as he looks after the financial side and I look after the Establishment side, we are both *de facto* heads of the Service.

He seemed eager to pursue this discussion, as if to prove a point. I simply avoided it by informing him that, in my view, I must remain aloof and judicial on the matter of Civil Service pay. I told him that it would be fatal, for the Service, if I lost the PM's confidence. [*Fatal for Sir Humphrey too, as he was well aware – Ed.*]

I encouraged Frank to make the running and assured him that when the time was ripe I would come down on his side.

Frank had another worry, this time quite legitimate. Quite rightly, he does not want the Cabinet to adjudicate on the claim.

We decided that it should be referred to an impartial committee, as usual. The question was: who should chair it? We agreed that Arnold[1] should be on it, but it seems improbable that the Cabinet will approve an ex-Civil Servant as an impartial chairman of a committee to decide upon Civil Service pay.

I suggested Professor Welsh. Frank has heard that he is a silly old buffer. Be that as it may, Welsh has asked me to put his name forward as the next chairman of the University Grants Committee. So he will understand what's required of him.

Frank agreed that Professor Welsh would be an excellent choice.
[*Appleby Papers BA/281/282*]

[*Hacker's diary continues – Ed.*]

March 15th

Only five days have elapsed since I instructed Humphrey to ensure that no more papers were bounced through Cabinet. On that very day we decided that MPs were not going to get their pay rise, and that the Treasury would be cancelling half our spending plans.

But what did I find on my desk today? A plan for a *Civil Service* pay rise!

Humphrey has had the temerity to suggest that because spending cuts mean a lot of extra work for the Civil Service, they deserve a pay rise for coping with them.

Ridiculous! And even if that were legitimate, how dare he try to get it through Cabinet tomorrow, after I told him to make sure that all Cabinet papers come through forty-eight hours in advance?

Humphrey claimed it was not his fault. 'Prime Minister, it is not for me to speak for Sir Frank.'

[1] Sir Arnold Robinson, the retired Cabinet Secretary.

'Speak for yourself,' I retorted. 'You're Cabinet Secretary. You're also Head of the Civil Service.'

'Am I?' Humphrey smiled. 'How gratifying.'

'At the moment,' I said significantly, regretting my momentary slip of the tongue.

'As Cabinet Secretary,' said Humphrey, 'I am most eager to reduce public spending, but as Head of the Civil Service I am responsible for the very real problems that will arise administratively if a pay rise does not come through soon. This is a difficult matter for me because I'm wearing two hats.'

'Isn't that rather awkward?' I enquired.

'Not if one is in two minds,' he replied smoothly.

'Or has two faces,' intervened Bernard, and I could see he instantly regretted it.

'Perhaps I should relieve you of one of them,' I suggested.

Humphrey panicked. 'Oh, no. No. I'm very happy with both of them.'

'Faces?' I asked with amusement.

'Hats,' he snapped.

'But,' I reminded him, 'you said you have very real problems.'

'The problem is low morale, which inevitably leads to the danger of a strike. Think of the effect of a strike of the computer men on the social services. Furthermore, we are already experiencing difficulties of recruitment.'

This was news to me. 'I thought you had about ten applicants for every place.'

'Yes,' he acknowledged with reluctance, 'but we are getting applicants of a very low quality, with very few first-class degrees. Most of them have lower seconds.'

Ridiculous intellectual snobbery! 'I got a third,' I remarked.

Humphrey hesitated, aware that he'd been less than tactful. Bernard tried to cover for him. 'A third's all right for a Prime Minister, but Sir Humphrey's talking about Civil Servants.'

Humphrey stuck to his guns. 'Non-cooperation by the Civil Service Unions brings government to a standstill.' Presuming that it was previously moving, I suppose. 'The FDA[1] has a huge membership now.'

'Including yourself?' I asked.

Humphrey assured me that even though he is a member of the union he will always cooperate with me to the same extent as usual.

[1] The First Division Association, the Union that represents the top Civil Servants in Whitehall.

Which is roughly what I'm complaining about.

I reiterated to him that I cannot possibly get this through, *even if I want to*. With the backbench revolt looming over the cuts, MPs will never okay a pay rise for the Civil Service. And the Cabinet is bound to resist.

Humphrey saw the point quickly. He suggested that we merely ask for Cabinet to agree, in principle, to look at the application. Then the matter could be put before an independent group of assessors to consider the claim in detail.

This seems a reasonable compromise. The only thing that puzzles me about it is that Humphrey's suggestion for chairman is Professor Welsh. I've heard he's a silly old buffer!

[*The Cabinet, the following day, did agree to look at the matter in principle, but made no other commitments. There the matter rested until the pay claim was worked out in detail. This was done in considerable haste, and only eleven days later the following letter was sent by Sir Frank Gordon to Sir Humphrey Appleby. Sir Frank was slightly less careful than Sir Humphrey about what he was prepared to put in writing. We found this personal, handwritten note in the Cabinet Office ourselves. Presumably it was carefully preserved by Sir Humphrey Appleby in case it should prove useful in his fight with Sir Frank for control of the Service. In the event, it was never shown to Hacker, but it reveals much about the way Civil Service pay claims were prepared in the late twentieth century. The complete note is reprinted opposite. – Ed.*]*

H M Treasury

Permanent Secretary

2?/III

Dear Humpy,

I enclose the working papers. I'm sure that you will agree that, in all fairness, the most senior grades of the service who really bear the heat of the battle should receive the greatest increase.

This means that there is a signif

H.M. Treasury
March 27th

Dear Humphrey,

I enclose the working papers. I'm sure that you will agree that, in all fairness, the most senior grades of the service who really bear the heat of the battle should receive the greatest increase.

This means that there is a significant percentage increase for Under Secretaries, Deputy Secretaries, Permanent Secretaries, and those two jobs which bear the greatest burden of all.[1] It comes to about 43%, alas!

The enclosed papers are not for submission. The submission papers, which follow shortly, go up to Appendix Q, so there is little chance that the Cabinet will read them all. The one-page summary for the Cabinet[2] is more or less the same as last time. It is headed 'Comparable Jobs in Industry', and is also enclosed.

You will recognise that the salary comparisons are based on directors of BP and IBM. I think that there is no risk of their being challenged because, in line with our usual custom and practice, we do not mention them by name. They are referred to as 'typical industrial firms'.

Then we take our own new examples of increase from the lowest point of the incremental scale,

e.g.: £3.50 a week rise for a Messenger
    £4.20 a week rise for a Registry Clerk
    £8.20 a week rise for a Scientific Officer

For the most senior grade[3] in the Service it would be a rise of £26,000 per annum. It hardly seems necessary to mention that in the Janet and John Bit, firstly because it can be calculated by the Cabinet Members themselves should they desire to do so, and secondly because it only applies to the two top jobs mentioned above. If there is criticism it is, as we said, just another cross we have to bear.

Sincerely,
FG

[*Sir Humphrey sent a carefully worded reply – Ed.*]

---

[1] The two jobs being Cabinet Secretary and Permanent Secretary of the Treasury, which, coincidentally, were held by the sender and the recipient of this letter.

[2] Known in the Civil Service as 'The Janet and John Bit'.

[3] Sir Frank and Sir Humphrey only.

70 WHITEHALL, LONDON SW1A 2AS

From the Secretary of the Cabinet and Head of the Home Civil Service

March 27th

Dear Frank,

I was glad to hear of your proposals for the Civil Service pay claim. Thank you for keeping me informed.

Thank you also for not showing me the full details. It would be most improper if I had full knowledge, since pay is within your purview. Do you think we should volunteer to forego some of the pay rise ourselves? And you have not mentioned pensions.

Are you quite sure that the Cabinet will not want to go through the proposals in much greater detail than the summary?

As ever,

[Sir Frank replied to Sir Humphrey – Ed.]

March 27th

Dear Humphrey,

If our own pay rises are brought up we can volunteer to *defer* the rise. And get it back later, when the fuss has died down.

I have not mentioned pensions. I find it is better not to, ever since we got the inflation indexing through. It creates animosity, confuses things, and pensions are so difficult to put a real value on.

I see no likelihood of Cabinet Ministers going into this matter more deeply. Ministers are briefed by their own officials, and we all know where their loyalties lie.

Frank.

[*And Sir Humphrey replied to Sir Frank – Ed.*]

March 28th

Dear Frank,

I shall put the matter on the agenda last item before lunch. The agenda is full, so with careful management there will only be about five minutes left.

So if should all be plain sailing, but for the vigorous scrutiny of Professor Welsh!

As ever,
H.A.

[*Hacker's diary continues – Ed.*]

March 29th

I had a most interesting phone call from Dorothy Wainwright this morning. I had asked her to do a paper on the Civil Service pay claim. She wanted to give me an immediate response.

I asked her what her answer was.

'I haven't an answer, more a series of questions,' she told me. 'Not for you, but for Humphrey. The claim is self-serving and inappropriate, and significant for the questions it leaves unanswered. But please treat my questions as highly confidential, or else you'll never catch Humphrey out.'

I've locked the list of questions in my desk and taken the key. So I can't list them here, but I shall come back to this matter tomorrow.

[*Fortunately for Sir Humphrey Appleby, this phone call was overheard by Bernard Woolley. He was not eavesdropping. It is the Principal Private Secretary's duty to listen in on all telephone calls to or from the Prime Minister, in order to minute and witness what was said, to give the Prime Minister an aide mémoire, and to protect the Prime Minister against subsequent misrepresentation. In this instance, Dorothy Wainwright made a tactical error in not calling on Mr*

Hacker's private line. Better still, she could have spoken to him in person.

It is also true to say that Bernard Woolley had a duty to respect the complete confidentiality of the call. It might be argued that he stuck to the letter of the rules – but it is clear from this entry in Sir Humphrey's diary that Bernard Woolley did not stick to the spirit of confidentiality. But then, like all Private Secretaries, he did have a difficult dual loyalty to maintain – Ed.]

En route to the Cabinet Room through the Private Office I was halted by an anxious BW.[1]

He informed me that there had been movement. Specifically, movement on a matter on which the Civil Service hoped there would be no movement.

I refrained from pointing out that the Civil Service generally hopes that there will be no movement on any matter.

BW seemed unable or unwilling to express himself with even his usual clarity. He told me that it was in relation to a subject that is normally wholly and exclusively within the control of the Civil Service that developments have developed. I told him that he was speaking in riddles. He thanked me.

Most unusually for me I had been slow on the uptake. I realised that his lips were sealed, and that he must be referring confidentially to minutes that he was duty-bound to make of a confidential conversation between the Prime Minister and one of his confidential advisers.

I asked if this were so. He acknowledged with a nod.

I asked for the name of the confidential adviser. He told me that he was not at liberty to divulge her name. Very helpful.

I questioned him closely, to find out whether the confidential advice concerned the financial crisis or the PM's foolish nuclear strategy. BW hinted that the matter was even more important than either of the above.

I realised at once that he must be referring to the Civil Service pay claim. I asked him, and he refused to confirm or deny it. Quite correctly. [*It might be argued that this refusal to confirm or deny was less than correct, since Bernard Woolley had given a clear negative response to all of Sir Humphrey's other questions. The inference was therefore unmistakeable – Ed.*]

I asked BW for his advice. He advised me to consider my position very carefully, perhaps temporarily adopting a middle-of-the-road posture, while keeping my ear to the ground, covering my retreat and watching my rear. A little undignified but I took heed of his warning.

I thanked him for his help. He replied that he had not told me anything. I agreed, for it would have been most improper had he done so.
[*Appleby Papers 638/T/RJC*]

[*Hacker's diary continues – Ed.*]

March 30th
I studied the Civil Service pay claim in great detail when I rose early

[1] Bernard Woolley.

this morning and, armed with Dorothy's excellent questions, I was ready to raise hell with Humphrey. I was delighted that her comments were given to me in complete confidence – because I learned something important about Humphrey today: he is *not* always on the side of the Civil Service. With no prior knowledge of the awkward questions I raised he performed reasonably and helpfully, and impressed me more than somewhat.

I handed him the very bulky Pay Claim file when he came in. It's incredibly long and verbose – goes up to Appendix Q, I think. Thank God Dorothy's a patient reader. And a quick one.

I asked Humphrey what he made of it. He said it was too large for an instant judgement. I told him to read the excellent one-page summary at the front.

He did so. Then he looked up at me, and remarked that I was putting him in a very difficult position.

I got heavy with him. 'Look, Humphrey,' I reminded him, 'I appreciate that you have a loyalty to your colleagues but you also have a broader loyalty to the Cabinet and its policies.'

'I agree,' he said.

I was confused. 'You agree?'

'Yes,' he said.

I wanted to get this quite clear. 'You mean you agree with me?' I asked.

'Yes, I agree,' he repeated.

I still wasn't quite sure that he wasn't playing some verbal or linguistic game. I wanted to be quite sure where I stood. 'Who, precisely, do you agree with?'

'With you,' he replied.

I wanted to be absolutely sure. 'Not with Sir Frank?'

'No,' he said.

I summed it up. 'So . . . you're not arguing with me at all?'

'No,' he answered. 'Perhaps I haven't made it quite clear, Prime Minister – I agree with you.'

Well, you can imagine how completely flabbergasted I was. So I asked him for *his* view of this self-serving pay claim.

'It's not excessive in itself,' he replied, 'but at a time of national stringency it is neither wise nor in the national interest. I don't like to criticise my colleagues, but in my opinion Sir Frank, though no doubt acting from the best of motives, should have placed the good of the nation before the narrower sectional interests of Civil Servants. This claim raises serious questions.'

How interesting that he should use that phrase. I told him I'd made a note of some questions too. I handed Dorothy's list over to him.

He stared at it. 'Good questions,' he said quietly. 'Where did they come from?'

I wasn't sure that I cared for the implication of his question. 'They . . . occurred to me,' I said.

He glanced at the paper again. 'Yes. Well, they're *very* good questions.'

This was exactly what I – and Dorothy – had thought. So I asked Humphrey what we should now do about these questions. He said that we should ask them. I thought I *was* asking them, but his view was that I should ask them of Sir Frank. 'I think you should invite him here to discuss them. He may well have answers. Indeed, he should have answers. This is his job, after all.'

I realised that he was quite right. I told him to speak to Bernard and arrange such a meeting. And I told Humphrey that I genuinely appreciated his impartiality on this subject. After all, there's no doubt that Humphrey himself would do quite well out of this pay claim if it went through.

Humphrey thanked me, but explained that he saw the rewards of his job as the knowledge that one has been of service to the nation. I'm sure he was telling the truth. And of course, I see my rewards in exactly the same light. Nonetheless, one must give credit where credit is due – Humphrey was extremely fair-minded today.

After he left I asked Bernard how the FDA[1] worked. How, if they are all in the Union, can they bargain with themselves over their own pay?

I could have predicted the answer – Bernard said it's not so difficult if they simply wear two hats.

'All very well,' I said, 'but what happens when there is industrial action?'

[*This phrase must be the only occasion on which the Civil Service uses the demeaning word 'industrial' to apply to itself. Though it frequently describes itself as 'industrious' – Ed.*]

'It can be awkward,' said Bernard. 'The Secretary of our Union was on the Council of Civil Service Unions which planned the last bout of disruption – and at the same time, as Number Three at Swansea, his duty was to make contingency plans for frustrating the disruption.'

I asked what happened. Bernard said he was very successful.

[1] First Division Association.

I couldn't see how. 'He must have known the other side's plans,' I said.

'Which other side?' asked Bernard.

'*Both* other sides,' I answered logically. 'Whichever side he wasn't on at whatever moment he was on the *other* side.'

This presented no problem for Bernard. 'Yes,' he agreed, 'but he never disclosed the other side's plans.'

'To whom?' I was getting confused.

'To his own side.'

'*Which* own side?' I asked.

'Whichever side', explained Bernard patiently, 'that he was on at whatever moment he wasn't on the *other* side.'

I was now groping blindly through the fog of logic. 'Yes, but even if he never disclosed the other side's plans to his own side, *he* knew the other side's plan because he was on the other side too!'

Bernard contemplated this question briefly. 'Therefore I imagine', he replied, 'that he never disclosed to himself what he knew.'

I asked Bernard how such a thing was possible. It seemed all too easy to Bernard. 'He was a model of discretion,' he said.

To me the Number Three man at Swansea sounded like a model of institutionalised schizophrenia. But there remained one vital un-answered question, 'When there is a genuine conflict of interest, Bernard, which side is the Civil Service really on?'

This time he replied without hesitation. 'The winning side, Prime Minister.' And he gave me a winning smile.

[*Sir Humphrey, having been forced by events to side against the Civil Service pay claim proposed by Sir Frank, was left in something of a dilemma. It had been useful to him to appear more loyal than Sir Frank, and, in any case, since the Prime Minister had found some of the key questions, the claim was inevitably doomed and any wise man would have distanced himself from it. Now, however, he was obliged to find a way to make the Civil Service pay claim seem acceptable – partly because it would consolidate his position with the PM and with his colleagues in the Service, and partly because he wanted the money.*

Accordingly, he consulted his eminent predecessor Sir Arnold Robinson. One of the many jobs Sir Arnold had accepted on his retirement was the Presidency of the Campaign for Freedom of Information. Strangely, however, Sir Arnold did not report the events described in this chapter to the press, nor to the Campaign. Indeed, his private notes only came to light comparatively recently when, under the

153

terms of his will, his private papers were released from the strongroom of his bank in Woking thirty years after his death – Ed.]

We lunched in the Athenaeum. Humphrey was concerned that he had not been able to support Frank's case. Deeply distressing, no doubt, but one does not support proposals that are clearly going to be rejected.

The Wainwright female had given Hacker a list of questions, plus the suggestion that the politicians stop letting us handle our own pay claim and let a Select Committee of Parliament decide on them. An *appalling* notion! The next thing we'd have is politicians removing Civil Servants on the grounds of incompetence, which would be the thin end of the wedge.

It is true, doubtless, that some Civil Servants are incompetent, but certainly not incompetent enough for a politician to notice. A better idea might be that Civil Servants could remove politicians on the grounds of incompetence, although that is a sadly improbable notion because it would virtually empty the House of Commons, remove all the Cabinet, be the end of democracy and the beginning of responsible government.

It appears that Frank used the normal formula – comparable jobs in industry. And they need a rise of 43%. I made the following suggestions:

1. Since virtually all the relevant staff work in London, there should be a big increase in the London Allowance. Allowances rank as expenses. Because they do not count as a rise, they do not show up in the percentage calculations.
2. Introduce a Special Graduate Allowance for those with First Class Degrees, and Upper Second-Class degrees. (Oxford does not give Upper Seconds, so count any Second at Oxford as an Upper Second.)
3. Double the Outstanding Merit Awards, which *everyone* gets. Awards rank as Bonuses and, like Allowances, do not count as pay rises.
4. Items 1–3 bring the claim down to about 18% for the top grades. Therefore it should be calculated from 1973, which was the high point in percentage increases [*not in income – Ed.*]. And take the calculation to the end of two years from now, *i.e.* the *end* of this claim period rather than the beginning.

These four measures bring the percentage increase down to about 6%. But that *still* means that the Civil Service overall pay bill will be too high. The only option is to reduce the size of the Civil Service. Thus, a comfortable rise for individuals would be a smaller rise in the total bill.

Of course, *real* reductions in the size of the Civil Service would be the end of civilisation as we know it. The answer is much less worrying: stop calling some officials by the name of Civil Servant.

E.g. Turn all museums into independent trusts. Then all the staff stop being classified as Civil Servants. They will still be the same people doing the same job and still paid by government grants. But grants, like allowances and bonuses, do not count in the pay statistics. It will look like a cutback, a most impressive cutback, unless anyone enquires very closely.[1]

---

[1] This procedure was followed in the 1980s, leading the British public to believe that the Civil Service numbered 680,000, its smallest size for many years.

There is only one problem: setting up a sufficient number of trusts. But it may not have to be done at all. It must only be *planned* for some time in the next two years in order to be reflected in the statistics. If it subsequently does not happen, it will not be anyone's fault.

Appleby thanked me profusely. I indicated that I was always happy to oblige. [*Especially, we suspect, with the Birthday Honours approaching. Sir Arnold did have the GCB[1] conferred upon him in June – Ed.*]

I offered to discuss the matter also with Frank Gordon at the Treasury. Humphrey was adamant that I should not do so. Apparently Frank Gordon has a lot of problems coming up at the moment. He hasn't mentioned them to me. [*This was because Sir Frank did not yet know about them – Ed.*]

Finally I suggested one major reform to Appleby:

Members of Parliament can be very small-minded about Civil Service pay, and there is often a struggle to get an increase past the House. But if MPs' pay were to be linked to a grade in the Civil Service, then every time they vote for a Civil Service pay rise they will accidentally be raising their own salaries. We could also index-link MPs' pensions. This could save much unpleasantness all round.[2]

This was not done in my time in the Cabinet office because Mr Hacker's predecessor as PM felt it might motivate parliament to frequent inflationary increases in government spending. I hope that MPs would not be so self-seeking, but politicians are a very mercenary lot and we in the Civil Service must not judge everyone by our own high standards.

[*Hacker's diary continues – Ed.*]

April 3rd

A most interesting meeting was held today. Present were Sir Humphrey, Bernard, Sir Frank and Dorothy Wainwright. Oh, and me, of course. I learned that Humphrey is a loyal, unselfish servant. I'm not sure about Frank.

Frank began the meeting by asserting that Civil Service pay has fallen significantly behind comparable jobs in industry. When I asked which comparable jobs, he avoided giving me a specific answer, and said that it was quite a complex formula which has been generally accepted for some time.

I confronted him with facts. 'According to my figures,' I informed him, 'a Permanent Secretary is already getting something over forty-five thousand a year. And the Cabinet Secretary and the Permanent Secretary to the Treasury get over fifty-one thousand pounds.'

---

[1] Knight Grand Commander of the Order of the Bath.

[2] This provision was enacted in 1983 without any legislation and with the minimum of publicity: it was announced in late July, to coincide with the summer holidays of the few journalists who would have seen its significance.

Frank hedged. 'Maybe you're right,' he said with a weak smile.

Ludicrous! Doesn't he know how much he earns? Or has it temporarily slipped his mind, perhaps?

I turned to Humphrey, sitting on my right at the Cabinet table, and asked him for his view.

He was cautious. Rightly so. 'It's not for me to say really, Prime Minister. I have a vested interest and Sir Frank is in charge of Civil Service pay. Aren't you, Frank?'

At least Humphrey had the decency to declare his interest. Dorothy, sitting on my left, spoke next.

'May I ask a question, Prime Minister?' I nodded. She stared hard at Frank, across the table. 'Sir Frank, what deduction do you make for job security?'

He was startled. This was obviously a question he'd not been asked before and was not expecting.

Dorothy explained further. 'Top people in industry can get sacked. Pushed out in take-overs, their firms can go bust. But your jobs are guaranteed.'

He hedged again. 'Well, there are swings and roundabouts.'

'What about the roundabouts?' Dorothy asked acidly.

Frank explained that top Civil Servants may have guaranteed jobs, but they have great pressure and long hours.

'Don't they have those in industry?' Dorothy wanted to know. Then she looked at me and added: 'Anyway, industrial leaders have to take decisions and stand by them.'

This angered Frank. His cheeks acquired small pink spots. 'So do Civil Servants,' he retorted.

Dorothy turned on him nastily. 'Really? I thought that Ministers took the decisions.'

'And the blame,' I chimed in. 'That's the deal, isn't it?'

Frank didn't really know whether to answer all these rhetorical questions or not. 'Yes . . . well . . . Ministers do, of course, take the decisions,' he acknowledged. 'But Civil Servants have to decide how to carry them out.'

Dorothy went for the jugular. 'Like a secretary deciding how to lay out a letter?'

'Yes,' said Frank. 'No,' he said, changing his mind instantly. And he appealed for help: 'I think Sir Humphrey knows what I mean.'

Humphrey's eyes were firmly fixed on the blank sheet of paper lying in front of him on the table. 'Well, Frank, it's up to you, you're in charge of Civil Service pay.'

Dorothy passed me a note. It said *What about the service element?*

I stared coldly at Frank. 'What about the service element?' I asked.

'Service element?' he repeated. 'What do you mean, service element?'

I wasn't quite sure what I meant, or what Dorothy meant. I'm sure it didn't show, though. I turned casually to Dorothy and indicated that she might speak for me.

'There is a strong service element about the job,' she began briskly, 'which is rewarded by honours – CBs, KCMGs, knighthoods.'

'To an extent,' conceded Frank with caution.

Dorothy turned to me again. 'You see, Prime Minister, I wonder whether we shouldn't compare civil servants with directors of charities rather than industry. I think,' she was rustling through all her papers, 'that they get about seventeen thousand.'

I smiled. 'That's an interesting proposal.'

Indeed it was. Frank was looking panicked. Humphrey wasn't looking any too pleased either.

'I don't think . . . well, we'd never recruit,' said Frank in a voice that was noticeably half an octave higher. 'Morale would plummet . . . I'm sure Sir Humphrey would agree.'

Humphrey stayed silent.

I looked at him. 'Humphrey?' I enquired.

'Well, Prime Minister, my opinion is that . . .' he looked up at Frank, with a distinctly unsupportive look in his eyes, 'Sir Frank is in charge of Civil Service pay. Though I do think, Frank, that the Prime Minister is entitled to an answer.'

Frank was visibly startled by this reply. He tried another weak smile. Nobody else at the table smiled.

The question of index-linked pensions was also on Dorothy's notes. I raised it next. Frank dismissed that as completely irrelevant. 'Those were agreed a long time ago.'

'But they have a considerable value,' I asserted.

He was disparging. 'A value, yes. But modest.'

I picked up one of the papers in the superb brief that Dorothy had prepared for this meeting. 'I have an estimate here that it would cost £650,000 to buy back a Permanent Secretary's pension.'

Frank smiled again. 'That's absurd!'

'How would you value it?' asked Dorothy.

Frank was foolish enough to suggest a figure. 'About £100,000.'

I pounced. 'In that case, Frank, I'll make you an offer. The government will buy back your pension – and anybody else's who will

157

sell – at your valuation. We'll give you a hundred thousand, cash, in exchange for your pension rights. Is that a deal?'

Frank was now doing the well-known Civil Servant impression of a headless chicken. 'Well, I mean, no, I was talking off the top of my head, it could be, that is, I haven't calculated it myself.'

Dorothy threw another dart straight at the bullseye. 'The figure of £650,000 came from the Society of Insurance and Pension Actuaries.'

'Yes, but when it was agreed,' whined Frank helplessly, 'I'm sure it was nothing like that.'

Dorothy was relentless. She had yet another idea. 'What about having index-linked pensions as an *alternative* to honours? Every Civil Servant could choose which way he wanted to take his reward – honours or cash!'

'But that's preposterous!' shrieked Frank.

'Why?' asked Dorothy.

I wanted the answer to that question too. It sounded like a damned good idea to me. On my right, Humphrey was looking very tight-lipped and was conspicious by his silence. Even Bernard was turning pale. I was thoroughly enjoying myself.

It was left for Frank to defend the indefensible. 'Such a choice would, it would, it, er, it would put us, er, put *them* in an impossible position. I mean, what about those who already have honours?'

Dorothy, of course, had an answer to that. Clearly she had worked out every implication in advance. 'It's quite simple. They could choose whether to renounce their honour or renounce their pension index-linking.' She leaned forward and smiled cheerfully across me at Humphrey. 'What do you think, Sir Humphrey – or will you be *Mr* Appleby?'

Humphrey was not amused. He had expected Frank to perform better than this – his own salary increase and honours were now under attack. 'I'm sure Sir Frank has gone into this very thoroughly,' he said.

'Not thoroughly enough,' I said. 'Frank, you personally would make a lot of money out of this pay claim, wouldn't you?'

Frank spluttered with indignation. 'Prime Minister, that is not a consideration,' he said. Which means *yes*, presumably.

Dorothy treated Frank to one of her acid smiles. 'You mean you'd be happy to be personally excluded from this rise?'

Frank was speechless. She turned to Humphrey. 'I'm sure the Cabinet Secretary would be, wouldn't you, Humphrey?'

I was sorry for Humphrey, but he was in a rather awkward position.

He stammered and stuttered about precedents, and thinking of the service as a whole, and considering long-term points of view. Then suddenly he found a brilliant way out. 'Yes!' he said, suddenly and very firmly. 'I would agree to be excluded from the pay rise *if*, and only if, the government did believe that senior people should be paid less than their subordinates, and if they extended the principle to Cabinet Ministers and their junior ministers.'

Naturally I had no such intention. And anyway, my purpose was not to corner Humphrey, who had taken my side on this matter. So I thanked everyone and dismissed them.

I kept Humphrey back for a quick private word. I asked him if he thought we were a bit hard on Frank. 'On the contrary,' he said. 'Most proper and penetrating questions, if I may say so, even though I do not like to be disloyal to colleagues.'

It's clear he's never been a Cabinet Minister.

April 5th

Humphrey really came through today. He has been hard at work on a new, much smaller Civil Service pay claim. He wanted to explain why.

'I'm afraid I thought all along,' he told me, 'that at a time of stringency the Treasury claim was excessive, not in the nation's interest. Nice for Civil Servants, of course, but not something the Cabinet Secretary with his higher loyalty could recommend. *That* is why we don't let the Permanent Secretary of the Treasury be Head of the Civil Service.' I took the point.

He then offered me a much more modest submission which amounts to only 11% over two years, with the top grades rising only by about the average. The overall Civil Service pay bill would only go up by about 6% a year over a period, in Humphrey's scheme.

This is obviously much more reasonable, and I'm perfectly willing to okay it. He wasn't even asking for that at once. He said that obviously the lower grades will have to go through the normal procedures, but he suggested that the First Division claim should be processed with the utmost secrecy and speed.

The reason is that he fears that his scheme could backfire if there is widespread discussion of it. Many members of the FDA might want to make a bigger claim – I'm sure he's right, if Frank is anything to go by. So Humphrey wants no one to see it now, even advisers.

That's only acceptable to me if he can get his colleagues to accept such a small rise, a mere 6%. He says he can swing it if I guarantee support and co-operation over the secrecy. I guaranteed it. I got a real bargain there!

But there was one outstanding problem: Parliament. The back-benchers always hate Civil Service pay rises. Humphrey had a solution – a brilliant solution. It involves a major reform that will be universally popular. [*By universally popular Hacker was referring to Parliament and the Civil Service, not the British public. To him, the universe consisted of Westminster and Whitehall – Ed.*]

'Prime Minister, if MPs' salaries were linked to a grade in the Civil Service, then they wouldn't have to keep voting themselves their own pay rises. Everytime the Civil Service got one, they'd get one too. Automatically. And if their pensions were index-linked too, that would help.'

'It certainly would,' I agreed. 'Excellent. Thank you.' Humphrey really has been a tower of strength, and thoroughly self-sacrificing. 'What grade should a backbencher's be, do you think?' I asked him.

'I think, perhaps, a Senior Principal.'

I was surprised. 'Isn't that rather low?'

'Backbenchers are rather low,' he said with a mischievous twinkle in his eye.

'And to what grade should Cabinet Ministers be linked?' I asked.

'Under Secretaries?' suggested Humphrey.

'And the Prime Minister?'

'Well,' said Humphrey, 'at present you earn even less than I do, but I think you should grade yourself as a Permanent Secretary. And you, like me, could have an index-linked pension. And it could be calculated not on your years as Prime Minister, but as if you had been doing the job all your life and it was your retirement salary.'[1]

A very fair offer. I thanked him. He shrugged off my thanks. 'After all, Prime Minister, this is a partnership.'

'Indeed it is,' I agreed. 'A real partnership.'

'Yes Prime Minister,' said Humphrey. What a nice man he is, underneath it all.

[1] This has been the practice since the 1980s.

6
A Victory For Democracy

April 10th
We had a drinks party at Number Ten tonight. Among the many guests was the American Ambassador. He cornered me in the yellow pillared room, and edged me towards one of the pillars.

'How are things in the White House?' I asked cheerfully.

He is a very tall, burly, amicable fellow. It's hard to believe that his words were threats. And yet . . . 'They've heard some talk about plans to cancel Trident, and coming on top of all this food war – er, that is this friendly rivalry from our European friends[1] it could just about blow the whole North Atlantic Alliance.'

One of those nice comfortable middle-aged ladies with those small silver trays of drinks passed by. I gratefully selected a Scotch. The US Ambassador waved her away.

'It's only a rumour, of course,' he continued. 'I can't personally believe the British Government would try to cancel Trident. But I know there's pressure on you.'

In reality, all the pressure to cancel Trident is coming from me. But I wasn't actually lying when I replied bravely, 'Yes, well, pressure's part of the job, isn't it?'

'But the White House has asked me to convey to you – informally, of course, not in my official role as Ambassador – that it might cause problems. The defence industries, you see, contain some of the biggest single contributors to party funds.'

This was the kind of American reaction that Humphrey had predicted. It was not news. 'Really?' I said, as if this were news.

The Ambassador came even closer to me. I'm sure he was only trying to be confidential, but it felt threatening. 'The White House would do a lot to stop cancellation. A lot!'

Again I was given a moment to think, this time by one of the ladies

[1] See page 31.

from Government Hospitality with a tray of mixed canapés. I took some brown bread with smoked salmon and asparagus rolled up in it. 'Delicious,' I said, and indicated to the Ambassador that he should enjoy our hospitality. He abstained.

'You can tell the White House, unofficially,' I said bravely, 'that you have made your point.'

'Unofficially?' He agreed to maintain the fiction. 'Fine. But the State Department and the Pentagon have other worries.'

'What about?' I couldn't think of anything else I'd done to offend the Americans.

The Ambassador sipped his Perrier. 'Well, you're aware of the East Yemen problem?'

I'd never heard of it. 'Absolutely,' I said. 'Big problem.'

The Ambassador seemed surprised at this response. 'Well, not at the moment, surely?'

'Not at the moment, of course,' I agreed hastily. 'But . . . potentially.'

'Right!' He was warming to his subject. 'And you know about St George's Island?'

Another place I'd never heard of. 'St George's Island?' I repeated, as if I were holding my cards close to my chest.

It didn't fool the Ambassador. 'It's part of your Commonwealth,' he explained.

'Oh, *that* St George's Island,' I said, as if everyone knew there were two.

'Well . . .' The Ambassador looked grim. 'It looks like the Communists might try and grab it.'

This sounded serious. 'Really?' I said. 'I'll speak to the Foreign Secretary.'

The Ambassador looked a little dubious. 'You think that'll do the trick?'

I didn't know, did I? For a start, I didn't know what trick was required. And speaking to Duncan rarely achieves anything anyway. So I prevaricated. 'Well, not in itself, perhaps – but . . .'

'The White House,' interjected the Ambassador, 'is worried that your Foreign Office might not be tough enough about it. They might just sit by and watch. The White House think your Foreign Office is full of pinkoes and traitors.'

I laughed. 'They've read too many newspapers . . . I mean, detective stories.' Freudian slip.

'That's what I tell them,' agreed the Ambassador with a sigh. 'But the Pentagon say they've read too many NATO secrets in Russian files. Prime Minister, the White House would be very upset if the Reds got hold of a strategic base like St George's Island.' So it's a strategic base! 'There's a talk of putting tariffs on British car exports. No more Jaguar sales to the United States.' He *was* threatening me!

I tried to interrupt but he was in full swing. 'Of course, I'd oppose it. But who am I? And the White House might tax US investment in Britain. That would cause a real run on the pound. They could demote GCHQ[1] and upgrade the listening post in Spain instead. They might even leave Britain out of Presidential visits to Europe.'

These were all humiliating threats, but the last was catastrophic. [*This was because it would have been humiliating to Jim Hacker personally – Ed.*] I was virtually speechless at this onslaught.

'But as I say,' the Ambassador went on, hopefully misinterpreting my silence as a counter-threat [*Hacker was always a wishful thinker – Ed.*], 'I would certainly not recommend that sort of reprisal against our friend, and old ally.'

I couldn't think who he was talking about. 'Who?' I asked.

'You,' he said.

I was about to edge away to talk to one of my other 200 guests, when the ambassador took me by the arm. 'Oh, by the way, I take it your man at the UN won't be supporting the Arab resolution condemning Israel? That would really make the White House burst a blood vessel. Freedom and democracy must be defended.'

I agree, obviously, that freedom and democracy must be defended. So does any right-thinking person. Whether a UN resolution makes such a difference to the future of freedom and democracy is anybody's guess. But the whole conversation was very unsettling. I'll see Duncan tomorrow.

April 11th

I didn't sleep too well last night. The American Ambassador had really worried me. This morning, first thing, I told Bernard all about it.

I asked Bernard, what is the big problem we have in East Yemen? 'Um' he said. He added that he would try and find out. I told him of the US worries about St George's Island, and that the US felt the Foreign Office couldn't help because it's full of pinkoes and traitors.

'It's not,' said Bernard indignantly. 'Well, not full.'

[1] The top security radar espionage centre in Cheltenham.

Bernard said he'd arrange a meeting with the Foreign Secretary for this afternoon. 'You can get him to sort it out,' he said reassuringly. 'After all, they are on our side.'

'Who are?' I asked.

'The Americans,' said Bernard.

'Oh. *They* are, yes.' I said. 'I thought for a moment you meant the Foreign Office.'

[*It appears that Duncan Short, the Secretary of State for Foreign Affairs, was unable to see the Prime Minister that day. A meeting was arranged at 10 Downing Street for the following morning. However, shortly after the Foreign Office received from Bernard Woolley the urgent request for a meeting with the Prime Minister, a different meeting was arranged for the same afternoon – between Sir Richard Wharton, the new Permanent Secretary of the Foreign Office, and Sir Humphrey Appleby. Sir Humphrey makes a note about it in his private diary. – Ed.*]

Dick Wharton of the FO came to my office for a quick chat. He was worried. I couldn't think why. I had understood that he had the Foreign Secretary eating out of his hand.

Dick confirmed that the Foreign Secretary was completely house-trained. The problem, apparently, is that the Prime Minister is starting to mistrust Foreign Office advice when Duncan gives it to him. It seems that the PM is even questioning Foreign Office policy.

Dick is beginning to see a danger of the Cabinet pursuing its own foreign policy. This would be absurd. The country can't have two foreign policies!

It is true that the PM is gravely under the influence of the White House. Except when it comes to Trident, which is the only time that he should be!

Dick told me of two matters on the horizon, over which the PM might need a little guidance in the right direction.

1. *St George's Island.* Dick had to remind me where it was: one of those few islands in the Indian Ocean to stay in the Commonwealth after independence. It is democratic, has free elections, but there is a group of Marxist guerrillas in the mountains who are reportedly planning a coup.

   These things happen, of course. But, according to Dick, the guerrillas are going to be helped by East Yemen – or, to give it its full title, the People's Democratic Republic of East Yemen. Like all People's Democratic Republics it is a communist dictatorship.

   These guerrillas from East Yemen are Soviet-backed and Libyan-backed. The FO is planning for Britain to stay out of the situation, because:

   a) We would only upset a lot of front-line African states if we got involved.

b) We don't want to antagonise the Soviets at the moment.

c) We have just landed a large contract to build the new St George's Island airport and harbour installation. If we back the wrong side we will lose the contract.

d) We don't mind whether the democrats or the Marxists win. It makes no difference to us.

The potential problem with the PM: He might get into one of his ghastly patriotic Churchillian moods. He might want to start some pro-British 'defending democracy' nonsense.

The Foreign Office solution: The PM must understand that once you start interfering in the internal squabbles of other countries you are on a very slippery slope. Even the Foreign Secretary has grasped that.

2. *The Israelis raided Lebanon last week.* It was a reprisal for the PLO bomb in Tel Aviv. The Arabs have put down a UN motion condemning Israel. Naturally we shall vote on the Arab side. But apparently the PM had indicated that he wants us to abstain. His reasons, as expressed to the Foreign Secretary, are unclear. But roughly:
a) the PLO started it this time;
b) faults on both sides;
c) concern about the Americans;
d) worries about the Holy Places.
The FO view is that points a) and b) are sentimental nonsense. With regard to c) the PM is dangerously sycophantic to the Americans as it is. As for point d), the PM should worry more about the oily places than the Holy Places.

The potential problem with the PM: Like all inhabitants of 10 Downing Street, he wants to take his place on the world stage. But people on stages are called actors. All they are required to do is look plausible, stay sober and say the lines they are given in the right order. Those that try to make up their own lines generally do not last long.

The Foreign Office solution: The PM must realise that as far as Foreign Affairs are concerned his job is to confine himself to the hospitality and ceremonial role.
[*Appleby Papers FO/RW/JHO*]

[*Hacker's diary continues – Ed.*]

April 12th
My meeting with Duncan was mysteriously postponed yesterday. He came along to Number Ten this morning.

I told him that the American Ambassador had had an 'unofficial' word with me the night before last.

'About what?' he asked nervously.

I sat back in my chair and watched him carefully. 'What do you know about St George's Island?'

Duncan's eyes moved shiftily from side to side. 'What do you know about it?' he asked. I didn't know whether he knew anything about it, or whether, like me, he was damned if he was going to reveal his total ignorance.

'You're the Foreign Secretary, not me.' I allowed myself to sound a little indignant. 'Do you think there's any danger of a Communist takeover?'

He still looked like a frightened rabbit. 'Did he say there was?'

'He hinted,' I informed him, and waited for Duncan's answer.

Duncan decided to take a firm, positive line. 'No. No danger at all.'

'Sure?'

I awaited definite assurances. I got them, but I didn't feel very reassured. 'Of course. The Foreign Office would have told me.'

'Are you sure,' I enquired, 'that they always tell you everything?'

'Everything they think I should know,' he said with a confident smile.

'That's what I was afraid of,' I retorted. 'But the White House is worried about it, apparently. And we mustn't upset them at the moment.'

'I'm sure we've got it all under control,' said Duncan with quiet confidence.

'Chamberlain was sure he'd got Hitler under control,' I reminded him. 'And Eden was sure he'd got Nasser under control.'

Duncan leapt belligerently to the defence of the Foreign Office. For Duncan, a natural thug, attack is always the best form of defence. 'Are you suggesting the Foreign Office doesn't know what it's doing?'

'No,' I said carefully, 'I'm suggesting the Foreign Office isn't letting us know what it's doing.'

Duncan said that this was an absurd accusation. 'I get full answers to any question I ask.'

'What about the questions you don't ask?' I countered.

'Such as?'

'Such as about St George's Island!'

He shrugged. 'Ah – well, I don't ask those.'

'Well, ask them,' I begged him. 'For me. All right?'

As if he'd do *anything* for me. He'll never forgive me. [*For becoming Prime Minister – Ed.*]

Duncan looked as though he was reluctant to ask the Foreign Office about St George's, though he said he would. But he admonished me. 'Don't forget that once you start interfering in the internal squabbles of other countries you're on a very slippery slope.'

I turned to the other matter the American Ambassador had raised. Was it true, I asked him, that we were proposing to vote against Israel in the UN again tonight?

'Of course,' he said, in a tone of slight astonishment that I could ask such a question.

'Why?'

'They bombed the PLO,' he said.

'But the PLO bombed Israel,' I said.

'But the Israelis dropped more bombs than the PLO did,' he said.

'But the PLO started it,' I said.

He was about to answer back again, but I stopped him with a gesture. I was getting tired of this. 'Anyway,' I said, 'it seems to me that they're both equally to blame.'

'Not according to my advice,' said Duncan with determination.

'Either way,' I said, fed up with the pros and cons and wishing to deal with known incontrovertible facts, 'I'm under a lot of American pressure about it. I want us to abstain tonight.'

Duncan looked genuinely anxious. And shifty. 'Oh, I don't think we could do that. The Foreign Office wouldn't wear it.'

I lost my temper. 'Are they here to follow our instructions, or are we here to follow theirs?'

'Don't be silly,' replied Duncan.

Obviously that's another question he doesn't ask.

April 14th

Two days have gone by. I've had no response from Duncan. It's making me edgy. I called in Humphrey after lunch for a discussion on Foreign Affairs – something we've never really had before.

We sat in the study, on either side of the fireplace, and had coffee while we talked. We had no agenda – I just wanted a chat really. But the afternoon certainly taught me a thing or two.

'Foreign affairs are so complicated, aren't they?' I began.

'Indeed, Prime Minister.' He took a chocolate digestive biscuit. 'That's why we leave them to the Foreign Office.'

I smelt a rat at once!

'So . . . do they know what they're doing?' I asked casually.

He smiled confidently. 'If they don't, who does?'

This hardly answered my question. I told Humphrey that I was worried about the Americans. It didn't seem to bother him at all.

167

'Yes, well, we're all worried about the Americans,' he remarked with a weary smile.

There is a general creeping anti-Americanism in opinion-forming circles in London – specifically in Whitehall – which worries me a little. But Humphrey can't just dismiss my worries so easily, he knows that I've got to do everything possible to keep in with them in the next few months if I'm to cancel a huge defence order for Trident.

Of course, I know what he'd suggest: don't cancel Trident! He's made his views perfectly clear on more than one occasion and I suspect he is doing everything possible to obstruct me in that area. In fact, this could account for his apparent unwillingness to help with this new American problem.

Nonetheless, I'm determined to cancel Trident and I have to be sure, therefore, that we don't upset the Americans any other way.

I came straight to the point. 'The American Ambassador mentioned something about St George's Island,' I said.

He looked surprised. 'Really?'

'Humphrey . . . do you know what's going on in that part of the world?'

'What part of the world is that?' he asked, staring at me with insolent blue eyes. Damn it, he realised that I didn't know exactly where it is!

Well, I *still* wasn't going to admit it. 'That part!' I said doggedly. 'The part where St George's Island is.'

'What part is that?'

I bluffed it out. 'If you don't know, Humphrey, I advise you to look at the map.'

'I do know, Prime Minister.'

'Good. Then we both know,' I said. I'm not sure that he was convinced. But I explained that the Americans fear that St George's will be taken over by Marxist guerrillas. He didn't seem to mind a bit. I wonder if he knew already.

'They think we ought to do something about it,' I continued.

Humphrey chuckled and shook his head sadly.

I admonished him. 'It's not funny, Humphrey.'

'No indeed, Prime Minister. Rather touching, actually.' Sometimes he is so superior I could wring his neck!

'It's *not funny*!' I said irritably.

The smile was wiped off his face instantly. 'Certainly not,' he agreed emphatically.

'It's a Commonwealth country. And a democratic one.'

168

'Yes, Prime Minister, but once you start interfering in the internal squabbles of other countries you're on a very slippery slope.'

Now I had proof that this conversation did not come as a surprise to him. That was exactly what the Foreign Secretary had said to me, word for word.

I turned to the matter of Israel. I pointed out that both sides were to blame, that the Middle East situation is a tragedy created by history, and that morally speaking we shouldn't condemn either without condemning both.

Humphrey didn't agree, which was no great surprise. 'Surely,' he argued, 'it's a question of maintaining our relationship with the Arabs. The power of Islam. Oil supplies.'

I tried to get him to understand. 'Humphrey, I am talking about right and wrong!'

He was shocked. 'Well, don't let the Foreign Office hear you,' he advised me with sudden vehemence.

I felt that I had to give him a basic history lesson. I reminded him that we in Britain are the flagbearers of democracy. We keep the torch of freedom alive. Our great duty, nay, our destiny, is to resist aggressors and oppressors and maintain the rule of law and the supremacy of justice. We are the trustees of civilisation. [*This was, presumably, the Churchillian outburst which Sir Humphrey Appleby had feared – Ed.*]

Humphrey agreed. Well, he had to! And he proposed a compromise: if I insist on an even-handed approach, the Foreign Office might agree to abstaining on the Israel vote, so long as we authorise a powerful speech by our man at the UN attacking Zionism.

I wasn't sure this was such a great idea either. 'Surely we should use the debate to create peace, harmony and goodwill.'

'That would be most unusual,' replied Humphrey, eyebrows raised. 'The UN is the accepted forum for the expression of international hatred.'

He seems to think that this is good. Presumably on the grounds that if we don't express hatred in a controlled environment we might all end up going to war again. But since there are sixty or seventy wars currently being fought in various parts of the world anyway, between member nations of the UN, I rather feel that expressing less hatred might not be a bad thing to encourage.

Humphrey would not budge in his approach to the defence of democracy or St George's. He made a couple of scathing references to what he called 'flagwaving and torchbearing'. He argued strenuously that defending democracy is not the priority if it harms British interests by upsetting those whom we wish to have as friends.

I was shocked. This is the voice of the people who appeased Hitler. The same Foreign Office, in fact, now I come to think of it.

But to my complete and total open-mouthed astonishment Humphrey defended the appeasers. 'They were quite right. All we achieved after six years of war was to leave Eastern Europe under a Communist dictatorship instead of a Fascist dictatorship. At a cost of millions of lives and the ruination of the country. That's what comes of not listening to the Foreign Office.'

I think that is one of the most shocking things Humphrey has ever said to me. I mean, he may be right, but it strikes at everything that we hold dear.

I challenged him. 'Humphrey, are you saying Britain should not be on the side of law and justice?'

'No, no, *of course* we should,' he answered emphatically. 'We just shouldn't allow it to affect our foreign policy, that's all.' He is completely amoral.

'We should always fight for the weak against the strong.'

'Oh really?' He was using his snide voice. 'Then why don't we send troops to Afghanistan, to fight the Russians?'

That was totally below the belt. I didn't bother to answer him. The Russians are *too* strong, obviously. In my opinion it didn't alter the validity of my argument, and I told him so. I instructed him to send assurances to the democratically elected Prime Minister of St George's Island that Britain will stand by him.

Humphrey stood up. 'Perhaps you wish to discuss this with the Foreign Secretary.'

'I'll tell him, if that's what you mean,' I replied coldly, and indicated that he could go. He had not been a great help. I sent for Bernard, and was forced to ask him a very embarrassing question. 'Where exactly is St George's Island?'

To my great relief and greater pleasure I realised that he didn't know either. 'Um . . . shall we look at the globe?' he said. 'There's one in your Private Office.'

We hurried down the grand circular staircase, decorated with photographs of past prime ministers, past the chattering tickertape, and into the Private Office. There were some clerks around. None of the other private secretaries were in there except Luke. He's the Foreign Affairs Private Secretary. He is the most Aryan-looking chap I've ever seen – tall, slim, blond – rather attractive actually, if he didn't have such a superior and patronising manner. Which really doesn't suit a man only in his late thirties.

He stood up as I came in, immaculate as ever in his perfectly pressed double-breasted grey-flannel suit. I wished him a good afternoon. He returned the compliment.

Bernard and I went straight to the globe, and Bernard pointed to a spot in the middle of the Arabian Sea – which is the part of the Indian Ocean which is close to the Persian Gulf.

'The Persian Gulf is the lifeline of the West,' said Bernard. 'Now look,' he went on, pointing to the land mass lying due north of the Arabian Sea. 'There is Afghanistan, which is now under Soviet control. If the Soviets ever took Pakistan . . .'

'Which they wouldn't,' interrupted Luke smoothly. I was suddenly aware that he had joined us at the globe and was standing right behind us.

'But if they did,' Bernard persisted, pointing to Pakistan which lies

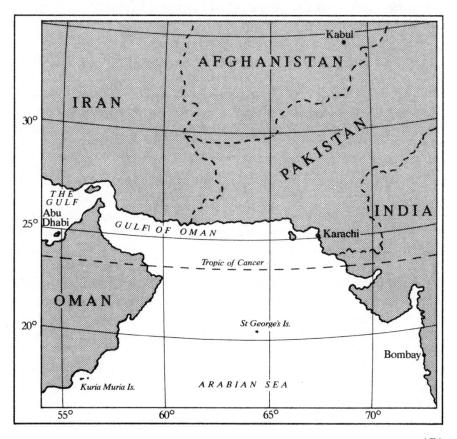

on the coast, south of Afghanistan and north of the Arabian Sea, 'the Soviets would then control the Persian Gulf, the Arabian Sea, and the Indian Ocean. And the Soviets have always wanted what they call a warm-water port.'

Luke smiled a superior smile. 'There's no risk. They wouldn't invade Pakistan and anyway the Americans have a fleet permanently stationed here.' He pointed to the Indian Ocean.

I turned to Luke and asked him, with his Foreign Affairs expertise, to tell me why the Americans are so worried about St George's. Is it because of the threat of Libyan and Soviet-backed guerrillas?

Luke said that we must remember that the front-line African states – and he pointed to the East African coast which also borders on the Indian Ocean – would be frightfully miffed if we interfered.

'Do they like Communist guerrillas?' I asked.

'They don't mind them,' Luke told me. 'Most of their governments started as Communist guerrillas. It can be argued that the guerrillas have the support of the people of St George's Island.'

'Who argues that?' I asked.

'The guerrillas,' said Bernard drily.

Luke emphasised that as we have a lot of trade with the front-line African states we don't want to upset them. When I suggested that we should be fighting for freedom and democracy on St George's Island, he sniggered and told me snootily that it's all rather more complicated than that, and that the Foreign Office took the view that we should do nothing. But the Foreign Office always takes the view that we should do nothing.

He then had the temerity to lecture me on peaceful coexistence. He said that the Americans can be too aggressive – well, we all know that. And he quoted his Permanent Secretary's view that the opposite of peaceful coexistence is warlike non-existence. The old FO appeasement line again.

Then, to my surprise, Bernard suddenly said that he wanted to have an urgent word with me about home affairs. I told him to wait but he started nodding and winking in a most peculiar way. At first I thought he was developing a nervous tick, then I realised that his back was to Luke and he was indicating that he wanted a private word with me.

We went into the Cabinet Room next door, and Bernard carefully shut the doors behind us.

'I don't want to be disloyal or anything,' he said in virtually a whisper, 'but I didn't really feel it was an awfully good idea to continue that conversation in front of Luke.'

'Luke? Why not?'

'Security,' whispered Bernard.

I was astounded. 'He's your colleague. One of my Private Secretaries. How could MI5 allow such a thing?'

Bernard corrected me hastily. 'No, Prime Minister, he's not that sort of security risk. It's just that he works for the Foreign Office.'

This was a revelation! I'd always thought that Luke worked for me. But it turns out that he is not only my man from the Foreign Office, he's also their man in Number Ten. In other words, he's a plant!

I understood this. But the implications were considerable. And worrying. It confirmed, definitively, what I've been suspecting for a while.

'Bernard,' I said, tiptoeing away from the doors in case Luke had his ear to them, 'do you mean that the Foreign Office is keeping something from me?'

'Yes,' he replied without hesitation.

'What?' I asked.

'I don't know,' he said helplessly. 'They're keeping it from me too.'

'Then how do you know?'

Bernard was confused. 'I don't.'

I began to get irritated. 'You just said you did.'

'No, I just said I didn't.'

What the hell was he talking about? I was now boiling with frustration. 'You said they were keeping things from me – *how do you know if you DON'T KNOW??*'

Bernard was beginning to look desperate. 'I don't know specifically what, Prime Minister, but I do know the Foreign Office always keeps everything from everybody. It's normal practice.'

'So who *would* know?' I asked.

Bernard thought for a moment. Then he gave me the full benefit of his education and training. 'May I just clarify the question? You're asking who would know what it is that *I* don't know and *you* don't know but the Foreign Office know that *they* know, that they are keeping from you so that *you* don't know but they *do* know, and all *we* know is that there is something *we* don't know and we want to know but we don't know *what* because we *don't know*.' I just stared at him in silence. 'Is that it?' he asked.

I took a deep breath. It was that, or grabbing him by the lapels and shaking him senseless. 'May *I* clarify the question?' I asked. 'Who knows Foreign Office secrets apart from the Foreign Office?'

'Ah, that's easy,' said Bernard. 'Only the Kremlin.'

[*Bernard Woolley sent notes to both Sir Humphrey Appleby and Sir Richard Wharton, asking for a meeting on the subject of St George's Island. Wharton's letter in reply was kept by Sir Bernard Woolley in his private papers and given to us for this edition of the Hacker diaries – Ed.*]

Foreign and Commonwealth Office

London SW1A 2AH

18th April

Dear Bernard

I shall be happy to attend your meeting tomorrow. This bit of bother on St. George's is getting to be a bit of a bore.

For your own background information, I believe that we made the real mistake twenty years ago when we gave them their independence.

Of course, with the wind of change and all that, independence was inevitable. But we should have partitioned the island as we did in India and Cyprus and Palestine and Ireland. This was our invariable practice when we gave independence to the colonies, and I can't think why we varied it. It always worked.

It has been argued by some people that the policy of partition always led to Civil War. It certainly did in India and Cyprus and Palestine and Ireland. This was no bad thing for Britain. It kept them busy and instead of fighting us they fought each other. This meant that it was no longer necessary to have a policy about them.

However, it's no use crying over spilt milk. The damage is done now.

See you at 3pm tomorrow.

Dick

[The following day, after lunch, Bernard Woolley had a meeting with the two wiliest mandarins in Whitehall. They had a frank conversation, in which Woolley learned for the first time how the Foreign Office really works. Fortunately for historians, Sir Humphrey Appleby made a careful note of the meeting and it was preserved amongst his private papers. Thus, for the first time, the general reader can be given an understanding of the Foreign Office approach to world affairs from the 1930s onwards – Ed.]

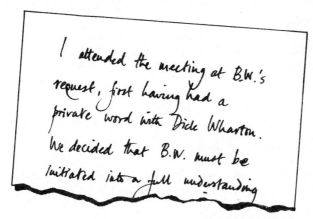

I attended the meeting at BW's request, first having had a private word with Dick Wharton. We decided that BW must be initiated into a full understanding of FO working methods.

BW began the meeting, which was technically about St George's Island, with his problem as he saw it: namely that the PM was completely in the dark. Dick said that this was good, and we began to encourage BW to see this not as a problem but as an opportunity.

This concept did not come easily to BW. He asked if there was anything else the PM did not know – a truly absurd question. I sometimes wonder about Bernard. Then he asked if there was something important that the PM doesn't know about St George's Island, and Dick correctly explained that the PM's proper course is to ask the Foreign Secretary to inform him of anything he needs to know. Then all that the FO has to do is ensure that the Foreign Secretary does not know the whole story either.

We were getting to the root of BW's problem. He was under the impression that the PM ought to know what is happening.

The basic rule for the safe handling of Foreign Affairs is that it is simply too dangerous to let politicians get involved with diplomacy. Diplomacy is about surviving till the next century – politics is about surviving till Friday afternoon.

There are 157 independent countries in the world. The FO has dealt with them for years. There's hardly an MP who knows anything about any of them. Show MPs a map of the world, and many of them would have difficulty finding the Isle of Wight.

Bernard was prepared to argue that MPs cannot be so ignorant. So Dick gave him a short quiz:

1. Where is Upper Volta?
2. What is the capital of Chad?
3. What language do they speak in Mali?
4. Who is the President of Peru?
5. What is the national religion of Cameroun?

Bernard scored nought per cent. Dick suggested that he stand for Parliament.

BW's problem is that he has studied too much constitutional history – or, at least, taken it too much too heart. He was arguing, not very articulately I may say, that 'if you've got a democracy, shouldn't people, sort of, discuss things a bit?'

We agreed that full discussion with the PM was essential. Therefore, Bernard argued, the PM should have the facts. There was the fallacy!

BW needs to understand the following argument clearly:

i)   Facts complicate things.
ii) The people don't want them.
iii) All that the press, the people and their elected representatives want to know is Who Are The Goodies? and Who Are The Baddies?
iv) Unfortunately, the interests of Britain usually involve doing deals with people the public think are Baddies.
v)   And sometimes British interests mean that we cannot help the Goodies.
vi) Therefore, discussion must be kept inside the Foreign Office. Then it produces one policy for the Foreign Secretary, which represents the FO's considered view, and he can act upon it. QED.

BW was concerned that the FO produces only one considered view, with no options and no alternatives.

In practice, this presents no problem. If pressed, the FO looks at the matter again, and comes up with the same view. If the Foreign Secretary demands options, the FO obliges him by presenting three options, two of which will be (on close examination) exactly the same. The third will, of course, be totally unacceptable, like bombing Warsaw, or invading France.

One further option is occasionally used: encouraging the Foreign Secretary to work out his own policy. The FO then shows him how it will inevitably lead to World War III, perhaps within 48 hours.

BW understood the idea, but – quite properly, since he is a Private Secretary at the moment – wanted to pursue the discussion from the point of view of the politicians. He remarked the Ministers are primarily concerned about the effect of policy on domestic political opinion. That's what they're good at, in fact. And the Foreign Office system does not really allow for this.

He was quite correct. The FO does indeed take a global view. It asks what is best for the world, whereas most Ministers would rather it asked: What is the *Daily Mail* leader going to say? This would be quite inappropriate for the

FO to consider: foreign policy cannot be made by yobbos like Fleet Street editors, backbench MPs and Cabinet Ministers. The job of the FO is to take the right decision, and let others sort out the politics afterwards.

Bernard was also concerned about what happens if the Foreign Secretary still will not accept the FO's advice after all the options have been presented. I explained to him that it is a free country, and the Foreign Secretary can always resign.

The whole basis of our conversation then took an unexpected turn. A Flash Telegram arrived. Dick read it, and informed us that East Yemen are preparing to invade St George's Island in support of the Marxist guerrillas.

BW thought this was bad news. It is, of course, moderately bad news for the government of St George's – but it's very good news for the guerrillas.

BW wanted to know, of all things, if it was good news for the islanders. I'm afraid he has been a Private Secretary too long – he is beginning to react like a politician.

Dick suggested, and I agreed, that we could do nothing to help the islanders. If they appeal to us, we shall give them every support short of help. If the Prime Minister insists that we help, then we follow the traditional four-stage strategy, the standard Foreign Office response to any crisis:

Stage One
We say that nothing is going to happen.
Stage Two
We say that something may be going to happen, but we should do nothing about it.
Stage Three
We say that maybe we should do something about it, but there's nothing we can do.
Stage Four
We say that maybe there was something we could have done but it's too late now.

[*Hacker's diary continues – Ed.*]

April 19th
Dramatic events today. I think I've had a major triumph.

It all came to a head this afternoon, when that insufferable young man Luke brought the old green box containing Foreign Office telegrams into the Cabinet Room.

Bernard wasn't there, for some reason. He'd left a message that he was at a meeting with Sir Humphrey.

I picked up the first telegram: it said there were troop movements in East Yemen. I looked at Luke. He said that this was not significant.

'But,' I told Luke, 'the American Ambassador mentioned something about East Yemen last week.'

'Really?' said Luke with a patronising smile. 'I'm surprised he's heard of it.'

177

I asked Luke why there were troop movements in East Yemen. He said that he presumed that they were just preparing one of their regular raids on West Yemen.

'Is there anything for us to worry about?'

'Nothing at all,' he assured me.

I sat back and thought. Then I said to Luke: 'The American Ambassador talked about St George's Island as well.'

'Really?' said Luke again. 'Educated man, for an American.'

'Is there a problem there?' I asked.

'No, Prime Minister, just the normal local squabbles.'

Luke was hiding something. I didn't know what. And, of course, the trick is not finding the right answers, it's finding the right questions. I didn't know what question I should be asking, the question that would oblige Luke to tell me what the FO was concealing.

'The American Ambassador seemed worried about a possible Communist takeover,' I said eventually.

'Americans always are,' he smiled.

And that seemed to be that. So I picked up the next telegram – and I did not like what I read! Apparently we voted against Israel in the UN last night. I showed it to Luke. He remained calm.

'Luke,' I said, 'I gave express instructions that we were to abstain.'

'I think not, Prime Minister,' he said with his usual smile. How dare he?

'I did,' I reiterated firmly. 'I told the Foreign Secretary I felt very strongly that we should not take sides.'

'That's quite right,' agreed Luke. 'The Foreign Secretary noted your very strong feelings.'

I was on my feet now, very angry indeed. 'Well, why did he do nothing about it?' I shouted.

'With respect, Prime Minister,' said Luke, manifestly lacking respect, 'he did do something. He asked our UN Ambassador whether we should consider abstaining.'

'And what did the Ambassador do?' I asked.

'He said no,' replied Luke.

I was appalled. It seems that the Foreign Office thinks it can simply defy the wishes of the Prime Minister.

Luke denied that this is what happened. He says that the FO takes full account of my wishes in coming to a decision. But events move rapidly. 'There were important factors in our relationships with the Arabs last night that were not known to you when you took your view. It wasn't possible to get through to you in time.'

Bloody ridiculous! 'I am on the phone, you know,' I said.

'It was not thought sufficiently important to wake you at three a.m.'

'It was extremely important,' I yelled at that supercilious snob. 'The White House will do its nut!'

Luke didn't look as if he cared all that much. 'Well, I suppose I could arrange for you to be telephoned before every UN vote. But there are two or three a night while they're in session.'

He was wilfully missing the point. I don't express a personal view about many UN votes, as he knows only too well. But when I do, I expect it to be acted upon.

It was useless arguing about the mistake. I considered the future. 'What can I do to reverse this?' I asked him.

'Nothing, Prime Minister,' he replied flatly. 'That would be embarrassing. Once government policy has been stated it can't be retracted.'

Perhaps he's right. All the more reason not to state a policy that hasn't been approved by the PM!

Then I had an idea – a great idea. One that, I now believe, will change history. At the time I didn't realise where it would lead. 'Luke,' I said, 'I'd like to talk to the Israeli Ambassador.'

He shook his head. 'I think not, Prime Minister.'

I could hardly believe my ears. Who does Luke think he is? I repeated that I wanted to talk to the Israeli Ambassador. Luke stuck to his guns, and repeated that in his opinion it would be rather unwise.

I pointed a forefinger to my mouth. 'Luke,' I said, 'can you hear what I'm saying? Watch my lips move. I – WANT – TO – TALK – TO . . .'

He got the point. Finally he understood that I meant what I said. Who put it about that all these Foreign Office types are bright? Expensively educated – yes!

Luke said that if that was my wish, then of course! I felt like a small child being indulged. 'I will contact the Foreign Secretary and Sir Richard, and then ring the Israeli Ambassador.'

'I don't want either of them,' I said, enjoying myself hugely with this whippersnapper. 'I just want the Ambassador.'

He began to get a little edgy. 'Prime Minister, I have to advise you that it would be most improper to see him without the Foreign Secretary present.'

'Why?' I asked. 'What do you think I want to talk to the Israeli Ambassador about?'

He paused, scenting a trap. 'Well, presumably the vote at the UN.'

'Really, Luke!' I admonished him, with apparent severity and complete humbug. 'That would be most improper.'

He was stuck. 'Oh,' he said feebly.

Now it was my turn to follow up a lecture on propriety with a patronising smile. This was fun! 'No, Luke, it's just that Lucy is thinking of spending her next university vacation on a kibbutz. Or perhaps, since she's at the University of Essex, I should say another kibbutz.'

'I see,' said Luke grimly.

I went on to explain that the Israeli Ambassador and I were at the LSE together, and I thought that Annie and I would get him round to the flat to give his advice on kibbutzim.

'Oh,' said Luke again.

I smiled at him unhumorously. Showed my teeth, really, that's all. 'Nothing wrong with that, I take it?'

'Um – no,' he said again.

I rubbed salt in the wound. 'Do we need the Foreign Secretary or Sir Richard to help choose Lucy's holiday place?'

'Um – no,' he repeated, completely defeated.

I told him to fix it for six p.m. this evening, and dismissed him with a regal wave.

At least I'd won one round. And I hoped that David Bilu, my Israeli friend, would be able to help me find some way of reversing Foreign Office reflexes in relation to Israel.

I didn't succeed. But I did find out something else, of much greater import.

David came at six, and we sat in the living-room up at the top. He accepted my apologies about the UN vote with equanimity. He said that the Israelis were completely used to it, and it happens all the time.

I assured him that I had told my people to abstain. He believed me. He nodded, his big brown eyes sad and full of resignation. 'It's well known,' he explained gently, 'that in the British Foreign Office an instruction from the Prime Minister becomes a request from the Foreign Secretary, then a recommendation from the Minister of State and finally just a suggestion to the ambassador. If it ever gets that far.'

He spoke such perfect English that I was amazed. Then I remembered he *was* English, and emigrated to Palestine just before it became Israel.

Thankful that my apology was over and accepted with such good grace, I stood up to pour him another scotch. I was just about to raise the subject of how to deal with the problem that he had just outlined so accurately when he dropped his first bombshell.

'Well, Jim, what are you going to do about St George's Island?'

Slowly I turned to face him. 'You know about that?'

He shrugged. 'Obviously.'

I brought the drinks back to the coffee table and sat down. 'That's not a serious problem, is it?'

He was astonished. His eyebrows raised themselves halfway to his curly greying hairline. 'Isn't it? Your information must be better than mine.'

'How can it be?' I asked. 'Mine comes from the Foreign Office.'

He sipped his scotch. 'Israeli Intelligence says that East Yemen is going to invade St George's in the next few days.'

So that was the connection! And I hadn't been told!

David Bilu explained that the FO have agreed with East Yemen that the British will make strong representations but do nothing. In return, the Yemenis will let the British keep the contract to build a new airport there, after they have taken over.

But that's only the start. Apparently David has been told by Israel's Ambassador to Washington that the Americans plan to support the present government of St George's. In battle! On the island! They intend to send in an airborne division backed up by the Seventh Fleet.

The Americans invading a Commonwealth country to protect freedom and democracy would be a profound humiliation for the British! The Palace would hit the roof!

'Why haven't the Americans told me?' I asked David. I didn't think he'd know. But he did.

'They don't trust you,' he replied sympathetically.

I was embarrassed. 'Why not?'

'Because you trust the Foreign Office.'

I could see their point. I couldn't really blame them. Then David offered me some great advice.

'Jim, you have an airborne battalion on standby in Germany that is not now wanted for NATO exercises.'

'How do you know?' I said.

'I know,' he said. He seemed very confident. 'And if you sent it to St George's it would frighten East Yemen off. They would never invade. But, of course, it's not for the Israeli Ambassador to advise the British Prime Minister.'

His eyes were crinkling humorously. I grinned back at him. 'And he wouldn't take your advice anyway,' I said, as I hurried to the phone to take his advice.

I told the switchboard to get me the Foreign Secretary and the Defence Secretary in that order. While I waited for them to be found, I speculated as to why the FO hadn't covered themselves on this. They usually do. I had been through all my boxes tonight, except one. So I rummaged about in it, and near the bottom was a very thick file labelled Northern Indian Ocean: Situation Report. I realised this was probably it. I counted the pages: 128. I *knew* that this was it! But I'll have to go through it with a fine toothcomb before tomorrow.

Duncan came through on the blower. I told him that I wanted the President of St George's Island to invite Britain to send an airborne battalion for a goodwill visit. As a friendly gesture.

He saw no objection. Of course not – he doesn't quite understand what's going on either. He did remark that 800 paratroopers armed to the teeth is an awful lot for a goodwill visit. I told him it's just an awful lot of goodwill!

Then Paul[1] came on the line. It's amazing how quickly the system can track us all down. I was inspired. I told him that as we have an airborne battalion on standby in Germany I want it sent off to St George's. He was a bit awkward. He wanted to know how I knew we had a battalion on standby. Bloody cheek! I told him I knew, that's all!

He wanted to know where St George's was. Extraordinary ignorance. I told him sort of between Africa and India and to look on a map. Not that it matters to him where it is.

He was also sceptical that it was for purely a show-the-flag goodwill visit. I assured him that we'd been invited, and told him to give orders to leave in six hours. I explained it was an instant goodwill visit.

Finally, I told him to tell the press that it is a routine visit. He amended it to routine surprise visit, which was all right with me. He asked how to explain it all, and I suggested he say that we were invited earlier but the NATO exercises prevented us accepting the invitation – and now they're not needed in Germany, they're going to St George's instead.

He was still stalling, this time on the ludicrous grounds that the story isn't true. I pointed out that nobody knows it's not true and in any case press statements aren't delivered under oath. I rang off after telling him they'd better be airborne by midnight or else.

[1] Paul Sidgwick, the Secretary of State for Defence.

Its now one a.m., as I dictate these notes. The troops did leave before midnight – I checked. I feel completely invigorated, not at all tired, fresh as daisy, very excited – quite Napoleonic, in fact.

I thanked David Bilu for his help. He was impressed. 'You won't only frighten the Yemenis, you'll terrify the Foreign Office,' he said as he departed discreetly into the night through a side door.

He's right. And I'm looking forward to it. The Foreign Office is a hotbed of cold feet.

April 20th

My victory was complete today. I didn't sleep well, I was too excited. So I was already busy in my usual place in the Cabinet Room when Humphrey arrived.

It hasn't taken long for the FO to let him know what was going on, for Humphrey came straight in to see me.

'I gather,' he said, in a voice pregnant with malice, 'that there's an airborne battalion in the air.'

'Sounds like the best place for it,' I said with a grin.

He stared at me coldly. 'I gather it's on the way to St George's,' he said.

'Yes, it's due to land in a couple of hours, actually,' I confirmed.

He was not mollified by my engagingly frank manner. 'Quite,' he said nastily. 'Isn't this all rather sudden?'

I nodded cheerfully. 'Yes, I had a sudden friendly impulse, Humphrey,' I said. 'I wanted to spread some goodwill.'

'There's not a lot of goodwill at the Foreign Office this morning,' he growled.

'Really?' I said, pretending innocence. 'Why not?'

'It could be construed as provocative, flying a fully-armed airborne battalion in to a trouble spot like that. Explosive situation.'

I picked him up immediately on the word explosive. 'But Humphrey, you told me there were no problems there.'

He tried to get out of this corner he'd painted himself into. 'Yes. No. There aren't. No problems at all. But it's explosive . . . *potentially*. Moving troops around.'

'Come, come, Humphrey.' I was openly amused now. 'We're always moving troops around Salisbury Plain. Is that potentially explosive?'

Bernard intervened, trying to save Humphrey's face. I think. 'There's a lot of unexploded shells on Salisbury Plain.'

I thanked Bernard for his contribution, and politely invited

Humphrey to explain precisely what the Foreign Office was worried about. I was fascinated to see how it would be argued.

'It's a very sensitive part of the world,' he began.

'But they've been telling me how stable it is.'

Again he was stuck. 'Oh, it is. Yes, yes, it is.' His eyes narrowed. 'But it's a very unstable sort of stability.'

Luke came in just then, with the box of Foreign Office telegrams. His lips were so tight-set that they had virtually disappeared. With frigid politeness he set the box down in front of me. I opened it. 'Ooh, rather a lot,' I said with feigned surprise. I looked at Luke for his comments.

'Yes, the, er, somewhat unorthodox visit to St George's seems to have stirred things up,' he said thinly. ['*Somewhat unorthodox' was Foreign Office code for 'irresponsible and idiotic' – Ed.*]

The first telegram contained the best news: East Yemen was moving its troops back to base. 'They decided not to invade West Yemen after all?' I said to Luke, who nodded grimly. I knew that he knew, and he knew that I *knew* that he knew that I knew.

The next telegram was from the White House expressing delight at our goodwill visit. I showed it to Humphrey.

'And look,' I pointed to the relevant passage. 'They say they have a whole airborne division ready if we want reinforcements.'

'Reinforcements of what?' he challenged me.

I was unmoved. 'Reinforcements of goodwill, Humphrey,' I said with charm.

Humphrey could contain himself no longer. 'Prime Minister, may I ask where the impulse for this escapade came from?'

'Of course you may, Humphrey,' I replied. 'It came from Luke.'

Humphrey didn't know whether to believe me or not. He turned to Luke, who had gone ashen.

'From *me*?' gasped Luke, horror-struck.

I produced the 128-page file, *Northern Indian Ocean: Situation Report*, and flourished it at him. 'You put together this masterly report, didn't you?'

Luke was beginning to panic. He swallowed. 'Yes, but it was arguing that we needn't do anything.'

I gave him a conspiratorial smile, told him he couldn't fool me, and that I could read between the lines. I told him that the one small paragraph on page 107 (which I know he'd only put in to cover himself, in the least obtrusive way possible) had made it quite clear that St George's needed urgent support. 'I took the hint,' I said. 'Thank you.

And I've given you full credit, and told the Foreign Secretary to tell Sir Richard Wharton that it was your prompt warning that sparked off the whole military manoeuvre.' This, at least, was true – I had told the Foreign Secretary to make it known that this was Luke's idea.

Luke was desperate, and so anxious to defend himself that he couldn't possibly think of blaming the Israeli Ambassador, the obvious tip-off man. 'No, no, it wasn't me,' he cried. 'You haven't!'

'And I don't think I'm giving away any secrets when I say you are to be rewarded,' I said in my most avuncular voice. 'You are being sent as ambassador to a very important embassy. Straightaway!'

'Which embassy?' Luke whispered, fearing the worst.

'Tel Aviv,' I said with delight.

'My God,' croaked Luke, a broken man. 'No! Please! You can't send me to Israel. What about my career?'

'Nonsense,' I replied briskly, knowing only too well that this would be the end of him. 'It's an honour. Promotion.'

Luke was trying anything to save himself. 'But what about the Israelis? You'll upset them. They won't want me, they know I'm on the Arabs' side!'

I didn't speak. I allowed the silence to speak for itself. Convicted

185

out of his own mouth. We all stared at Luke, and I heard the grandfather clock ticking. 'Not that I meant . . .' he said feebly, then stopped.

Bernard and Humphrey averted their eyes. They didn't like being present at the end of a colleague's career.

I answered him. 'I thought you were supposed to be on our side,' I remarked quietly.

Luke was silent.

'Anyway,' I said with a brisk smile, 'we need someone like you in Tel Aviv to explain to them why we always vote against them in the UN. Don't we, Humphrey?'

Humphrey looked up at me. He knew when the game was lost. 'Yes Prime Minister,' he said humbly.

7

The Smokescreen

[*Some three and a half months after Hacker became Prime Minister he had to face his first Cabinet crisis, and the way in which he overcame it was a tribute to his increasing political skills. The crisis involved many issues simultaneously – his fight to save his Grand Design, threatened leaks, the threatened resignation of at least one and possibly two junior ministers, and his use of the powerful tobacco lobby in a fight to outwit the Treasury and obtain tax cuts to give him some short-term electoral advantage.*

The origins of the crisis may be seen in the notes of a meeting that took place early in May between Sir Humphrey Appleby, the Cabinet Secretary, and Sir Frank Gordon, the Permanent Secretary of the Treasury. There is no reference to this meeting in Sir Humphrey's diary but Sir Frank's notes were recently found in the Civil Service archives in Walthamstow – Ed.]

Lunched with Appleby at the Reform Club. Appleby was concerned because our new Prime Minister wishes to cut either taxes or public expenditure.

This should be resisted. Politicians are like children – you can't just give them what they want, it only encourages them.

Nonetheless, Appleby should not even have allowed it to get as far as being a *Formal Proposal*. It should not have been allowed to get past *Informal Discussions*.

[*Sir Frank Gordon could not have been seriously worried. There are nine further preliminary stages after Informal Discussions and Formal Proposals. All eleven stages are as follows:*

1. *Informal discussions*
2. *Formal proposals*
3. *Preliminary study*
4. *Discussion document*
5. *In-depth study*
6. *Revised proposal*
7. *Policy*
8. *Strategy*
9. *Implementation plan circulated*
10. *Revised implementation plan*
11. *Cabinet authorisation*

Any competent Civil Servant should be able to ensure that if a policy is unwelcome, stage 11 will not be reached until the run-up to the next General Election – Ed.]

Humphrey is unduly relaxed about the matter, in my humble opinion. The possible tax cut is contingent upon Hacker's fantasy about cancelling Trident and switching to conscription to create large conventional forces. The Services will never wear it because, however much they dislike Trident, they hate conscription.

But my staff are horrified. There are waves of panic running through the Treasury. Giving away one and a half billion pounds of our money is unthinkable. [*Hacker was arguing that the money was the taxpayers', and that – in the event of a tax cut – the Treasury would merely* not *be taking it away from them. This has never been the Treasury view – Ed.*]

I indicated to Humphrey Appleby that Arnold[1] would never have allowed such a notion to become a Proposal. Appleby observed, with some justice, that Arnold was not at Number Ten with the present inmate.[2]

As Humphrey Appleby is relatively new to the job I made the following matters clear to him:

1) The entire system depends on the supposition that he can control the PM and that I can control the Chancellor.
2) For this control to be maintained there must be an agreeable mistrust between them.
3) Hostility between them would be preferable.
4) Tax cuts unite them. Politicians win votes with them.
5) Even *proposed* tax cuts unite them, because they give the promise of votes to be won.

Appleby was confident. One might almost say complacent. He is confident that the Prime Minister and the Chancellor will manage their hostility without our help. Eric,[3] he believes, will never forgive Jim for winning

---

[1] Sir Arnold Robinson, the previous Cabinet Secretary.
[2] Hacker.
[3] Eric Jeffries, the Chancellor of the Exchequer.

Number Ten, and Jim can never trust Eric again – after all, one never trusts anyone that one has deceived.

I have *ensured*, however, that Eric opposes any tax cuts. I used the usual bait – told him we needed the money for hospitals, schools and the old people. [*This argument was known in the Treasury as the Kidney Machine Gambit. It hardly ever failed. It was followed up with the suggestion that the incumbent would be known to history as The Caring Chancellor. This never failed – Ed.*]

Appleby still felt that I was overly concerned about a tax cut of a mere one and a half billion pounds. It is true that the amount is not much in itself. But I indicated that some of our senior colleagues are worried that he (Appleby) is not in control. This cut has been proposed far too soon. Is Appleby able to keep up Arnold's tradition – the iron fist in the iron glove? It would, after all, be a black day for Britain if the politicians started running the country.

[*Sir Humphrey Appleby did not seem unduly worried by Sir Frank's hints, anxieties and veiled threats. He records his own dry comments in his diary.*]

Frank was worried about Hacker's proposed tax cuts. They are serious, I know, but if I were in his shoes I should be much more worried about the state of the economy and low productivity. Of course, there's not much Frank can do about that. The British worker is fundamentally lazy and wants something for nothing. Nobody wants to do an honest day's work any more.

This afternoon I went to Lords. When I got there England were seventy for four. Another collapse by England. What with the state of the pound and the state of our batting one sometimes wonders whether England has any future at all.

Still, it was a delightful afternoon. Warm sunshine, cold champagne, and the characteristic smack of willow on leather – occasionally, anyway.

I was there on government business, of course, as the guest of Gerald Baron, Chairman of the British Tobacco Group. The BTG are national benefactors in my opinion. I took the opportunity to ask Gerald for more sponsorship for the Garden.[1] Gerald was fairly open to the idea, though he mentioned that the Minister for Sport might also drop in at Lords this afternoon, twisting his arm on behalf of Wimbledon, Brands Hatch or some snooker tournament. I don't know where we'd all be without the BTG.

I did notice, however, that Dr Peter Thorn, the Minister of State for Health, was again conspicuous by his absence. Apparently he's been got at by the anti-smoking lobby. Gerald asked me if Dr Thorn has much clout in Whitehall. I was able to reassure him on that score. Dr Thorn is only a Minister, and has no clout at all.

[*Appleby Papers WHS/41/DE*]

---

[1] The Royal Opera House, in Covent Garden, which was more or less run from the Cabinet Office.

[*Hacker's diary continues – Ed.*]

May 3rd

Humphrey and I had a meeting about a study paper that he had sent me on the subject of cancelling Trident and reintroducing conscription. It was very long, very full, very fat, and completely unreadable.

I showed it to him. He was pleased with it. 'Ah yes, we can't get enough papers on that,' he remarked smugly. 'We need lots of input. We don't want to make any announcements until we have examined every implication and ramification.' Familiar delaying tactics.

'This *is* going to happen, Humphrey,' I told him firmly.

'Oh yes, Prime Minister.' By *yes* he meant *no*. 'Indeed it is, beyond question, at the appropriate juncture, in due course, in the fullness of time.'

'No Humphrey,' I replied sharply. 'This century. This Parliament, in fact.'

He shook his head sadly. 'This Parliament? I'm not sure it would be fruitful. The time may not be ripe. It could turn out to be a banana skin.'

Perhaps his doubts are a reflection of the curious obstinacy that I am encountering from Eric. The paper shows that if my plan goes ahead we'll have one and a half billion pounds available for tax cuts. And the Chancellor, of all people, opposes it. How can he oppose such a chance to win popularity from the voters? The only possibility, according to Humphrey, is that Eric is being advised by the Treasury, which apparently doesn't believe in giving money back.

This is always hard for a non-Treasury man to understand. I explained that the money is not the Treasury's, it is the taxpayers'.

'That *is* one view,' Humphrey acknowledged. 'But it is not the view that the Treasury takes. Not once they have got their hands on it.'

'But if they don't need the money . . .' I began.

He interrupted me, puzzled. 'I'm sorry?' he asked.

'If they don't need it . . .' I reiterated, and was again stopped in mid-sentence.

'Taxation,' said Humphrey loftily, 'isn't about what you need. The Treasury does not work out what it needs and then think how to raise the money. The Treasury pitches for as much as it can get away with and then thinks how to spend it. If the government started to give money back just because we didn't need it, we would be breaking with centuries of tradition. What would happen to the British Navy, for instance?'

I couldn't see any relevance to the question. 'It would still be there. We still need a Navy.'

Humphrey explained that, as we only have four capital ships, we only would *need* four Admirals and one Admiral of the Fleet. Whereas we have a total of sixty Admirals. And tempting though it would be to do away with fifty-six of them, the effect would be to reduce the number of serving officers all the way down, until there was hardly anybody left in the Navy at all.

I felt this was a red herring. My conversation with Humphrey was completely circular. To summarise it: the Treasury is the most powerful department of government because it controls all the money. Every time you take away some of its money you take away some of its power. Therefore it resists. The only way to get the Treasury to agree to tax cuts is to get the Chancellor to agree. But the Chancellor won't agree unless the Treasury agrees. So how do you force the Treasury's hand? Only by forcing the Chancellor's hand. And how do you force the Chancellor's hand? Only by forcing the Treasury's hand.

Humphrey suggested that I try to persuade the Chancellor to give me his active support. He is my Cabinet colleague. That, briefly, is the drawback – I need help from somebody who is on *my* side.

We got nowhere. I'll have to give this a lot of thought.

May 10th

Today I saw the way to get my tax cuts. And the help is going to come from a most unlikely source: the Minister of State for Health. Not only is he an unlikely source of help, he doesn't even know that he's going to help. And I'm certainly not going to tell him!

This is how it happened. Dr Thorn came to see me. He had sent me a paper on cigarettes, apparently, and the power and influence of the tobacco lobby in this country. Unfortunately I hadn't had time to read it. He asked me for my reaction to it, so I asked him to summarise it in his own words.

'Those were my own words,' he said, slightly nonplussed.

Bernard came to the rescue, very skilfully. 'The Prime Minister often finds that a brief verbatim summary clarifies the emphasis and focuses on the salient points.'

'Salient points,' I echoed, to encourage Dr Thorn.

So he told me what he had in mind, I was staggered. His idea was for the government to take action to eliminate smoking. He had a five-point plan:

1. A complete ban on all cigarette sponsorship.
2. A complete ban on all cigarette advertising, even at the point of sale.
3. Fifty million pounds to be spent on anti-smoking publicity.
4. A ban on smoking in all public places.
5. Progressive deterrent tax rises over five years until a packet of twenty costs about the same as a bottle of whisky.

It is a drastic scheme. He claims it should reduce smoking by at least eighty per cent. Even ninety per cent, perhaps. He reckons it will drive the tobacco companies out of business.

I had no immediate answer for such radical proposals. Of course, it would have helped if I'd read his paper before the meeting, but one can't find time for everything! But he was very serious and I had to keep him happy. So I told him that obviously I agreed with him, basically, that smoking ought to be stopped. No question. And I told him that we would definitely stop it in due course, at the appropriate juncture, in the fullness of time. I could see Bernard nodding with approval in the background. I'm getting very good at Civil Service stalling techniques.

Dr Thorn could see what I was doing, though. 'You mean, forget it?'

I assured him that that wasn't what I meant. And it wasn't! Well, not exactly! But we do have to be realistic. 'After all,' I remarked, 'we weren't born yesterday.'

'No.' He was very tight-lipped. 'And we didn't die yesterday.'

'What do you mean?' I asked.

'Three hundred people did die yesterday, prematurely, as a result of smoking. There are a hundred thousand deaths a year, at least.'

I tried to show Peter just how unrealistic he was being. If I took his proposal to Cabinet, the Treasury and the Chancellor would surely say that smoking brings in four billion pounds a year in revenue, and that we can't possibly manage without it.

Peter insisted that he wasn't unrealistic. 'I know you can't beat the Treasury with financial arguments. But this is a moral argument.'

And then my *brilliant* idea occurred to me! A way to beat the Treasury. With Dr Peter Thorn's help, but without his knowledge. And *not* on the issue of smoking, but as a means of securing the tax cuts that I want.

I was very careful. I didn't *exactly* tell Thorn that I'd support him. But I told him he'd made his case, and that we could give his plan a try. I told him I'd even read his paper. I added 'again' just in time.

He tried to pin me down on the issue of actual support for him. I explained that I couldn't give him *public* support – not yet. 'It would undermine my position if I took sides at this stage. I have to be seen as the impartial judge who is persuaded by the strength of the case.'

He said he saw the sense of that. He is a bit gullible. I must remember that, it could be dangerous. Or useful, come to think of it.

'But off the record,' I concluded, 'I'd like to see this pushed very hard. Very hard indeed. I'd like to see you make some speeches on it.'

Bernard looked alarmed, but Dr Thorn's face lit up. He flushed with pleasure, and thanked me profusely for my help. I thanked him for his cigarette paper. [*Presumably Dr Thorn understood that Hacker meant his paper on cigarettes – Ed.*]

After Peter Thorn left Bernard asked me if I were serious. He explained that it has been the practice in the past to discourage anti-smoking speeches by Ministers, and not to print or distribute their speeches if they make them. I asked Bernard if there had ever been a written directive on this. He said that it wouldn't be cricket, and that there was just a gentleman's agreement of the matter.

I instructed Bernard to check that Peter Thorn's anti-smoking speeches are printed and distributed, and to make sure that everyone knows. It is particularly important that the Treasury gets to hear of it all soon.

Bernard, of course, had no idea of my plan and he asked me if I thought I could possibly win this fight.

I smiled cheerfully. 'Some you win, Bernard, and some you lose. This one I shall definitely lose.'

Now he was completely baffled. 'Then why . . . ?'

I saved his breath for him. 'Because *when* I lose they'll have to give me something in return. If you were the Treasury, which would you rather give up – one and a half billion pounds of income tax revenue or four billion pounds of tobacco tax revenue?'

He smiled. 'I'd prefer the income tax cut.'

I nodded. 'And that, as you know, is what I've wanted all along.'

His face was full of admiration and respect. 'So you're using cigarettes to create a sort of smokescreen?'

'Precisely,' I said.

May 11th

Humphrey came to see me this morning. He was very tense. Clearly Bernard has been doing an excellent job of making sure that everyone knows about Dr Thorn's new policies.

193

'Prime Minister,' he began, 'I just wondered . . . did you have an interesting chat with Dr Thorn?'

'Yes. He has proposed the elimination of smoking.'

Sir Humphrey laughed derisively. 'And how, pray, does he intend to achieve this? A campaign of mass hypnosis, perhaps?'

I remained calm. I leaned back in my chair and smiled confidently at him. 'No. By raising taxes on tobacco sky high, and simultaneously prohibiting all cigarette advertising including at the point of sale.'

Humphrey chuckled confidently, but said nothing.

'Don't you think,' I asked, 'that his position is admirably moral?'

He was as superior as only Humphrey can be. 'Moral perhaps, but extremely silly. No one in their right mind could seriously contemplate such a proposal.'

'I'm contemplating it,' I said.

'Yes, of *course*,' he replied without a moment's hesitation, the patronising smile wiped instantly from his face. 'Don't misunderstand me, of course it's right to contemplate all proposals that come from your government, but no sane man could ever *support* it.'

'I'm supporting it,' I said.

'And quite right too, Prime Minister, if I may say so.' His footwork is so fast that one might be forgiven for not noticing that he totally reversed his opinion with each sentence he uttered.

I gave him the chance to come over to my side. 'So you'll support it?' I asked.

'Support it?' He was emphatic. 'I support it wholeheartedly! A splended, novel, romantic, well-meaning, imaginative, do-gooding notion.'

As I thought. He is totally against it!

'The only problem is', he continued, 'that there are powerful arguments against such a policy.'

'And powerful arguments for it,' I replied.

Oh, *absolutely*! But *against* it,' he persisted, 'there are those who will point out that the tax on tobacco is a major source of revenue to the government.'

'But there are also those who would point out that tobacco is a major cause of death from a number of killer diseases[1].'

---

[1] Cancers of the lung, larynx, mouth, oesophagus, pancreas, bladder and kidney; emphesyma and chronic bronchitis; coronary heart disease; strokes; peri-natal mortality; and smoking in pregnancy carries a higher risk of still birth. Also there were about 10,000 fires per annum, in the 1980s, attributed to smoking, causing about 250 deaths a year.

Humphrey nodded earnestly. 'Yes. Indeed. Shocking. If it's true. But of course, no *definite* causal link has ever been proved, has it?'

'The statistics are unarguable,' I said.

He looked amused. 'Statistics? You can prove anything with statistics.'

'Even the truth,' I remarked.

'Ye-es,' he acknowledged with some reluctance. 'But £4 billion revenue per annum is a considerable sum. They would say,' he added hastily, for fear of it being thought that he was taking sides in this dispute. *They* were clearly the Treasury.

I remarked that a hundred thousand unnecessary deaths a year – minimum – is a hideous epidemic. He agreed that it was appalling. So I went for the kill. 'It costs the NHS[1] a fortune to deal with the victims. So the Treasury would be delighted if we discouraged it.'

This was a tactical error. Sir Humphrey swung confidently on to the offensive. 'Now I think you're wrong there, Prime Minister.'

I couldn't see how I could be wrong. 'Smoking-related diseases,' I said, referring to Dr Thorn's paper which I had in front of me, 'cost the NHS £165 million a year.'

But Sir Humphrey had been well briefed too, by the Treasury and by their friends in the tobacco lobby. 'We have gone into that,' he replied. 'It's been shown that, if those extra 100,000 people a year had lived to a ripe old age, they would have cost us even more in pensions and social security than they did in medical treatment. So, financially, it is unquestionably better that they continue to die at about the present rate.'

I was shocked. I've been in politics a long time and not much shocks me any more. But his cynicism is truly appalling. [*Interestingly, Hacker was shocked by Sir Humphrey's cynical desire to encourage smoking, but was not shocked by his own self-declared plan to use the smoking issue merely as a way to force the Treasury into conceding income tax cuts. He had no more intention than Sir Humphrey of following Dr Thorn's advice. But he was able to convince himself, temporarily, that he was less hypocritical than his Cabinet Secretary. Of such self-deceptions are great political leaders made. Thus Hacker was able to conduct the argument with Sir Humphrey in moral terms – Ed.*]

'Humphrey,' I said, 'when cholera killed 30,000 people in 1833 we got the Public Health Act. When smog killed 2500 people in 1952 we got the Clean Air Act. When a commercial drug kills fifty or sixty people we get it withdrawn from sale, even if it's doing lots of good to

[1] National Health Service.

many patients. But cigarettes kill 100,000 people a year and what do we get?'

'Four billion pounds a year,' he replied promptly. 'Plus about 25,000 jobs in the tobacco industry, a flourishing cigarette export business which helps the balance of trade. Also, 250,000 jobs indirectly related to tobacco – newsagents, packing, transport . . .'

I interrupted. 'These figures are just guesses.'

'No,' he said, 'they are government statistics.' He saw me smile, and hurriedly continued: 'That is to say, they are facts.'

I couldn't resist it. 'You mean, your statistics are facts, but my facts are just statistics?'

Sir Humphrey decided it was time to tell another little untruth. 'Look, I'm on your side, Prime Minister. I'm only giving you arguments you will encounter.'

I thanked him, and told him that I was glad to know that I should have support such as his. I hoped that would bring the conversation to a close – but no! He was determined to give me *all* the arguments I shall encounter.

'It will also be pointed out that the tobacco industry is a great sponsor of sport. They give much innocent pleasure to millions of people, and you would be taking it all away. After all, where would the BBC sports programmes be if the cigarette companies couldn't advertise on them?' [*This was a slip of the tongue by Appleby. Until the late 1980s the BBC maintained the fiction that it did not screen advertisements. Of course, he must have intended to ask where BBC sports programmes would be if cigarette companies could not 'sponsor' the events that are televised – Ed.*]

I reiterated that we were discussing over 100,000 deaths each year. Humphrey agreed immediately.

'Yes, Prime Minister . . . but in a very overpopulated island. And there aren't enough jobs for everyone anyway. The benefits of smoking greatly outweigh the ill-effects: cigarettes pay for *one-third* of the total cost of the National Health Service. We are saving many more lives than we otherwise could because of those smokers who voluntarily lay down their lives for their friends. Smokers are national benefactors.'

'So long as they live,' I reminded him grimly.

'So long as they live.' He nodded. 'And when they die they save the rest of us a lot of money. And anyway, there's always more coming along to replace them. Not that any direct causal link has been proved, as I said before.'

This nonsense about no direct causal link was beginning to irritate me. I reminded Humphrey that the US Surgeon-General says that 'cigarette smoking is the chief avoidable cause of death in our society and the most important public health issue of our time'.

Humphrey dismissed the US Surgeon-General's report with a patronising smile. 'In his society, maybe. But do remember, Prime Minister, that Americans do love overstating everything, bless their warm little hearts.' He begged me to do nothing rash, to be very sure of my ground, and be very careful before I made any move. Of course, that's what he says about virtually everything.

Bernard interrupted us. It was time for Cabinet Committee, to be followed by lunch at the House – where the Minister for Sport wanted an urgent word with me.

The news is certainly getting round fast. I stared accusingly at Humphrey, pretending to be angry.

'Who tipped him off?' I enquired.

Humphrey and Bernard looked at each other. Then they looked at me. They remained silent.

'He's part of the tobacco lobby,' I said to Humphrey.

Humphrey pretended he didn't know. 'A member of your government?' he asked, with a feeble pretence of shock-horror.

This ploy was unworthy of Humphrey. *Obviously* the Minister for Sport has a vested interest in tobacco – all that sponsorship. Furthermore, this particular Minister for Sport [*Leslie Potts MP – Ed.*] is the Member for one of the Nottingham constituencies – and there are thousands of tobacco workers in Nottingham.

I told Bernard to tell the Minister I'd give him ten minutes at 2.30.

'With pleasure, Prime Minister.'

'Not with pleasure, Bernard,' I replied, 'but I'll see him anyway.'

At 2.30 we had our meeting. I have inherited Leslie Potts from the previous administration. He really is a dreadfully unappealing, unattractive figure. He is short, very thin, with bulging pop-eyes that seem to bulge even more than nature intended because they are so heavily magnified behind his inch-thick spectacles. He coughs and wheezes, his fingers are permanently stained yellow with nicotine, he chain-smokes and spreads ash all around him like an ancient volcano. His hair is greasy, his teeth are yellow, and he smells like a smoker's railway compartment, second class. I can only suppose that when my predecessor appointed him Minister for Sport he must have been giving a rare outing to his little-known sense of humour.

'Mind if I smoke?' rasped Potts.

I shook my head, whereupon a lit cigarette appeared instantly from inside his half-closed fist. He took a deep drag on it, coughed a bit, and asked about the rumour that I intended making a personal attack on the tobacco industry.

I gave a truthful but irrelevant answer. 'I haven't heard that rumour,' I said.

'Is it true?' asked Leslie, not deceived.

'The Minister of Health is considering the matter. No decision has been taken.'

'There's no smoke without fire,' said Leslie. He should know!

'Naturally you'd be consulted,' I said, in my most consultative voice. 'As Minister for Sport I realise that you have an interest in the matter.'

'I don't give a stuff about sport! I've got 4000 tobacco workers in my constituency. What about my seat?'

'What about your lungs?' I said.

'My lungs are fine,' he snarled.

'And he doesn't breathe through his seat,' said Bernard, not very helpfully.

'What did you say?' wheezed Potts.

'Oh,' said Bernard. 'Your seat. I see. Sorry.'

I tried not to laugh. I silenced Bernard with a wave and turned back to Leslie.

'I am aware, of course, that your constituency has a cigarette factory in it. But sometimes one must take a broader view.'

'Even *broader* than your seat,' added Bernard mischievously. I didn't dare meet his eyes – I might have burst out laughing.

Leslie Potts MP was not amused. 'It's not just *my* seat,' he snapped. 'There are marginal seats in Bristol, Nottingham, Glasgow, Basildon and Northern Ireland, all with tobacco works. And then there's all the brewery towns, which are owned by the tobacco manufacturers.'

'I can see there's a problem,' I acknowledged. 'But if something is right for the country, don't you agree that the government should do it regardless?'

There was no contest as far as Leslie Potts was concerned. 'Of *course* the government must do what's right – but not if it affects marginal constituencies! There's obviously a limit.'

I reassured him that no decision had yet been taken. And of course the decision he fears never will be – it's a *different* result that I'm after. But he wouldn't let it drop. He told me that, for the good of the party,

I couldn't interfere in the smoking issue.

I disliked being told what I can and can't do by junior members of my government! 'It's no good huffing and puffing at me, Leslie,' I complained.

'Sorry,' he said, waving away clouds of second-hand blue smoke.

'Weren't you.' I went on, 'a paid consultant for the British Tobacco Group?'

He drew himself up majestically to his full height of five foot two and a half, and replied in his most self-righteous tone. 'The fact that BTG paid me a small retainer is totally beside the point.' I managed to keep a straight face. 'They are a very generous corporation with a strong sense of responsibility towards the community. Look at all the money they give to sports. And now you're trying to stop them!'

I'd had enough of all this rubbish. 'Leslie,' I said firmly, 'they only give money to help sell more cigarettes.'

'No,' he insisted doggedly, 'they're doing it out of a genuine wish to serve the community.'

'That's fine,' I answered. 'In that case, they can go on giving the money anonymously, if they like.'

'Ah,' he said, and hesitated. 'Well . . . of course, they would be very happy to, provided they could publicise the fact that they were doing it anonymously.' He saw no problem there. 'Tell me, Jim, is it true that Peter Thorn is also trying to change the government health warning?'

I didn't want to reply, so I looked to Bernard for help. But Bernard was still not taking the conversation absolutely seriously. 'I believe,' he replied, deadpan, 'that Dr Thorn is proposing something like *Dying of cancer can seriously damage your health.*'

Leslie Potts was outraged. 'It's simply not true!' he exclaimed. I wonder if he believes it himself. By now I am really coming to believe that we must actually do something about this smoking and health problem – but not until the time is ripe, I think.

'Look, Leslie,' I said, 'if we do nothing there'll be a million premature deaths in this country over the next ten years – minimum.' I actually shocked myself as I uttered that statistic.

'I agree,' he answered desperately. 'A million deaths. Terrible. But they'll be *evenly spread*, not just in the marginal constituencies. Listen, Jim, there is no conclusive proof of any causal link between smoking and . . .'

I couldn't understand the rest of his sentence. It was lost in another paroxysm of coughing and choking. But I think I got the gist.

[Meanwhile, an anxious correspondence was taking place between Sir Humphrey Appleby and Sir Frank Gordon, Permanent Secretary of the Treasury. Copies of the letters have been found in both the Cabinet Office files and the Treasury files, all now available to us under the Thirty Year Rule. As the discussion was in writing, both gentlemen were careful to express their enthusiasm for government policy. Their real feelings must be read between the lines – Ed.]

70 WHITEHALL, LONDON SW1A 2AS

From the Secretary of the Cabinet and Head of the Home Civil Service

May 15 th

Dear Frank,

We are, of course, agreed that in an ideal world cigarette smoking would be discouraged. And we agree, obviously, that it is our duty to help the Prime Minister achieve his objectives. Nonetheless, we may have to help him understand that we are not in an ideal world and that he might be wise to reappraise not his objectives but his priorities.

He is unfortunately subject to silly pressure groups and fanatics such as the Royal College of Physicians. These fanatics want the Government to have a policy about smoking.

This is wishful thinking, I regret to say. It is not how the world works. Everyone outside government wants government policies. But none of us in government want them including, I venture to suggest, the Prime Minister when he fully understands the risks and the downside.

If you have a policy someone can hold you to it. And although the anti-smoking lobby see the whole matter in terms of black and white, merely preventing death and so forth, we know that the whole issue is much more complex than this.

As in all government, I'm sure that you agree that there has to be a balance. For instance the Minister of Health may be anti-smoking, but the Minister for Sport needs the tobacco companies.

It would be easier if the government were a team. But as, in fact, it is a loose confederation of warring tribes, it is up to us to find the common ground.

Comments, please.

[The following day a reply was received – Ed.]

H M Treasury

Permanent Secretary   May 16

Dear Humphrey,

The Minister for Health wishes the smoking problem dealt with by high taxation. The Chancellor, however, will not let me raise taxes too high – he is concerned about his own popularity with the electorate.

I must agree with him, for other reasons. The inflationary effect of such a high rise in cigarette taxes would be considerable.

Nonetheless, it must be admitted that there is a moral principle involved. And we at the Treasury fully understand and applaud the PM's concern. We earnestly believe in the moral principle.

But when four billion pounds of revenue is at stake I think that we have to consider very seriously how far we are entitled to indulge ourselves in the rather selfish luxury of pursuing moral principles.

As you recall, I have been worried about a suggested income tax cut of one and a half billion, and that was in a proposal that may not now happen. A cut of four billion would be a catastrophe!

I suggest we get Noel's opinion and advice. I have copied these letters to him.

Frank

[The copies of the correspondence were sent to the DHSS[1] for the comments of Sir Noel Whittington, the Permanent Secretary. Two days later this letter was sent to Sir Frank, with a copy to Sir Humphrey – Ed.]

[1] Department of Health and Social Security.

Department of Health and Social Security

LP1

May 18th

Dear Frank,

There are several worrying implications raised by this potential cigarette tax increase:

1. It is not just a matter of revenue loss. There is also the question of scrutiny. If we 'took on' the tobacco companies they would put a host of people on to scrutinising everything we do. They would point out, publicly, any errors of facts, inconsistencies of argument, inaccurate or misleading published figures, and so forth. Of course, it is said that our work should be able to stand up to scrutiny. Quite right too! Parliamentary scrutiny and press scrutiny are to be applauded. But not professional scrutiny, which could take up far too much government time. It is therefore not in the public interest to provoke it.

2. The tobacco companies might attempt to embarrass us by threatening to drag up all the times we have accepted invitations to lunches and free tickets at Wimbledon, Glyndebourne, etc.

3. Where would the arts be without tobacco sponsorship? They would be at the mercy of the Arts Council!

4. Above all, and here I speak for the DHSS specifically, we must remind the PM that there is a moral issue here: Government must be impartial. It is not proper for us to take sides as between health and cigarettes. This is especially true in the DHSS, which is the Department

Cont.

2.

of Health <u>and Social Security</u>. We have a dual responsibility. What will happen, if we lose the tobacco revenues,to the extra 100,000 people per year who would be alive and drawing pensions?

It is clear that we must, as always, maintain a balance. We want a healthy nation, but we also need a healthy tobacco industry.

We have a duty to be even-handed: tobacco sponsorship may encourage people to smoke, but sponsored sport encourages them to take exercise.

In my view, the DHSS may already go too far on this anti-smoking matter. We already devote one third of an Assistant Secretary's time and half a Principal's time to reducing smoking. Surely this is enough in a free society.

In summation I make two suggestions:

1) that Humphrey Appleby arranges for the PM to meet some of the tobacco people. He would then see what jolly good chaps they are, and how genuinely concerned about health risks. In my view, there cannot be anything seriously wrong with BTG, for instance: they have an ex-Permanent Secretary on their Board. And it has been suggested that they could well need another, in the fullness of time.

2) I think we might raise some questions about our junior Minister, Dr Peter Thorn. He is a highly intelligent, very imaginative Minister. But he is inexperienced, and not at all even-handed. Unfortunately, he comes to his post with severe bias: he is a doctor and, as such, he is unable to take the broader view. His <u>sole point</u> is keeping people alive. Seeing patients die must have, regrettably, distorted his judgement. It is understandable, of course, but emotional responses are a great handicap to cool decision-taking.

I look forward to hearing your conclusions. I think it is vital that Sir Humphrey takes some immediate action.

[Sir Humphrey considered this correspondence carefully, and made the following note in his private diary – Ed.]

[1] This suggests that hints had been dropped to Sir Noel himself.

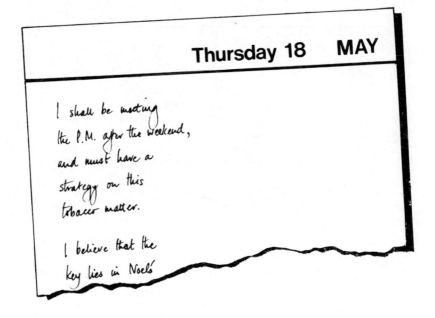

I shall be meeting
the P.M. after the weekend,
and must have a
strategy on this
tobacco matter.

I believe that the
key lies in Noel's

I shall be meeting the PM after the weekend, and must have a strategy on this tobacco matter.

I believe that the key lies in Noel's comment that we are a free society. Therefore people should be free to make their own decisions. Government should not be a nursemaid. We do not want the Nanny State.

The only drawback to this view is that it is also an argument for legalising the sale of marijuana, heroin, cocaine, arsenic and gelignite.

My strategy, therefore, is as follows: When Hacker was Minister for Administrative Affairs[1] he accompanied me not only to Glyndebourne as the guest of the BTG, but also Wimbledon, Lords, the opera and the ballet.

At *The Sleeping Beauty* one might have thought he was auditioning for the title role. He has no interest at all in the arts, which is why using sponsorship to save the arts from the Arts Council is likely to be an unproductive line of argument. At the ballet he kept quiet, apart from his snoring. When Act IV of the Wagner started at the Garden he asked why they were playing extra time. And he referred to Act V as 'injury time'. A total philistine.

But I digress. It seems that he is implicated in receiving tobacco hospitality worth hundreds of pounds, if not thousands, from the BTG. If this were to leak, shocking though a leak might be, it could be a grave embarrassment for him.

[*Sir Humphrey overestimated his threat. At the meeting four days later Hacker was able to deal with it with an ease that surprised the Cabinet Secretary – Ed.*]

[1] See *Yes Minister*, Vols 1–3, and *The Complete Yes Minister*.

SIR BERNARD WOOLLEY RECALLS:[1]

The Prime Minister was in very bullish mood on the morning of 22 May. He informed me that things were going very well, and that he had the Treasury on the run. And the Chancellor.

I asked him if this was entirely to the good. After all, the Chancellor is a member of the Prime Minister's own government.

'Of course it's good,' he told me. 'He's got to be brought to heel. He's got to learn to co-operate.'

I asked him what he meant, precisely, by co-operate. He revealed that he defined co-operation as obeying his commands! 'That', he said, 'is what co-operation means if you are Prime Minister.'

It reminded me not a little of Humpty Dumpty.[2]

'The Chancellor wanted to be Premier, remember? He was the front runner. And I outsmarted him.' How well I remember this! The Prime Minister did a little dance of glee in front of his study windows. 'Now I'm outsmarting him again. He knows that if he loses £4 billion of tobacco revenue he'll either have to impose four billion more in other taxes, which will make him frightfully unpopular in the country, or cut £4 billion of government expenditure, which will make him even more unpopular in the Cabinet. They're all terrified about Peter Thorn's policies – loss of smokers' votes, loss of tobacco taxes, loss of jobs – it's wonderful! So I shall support Peter Thorn until I get the Treasury to stop obstructing me on the income tax cut of 1.5 billion that *I* want.'

[*Hacker's diary continues – Ed.*]

May 22nd

A good meeting with Humphrey. He began it by showing me some impenetrable piece of paper, always a good sign I now realise. He can no longer bamboozle me like that. It's merely an indication of his own insecurity. [*A sign of Hacker's growing awareness and administrative skill – Ed.*]

[*The piece of paper contained Sir Humphrey's comments on a submission concerning Dr Thorn's plans, which had been submitted by the DHSS. The entire submission survives. Sir Humphrey's comments are reproduced overleaf – Ed.*]

---

[1] In conversation with the Editors.

[2] 'When I use a word,' Humpty Dumpty said in a rather scornful tone, 'it means just what I use it to mean – neither more nor less.'

'The question is,' said Alice, 'whether you *can* make words mean so many different things.'

'The question is,' said Humpty Dumpty, 'which is to be master – that's all.'
Through the Looking-Glass, Chapter 5, by Lewis Carroll.

(1)

Notwithstanding the fact that the
proposal could conceivably encompass
certain concomitant benefits of a marginal
and peripheral relevance, there is a
consideration of infinitely superior
magnitude involving your personal
complicity and corroborative
malfeasance, with the consequence that
the taint and stigma of your former
associations and diversions could
irredeemably and irretrievably
invalidate your position and culminate
in public revelations and recriminations
of a profoundly embarrassing
and ultimately indefensible character.

I asked Humphrey for a précis. In one short sentence.

He thought for a moment. 'There's nicotine on your hands,' he said.

I couldn't think what he meant. I'm a non-smoker. Then I realised he was speaking not literally but figuratively. 'All the hospitality you have enjoyed at BTG's expense,' he reproached me in a sorrowful voice. 'Champagne receptions, buffet lunches, the best seats at sporting and cultural events.'

He seemed to think that the tobacco companies might release this embarrassing information to the press if I legislated against them.

But I can't see anything embarrassing about that. I've had drinks at the Soviet Embassy – that doesn't make me a spy. If that's the best idea Humphrey can come up with to block me, I may have to put Dr Thorn's proposals through after all! I think Humphrey may be losing his grip – it's the feeblest threat I ever heard.

Humphrey realised it himself, because he fell silent. 'Anything else?' I asked, hopeful that he'd do better.

'Yes, Prime Minister.' He was fighting on, but not looking too confident. 'It has been put to me that since smoking is not a political issue the government should not take sides.'

'You mean we have to be impartial?'

'Exactly,' he replied with gratitude.

'You mean,' I enquired innocently, 'impartial as between the fire engine and the fire?'

He hurried straight on. He knows when he's backing a loser. 'And there is a much graver objection. A large number of people, *eminent* people, *influential* people, have argued that Dr Thorn's legislation would be a blow against freedom of choice.'

I asked why. He rabbited on about how it is a serious attack on freedom to introduce penal taxation and prohibit the advertising of a product which is perfectly legal in itself. I told him this was complete and utter rubbish! We are not talking about prohibiting smoking itself. And I asked him if every tax increase is a blow against freedom?

He hedged. 'That depends on how big a tax increase.'

A fascinating answer. 'So,' I asked, 'is twenty pence a blow against freedom?'

He began to protest. 'Prime Minister . . .'

I brushed him aside. 'Is twenty-five pence? Thirty pence? Thirty-*one* pence? Is something a blow against freedom just because it can seriously damage your wealth?'

Rather good that, I thought! He didn't laugh though. He just remarked grimly that it was very droll.

So I took him through the freedom of choice argument. We agreed that advertising is essential if there is to be a free choice because free choice depends on full information. Therefore there should be advertising on both sides. Why, since the tobacco companies spend at least £100 million on advertising and promotion, shouldn't they pay an equal amount to advertise the arguments *against* smoking? This, I suggested to Humphrey, would be a point of view that would appeal to all those eminent and influential people who favour freedom of choice.

'Prime Minister,' he said, gritting his teeth. 'I do have to advise you that this proposal will cause grave difficulties. I foresee all sorts of unforeseen problems.'

'Such as?' I asked.

Humphrey was getting irritable. 'If I could foresee them, they wouldn't be unforeseen!' he snapped.

'But you said you could foresee them,' I reminded him cheerfully.

He was cornered. He had now reached his last refuge. 'Look, how about setting up an interdepartmental committee . . . a Parliamentary enquiry . . . a Royal Commission?'

I asked the question that I've been wanting to ask for days now. 'Humphrey, why are you so keen on the tobacco industry?'

He ignored the question. I knew he would, of course. 'Prime Minister, how about a Treasury Committee in the first instance?'

This was my opening. 'Don't talk to me about the Treasury,' I sighed sadly. 'They're blocking my plan for including a one and a half billion tax cut in my new defence strategy.' I sighed again heavily, theatrically, wondered if I were overdoing it a bit, then pressed on. 'Of course, if *only* the Treasury would show some flexibility . . .'

Humphrey saw the point immediately, or even sooner. 'Oh,' he said, brightening up considerably. 'Er . . . Prime Minister, I don't think they're fully committed to that other matter yet.'

'Really?' I pretended surprise.

'Absolutely not. Oh no. Flexible. I'm sure they could find a way.'

'Could they?' I asked with wide-eyed amazement. I should have got an Oscar for this one.

'The only stumbling block,' said Humphrey, adjusting rapidly to his new negotiating position, 'would be that if the anti-smoking proposals go through, the Treasury will be too busy working on those to look for a way to help with the other cuts.'

We were now talking in a code that we both understood. 'Well,' I said, 'the anti-smoking proposals don't have nearly such a high priority as defence.'

Humphrey now knew what deal I'd accept. The quid pro quo was acceptable to him, I could see. It's just a question of clearing it with the Treasury.

May 23rd

A slight complication developed today.

Peter Thorn came to see me in my room at the Commons. 'I've just had some very exciting news, Prime Minister,' he began. 'We have just got full backing from the BMA, the Royal College of Physicians, and eight other top scientific and medical colleges.'

My heart sank into my boots. I hadn't expected him to make so much progress so soon. I told him that this was excellent news, but that his legislation couldn't happen immediately.

'No,' he said, 'but their support only requires it to be announced as government policy within three months and a White Paper in a year. So that's bags of time.'

His enthusiasm was touching. I was genuinely sorry that I was about to ditch his scheme, particularly as I'd argued it so successfully with Humphrey that now I had even begun to believe in it myself.

I told him I'd encountered problems with the Treasury. He immediately saw the turn that the conversation was taking.

His eyes narrowed. 'It can't be anything you didn't know about before.'

'It's not as simple as you think, Peter.' I knew I sounded unconvincing.

Peter took a deep breath. And then he made a threat that was a *real* threat. 'Look, Jim, I really am serious about this. It's the one really important and worthwhile thing I believe I can do in politics. If you stall it, I shall have to resign. And say why.'

I told him to calm down, but he said he was perfectly calm already. 'Jim, the medical bodies are even more committed than I am. Perhaps I shouldn't have told them about your support, but they say they'll announce that you've capitulated to the tobacco companies.'

His strategy was all worked out. Clearly he was not a bit surprised by my new position on this matter – in fact, he must have been half expecting it.

I really didn't know what to say or do. But I was saved by the bell. The telephone bell, to be precise.

Bernard answered it. 'Excuse me, Prime Minister, could Sir Humphrey see you urgently, just for a moment?'

I asked Thorn to wait outside. Humphrey came bursting in with *good* news: he'd spoken to the Treasury first thing this morning and, surprise! surprise! they can encompass my income-tax cut. This is on the understanding that no further work would be needed on the anti-smoking proposal.

I briefly filled Humphrey in about the new complication – Dr Thorn's threatened resignation and the ensuing public condemnation of me by the entire British medical establishment.

Humphrey was worried – but only for a moment. Then he had a

brilliant idea, the kind of idea that makes him worth all the trouble he causes me – well, almost all!

'Prime Minister, you still have that government vacancy in the Treasury, don't you?'

It was genius, pure genius. It would be a big promotion, a very rapid promotion, for Peter Thorn. But why not, for such an able Minister?

We got him back in.

'Peter,' I said, 'I have just remembered that we still have a vacancy at the Treasury. I couldn't think how to fill it – but your work on this proposal, I have to tell you, has impressed me a lot.'

He was suspicious. Well, who wouldn't be? 'You're not trying to get rid of me?'

'Absolutely not. Quite the reverse.'

He was tempted. 'Well . . . it's a terrific step up.'

'But merited,' I said in my warmest father-figure voice. '*Thoroughly* merited.'

Thorn was torn. 'I don't see how I can take it if it means dropping the anti-smoking bill.'

'Peter, let me be absolutely honest with you. The bill would have been . . . will be . . .' I think I managed to correct myself without his noticing . . . 'very difficult to get through. The Treasury is the key place, the true stumbling block, not the Department of Health. It may take a bit longer, but if you're inside there, if you learn the ropes, there's a much better chance of a really foolproof watertight Act when it finally gets on to the statute books. Believe me.' It sounded so convincing an argument that I almost believed it myself.

Fortunately he bought it. 'So my proposals aren't dropped?' he asked, *wanting* the answer no.

'Absolutely not,' I said. I wasn't exactly lying – maybe I will come back to them in due course. In the fullness of time. When the time is ripe.

He only hesitated for a second. 'Okay,' he answered. 'I'll take the Treasury job. Thanks a lot.'

We shook hands and he left, walking on air. The great thing about being Prime Minister is that you can give people so much happiness and such a great sense of achievement.

May 24th

Peter Thorn's promotion to the Treasury left me with another vacancy, in the Ministry of Health. Clearly we now want to avoid a

Minister who will antagonise the tobacco lobby. So an obvious candidate sprang to mind.

I sent for Leslie Potts this morning. It didn't take him long to drive over from Marsham Street.[1] He wheezed into my study enveloped in his usual cloud of pollution, a lit cigarette clamped between his stubby yellow fingertips.

I welcomed him warmly. 'My dear chap, do come in. How would you like to be the Minister of Health?'

He was extremely surprised. 'Me?'

I nodded.

He coughed for a while, a good chesty wet rasping cough. Even *I* felt better after it.

'It is a considerable promotion' he said at last, eyeing me with caution and wondering what I was playing at.

'But merited,' I said warmly.

He thought for a moment, but could see no signs of a trap. Indeed, there were none. 'Well, of course, I can't refuse. Thank you, Prime Minister.'

I sent for Humphrey and introduced him to our new Minister of Health. Humphrey pretended slight surprise, even though it had been Humphrey's idea.

Meanwhile, Leslie thought he'd found the catch. 'Wait a minute,' he croaked suddenly. 'I don't want the job if it means attacking the tobacco industry.'

I was able to reassure him completely. 'No, Leslie, we in government have to be realists. I want you to work with the tobacco industry: they're nice chaps, caring people, fabulous employers, and they really want to help – I want you to work with them, not against them. All right?'

Leslie Potts looked pleased but, as he tried to reply, he was overwhelmed by a fit of uncontrollable coughing. He went purple, and struggled to say something – I simply couldn't tell what it was.

I turned to Humphrey. 'What did he say?' I asked.

'I think,' said Humphrey cheerfully, 'that he said "Yes Prime Minister".'

---

[1] Where the Department of the Environment has its headquarters.

8
The Bishop's Gambit

Finished work by six p.m. tonight, except for my red boxes. So Bernard and I watched the six o'clock news. There was nothing new. But the media are making a big story out of a young British nurse called Fiona McGregor who is being held in the Gulf state of Qumran for the alleged possession of a bottle of whisky.

They've given her ten years' imprisonment and forty lashes, but apparently the sentence is not to be carried out till it is 'confirmed', whatever that means.

On the news they showed her mother and her MP (Stuart Gordon, one of our backbenchers) taking a petition to the Qumran Embassy. The officials refused to accept the petition.

The final item of this story was the official response from the Foreign Office, which said that the Foreign Secretary has described the incident as 'regrettable', but that no action is planned.

The news moved on to telling us that there has been another bad day for the pound. I switched off, and sent for Humphrey. When he came I told him that this situation with the nurse is a big worry. There's a lot of public sympathy for her.

He agreed.

'What's the best thing to do?' I asked.

'I'm sure the Foreign Secretary will advise you,' he said.

'He advises me to do nothing,' I said.

'I'm sure that's very good advice,' said Humphrey.

The usual obstruction from the FO. This has been going on too long already. 'If we don't do anything we look heartless,' I explained. 'We also look feeble. It doesn't do the government any good to look heartless and feeble simultaneously.' I turned to Bernard. 'What do you think, Bernard?'

Bernard perked up. 'Perhaps you could manage it so that you only look heartless and feeble alternately.'

I ignored him, and simply reiterated to Humphrey that we have to do *something*. My hope is that since I trounced Humphrey and his Foreign Office pal Dick Wharton[1] only recently, this time they may knuckle under with less pressure from me.

However, it doesn't look hopeful at the moment. Humphrey informed me politely that the Foreign Secretary doesn't think that we have to do anything. Well, *obviously* not – he's been told what to think by the Foreign Office, and the officials there do not know or care what the electorate wants.

Humphrey gave me the official view. 'The Qumranis are good friends of Britain. They have just placed a huge defence contract with us. They tell us what the Soviets are up to in Iraq. They even sabotage OPEC agreements for us. We can't afford to upset them.'

'I *know* all that, Humphrey,' I said wearily. Sometimes he talks to me as if I'm a complete idiot. 'But the point is, a British citizen is facing a barbaric punishment for a trivial offence in a foreign country. And the Foreign Office is there to protect British subjects.'

He shook his head and smiled sadly. 'They are there to protect British interests.'

'It's not in her interests to be flogged,' I said.

'It's not in our interests to prevent it,' he replied with sudden firmness.

I did not and do not accept this view. I have refused to accept it for days now and I still refuse. [*The Foreign Office would have been perfectly content for Hacker to refuse continuously to accept their view, for his refusal appeared to satisfy him emotionally, so long as this did not result in his forcing the FO to accept a change in policy – Ed.*] Humphrey argued that this is one of those little bush fires that flares up and dies down in a few days. The only mistake we can make is to put fuel on it. Statements, actions, ultimata, sanctions – they would all only make it worse. The Foreign Office wants me to sit back and do nothing.

He claims that the FO is doing something. Tomorrow, apparently, we are to deliver a strongly worded note of protest to the Qumranis.

'Why can't we do it now?' I asked.

'Because we haven't got their agreement yet,' he explained. 'We're talking to the Ambassador privately now. When they have approved the wording we shall hand it to them. Then,' he remarked smugly, 'we'll have done all we can.'

[1] The Permanent Secretary of the FCO.

It seems like a pretty odd way to protest. It's a purely diplomatic protest, for public consumption only. No teeth at all. And Humphrey thinks that this would be sufficient action to take on behalf of that poor girl. 'I suppose the Foreign Office thinks Pontius Pilate did all he could.'

To my surprise, Humphrey agreed enthusiastically. 'Yes indeed, Pontius Pilate would have made an excellent Foreign Secretary. You can't put the nation's interests at risk just because of some silly sentimentality about justice. If we took moral positions on individual injustices and cruelties we'd never have been able to hand Hong Kong over to the Chinese, or put Mugabe in power in Zimbabwe. Morality was what fouled up the Foreign Office's plans for a quiet handover of the Falklands to Argentina – they don't want to take any moral positions for a long time now.'

I sighed. He seemed to be right, in purely practical terms. There seems to be nothing we can do. 'It's very heartless,' I said gloomily.

Humphrey leaned forward encouragingly. 'It's safer to be heartless than mindless. The history of the world is the triumph of the heartless over the mindless.'

He'd won and he knew it. We all fell silent for a moment, then Humphrey rose and asked if he might leave as he had a dinner engagement. As he walked to the door I called after him that the Foreign Office will never get the Cabinet to agree to this policy.

He turned in the doorway. 'The Foreign Office never expect the Cabinet to agree to any of their policies. That's why they never fully explain them. All they require is that the Cabinet acquiesce in their decisions after they've been taken.'

And he was gone.

I stared morosely at Bernard. 'Bernard, is there anyone else in public life who is quite as spineless as our Foreign Office officials?'

Bernard was surprised. 'They're not spineless, Prime Minister. It takes a great deal of strength to do nothing at all.'

I'd never thought of it that way. 'Does it?' I asked.

'Yes, Prime Minister, that's why people regard *you* as a strong leader.'

Was this a compliment or an insult? It seemed that Bernard wasn't too sure either because he continued hurriedly: 'I mean, because you resist pressures.' Then he reminded me that I should get ready for the Reception tonight.

I asked him to give me a rundown of the list of significant guests. The most significant tonight were representatives of the Synod of the

Church of England. There is a vacancy in the diocese of Bury St Edmunds, and I have to make the choice between two names which they will be submitting to me.

But although, by tradition, they have to submit two names, they will be anxious that I don't pick the wrong one. I asked Bernard how I will know which to pick.

'It's like any Civil Service option, Prime Minister. It'll be a conjuring trick. You know, "take any card" – you always end up with the card the magician forces you to take.'

It was very bold of Bernard to admit this. So I asked, 'What if I don't take it?'

He smiled confidently. 'You will.'

We'll see about that, I thought to myself. 'Who are these clerical cards they're going to offer me, Bernard?'

'With the church,' he grinned, 'you're usually given the choice of a knave or a queen.'

[*Sir Humphrey Appleby's dinner engagement that evening was at the High Table of his alma mater, Baillie College, Oxford. There, by chance, the subject of Sir Humphrey's retirement impinged unexpectedly on the Prime Minister's forthcoming choice of a bishop. The conversation at High Table, which Sir Humphrey reports in his private diary, was of course not known to the Prime Minister – Ed.*]

We had the usual adequate dinner. As always the claret was better than the food, the port was better than the claret, and the conversation was better than the port.

The serious conversation, as always, began as we reached the port and walnuts. After the customary courtesies, the Master thanking me for coming to dine with them and my replying that it is always a pleasure to dine with old friends, the Master came to the point. He told me that he would be retiring in four or five years, roughly when I shall be retiring from the Civil Service.

The juxtaposition could hardly have been coincidental. So I was alerted for his next remark: 'The Bursar and I think you could be just the chap to succeed me as Master of Baillie.' Sweet words. Music to my ears.

However, it soon became clear that there is an obstacle. This obstacle is known as The Dean. Somewhat reluctantly, but without pulling any punches, the Master revealed that the Dean does not like me.

This astonishes me. Why should he dislike me, I've never done anything that he should be grateful for?

Nevertheless, it seems to be a fact. The Bursar's theory is that the Dean believes that I'm too clever by half. One would have thought that, at Oxford, to be called clever might be rather a compliment.

Apparently, the Dean also thinks I'm smug. I got that from the Bursar too, who seemed to be enjoying the whole conversation a little too much for my liking.

The Bursar may have realised that I wasn't appreciative of his candour, because he told me that in his opinion it did not matter. I thought he was saying that it didn't matter what the Dean thought – but no, he was saying that it didn't matter that I am smug!

And he went on and on about it. He told me that it was perfectly obvious, and that furthermore I have a lot to be smug about. If he had £75,000 a year, a knighthood, an index-linked pension and a bunch of politicians to take the blame for all his mistakes, he informed me, *he* would be pretty smug too.

This remark was very revealing. Envy is at the root of the Dean's dislike for me, and the Bursar's belief that I am smug. There can be no other explanation. It is yet another cross to bear. But I shall do my best to bear it with grace.

The Master added that the Dean hates intrigue and does not like politicians. For a ghastly moment I thought that the Master was suggesting that *I* am a politician. I decided that we had spent enough time discussing their distorted vision of my personal qualities, and asked to know more about the Dean.

The Bursar explained that the Dean is paranoid that the Master and the Bursar are intriguing about this matter behind his back. Which is why they decided to discuss it with me while he's away. They made two matters quite clear: first, that they do *not* go in for intrigue; second, that the only way I can become Master of Baillie is if they can dump the Dean.

This could be a problem. The Dean is a lazy bugger. He only has to do four hours work a week, give one lecture and a couple of tutorials – and he has tenure for life. They say that he only has two interests: cricket and steam engines. He never has to read a new book or think a new thought, so being an Oxford don is the perfect job for him. Why would he ever move?

The Master and the Bursar have concluded that only a bishopric would get him away from Baillie and they were wondering about the Diocese of Bury St Edmunds, which is up for grabs.

It is a very appealing Diocese. It is one of the old ones, with a seat in the Lords. This, I know, would appeal greatly to the Dean. In *my* observation of him, his principal hobby is sucking up to the aristocracy.

Unfortunately, I'm not sure if I can do anything about getting Bury St Edmunds for the Dean. It's rather late in the day. Furthermore, as I explained to them, the Church is looking for a candidate to maintain the balance between those who believe in God and those who don't.

It comes as a surprise to many, including the Master and the Bursar, to learn that many people in the church do not believe in God, including most of the bishops.

Bury St Edmunds is sewn up. It has been arranged by the Church that Canon Mike Stanford will get the job. In theory Hacker has to recommend the appointment. But the Church customarily puts up the candidate they want plus an impossible second candidate, to ensure that the PM has no real choice.

Furthermore, the Dean has not done enough public service even to qualify for Bury St Edmunds.

But this is a serious matter for my own future, especially as there are no other dioceses coming free in the near future. Bishops don't retire as often as they should. The older appointees don't have to retire at sixty, and bishops tend to live long lives – apparently the Lord is not all that keen for them to join Him. Ὃν οἱ θεοὶ φιλοῦσιν, ἀποθνῄσκει νέος[1], which perhaps explains why bishops live to a ripe old age.

We concentrated on the only hopeful line of attack: more public service for the Dean. He is an expert on Islamic studies, and he loves the Arabs. One of his few good qualities. I had a flash of inspiration: I suggested that the Master gets his bishop to send him to Qumran to intercede on behalf of that nurse. They were delighted with the idea.

It is a situation in which we cannot lose. If he fails, he has at least tried. If he succeeds, he will be a hero. And if he doesn't come back he won't be missed.

I wouldn't want to go there, though. It's an awful country. They cut people's hands off for theft, and women get stoned when they commit adultery. Unlike Britain, where women commit adultery when they get stoned.

He might even come back with certain parts missing.

Look, no hands!

[*Appleby Papers 42/43/12 BD*]

[*Hacker's Diary continues – Ed.*]

June 6th

A meeting with Peter Harding, the Appointments Secretary. He's about sixty, and he's a quietly confident sort of chap. Very sound, apparently.

I was a little hesitant because I've never appointed a bishop before. [*Recommended the appointment to the Sovereign – Ed.*]

There were two candidates. First, Canon Mike Stanford. Michael, I suppose, though it seems they all call him Mike. People never called bishops 'Mike' when I was a kid! Not in public, anyway. Perhaps he's called Mike because he's always on the radio.

Peter told me that Mike is a Modernist. This was new terminology to me. 'A theological term, Prime Minister. It seems that he accepts that some of the events described in the Bible are not *literally* true – he sees them as metaphors, legends or myths. He is interested in the spiritual and philosophical truth behind the stories.'

---

[1] Menander. Pronounced *Hon hoi theoi philousin apothneeskei neos*. Translation: Those whom the gods love die young.

I expressed it my way, to be sure I understood. 'You mean, he doesn't think God created the world in seven days, or that Eve came out of Adam's rib, that sort of thing?'

Peter was delighted. It seems it's that sort of thing *exactly*, which sounds very sensible. The only other things Peter said I need to know about Mike Stanford are that he went to Winchester and New College, Oxford, and his name is first on the list. 'And,' added Peter, 'he has an eminently suitable wife.'

'You mean she's devout and full of good works?' I asked.

He was surprised. 'No, I mean she's the daughter of the Earl of Dorchester.'

Now it was my turn to be surprised. So what? I wondered. I asked him who was second on the list.

'Well . . . second is Dr Paul Harvey.'

And I waited. But Peter seemed reluctant to say more.

'And?' I prompted him.

'Well, he's an admirable man,' said Peter. This was damning with praise if I ever heard it. Peter was staring at his shoes.

'But?' I wanted an explanation.

Peter sighed, then looked me straight in the eye. 'Of course, it's your choice, Prime Minister. But there is a suspicion that he tends towards disestablishmentarianism.'

'Ah,' I said knowledgeably, then realised to my embarrassment that I wasn't *absolutely* sure what he meant. I asked him for details.

'It's the view that the Church of England shouldn't be part of the state. Some people feel it should be separate, like Methodists or Catholics. They think ordinary people feel the established church is a club for the ruling classes, not a faith.'

He sounded like an awfully good chap to me, and I said so. But Peter maintained a pained silence. So I asked him what was the matter.

'Well, it's entirely up to you, of course, Prime Minister. But I suspect that Her Majesty might be a little surprised if you asked her to appoint a man who believes she should be made to break her Coronation vow to defend the church.'

Fair enough. But then why is he on the list at all? Peter prevaricated. He explained that Harvey is not *exactly* a *card-carrying* disestablishmentarian *yet*. It's just the way his mind seems to be moving. But as a result of the discussions his name emerged. His health may be suspect too. Also he's getting on a bit.

One thing is clear to me: someone is bad-mouthing him! Or else he was never a suitable candidate to start with. In any case, this is not what I call a choice. 'You're saying I can choose Canon Stanford or Canon Stanford,' I said to Peter.

'No,' he replied blandly. 'It's entirely your decision. But in this case, may I suggest, quite an easy one.' He refused to admit anything. His face was expressionless. 'Prime Minister, the Commission is offering you the two names which emerged.'

'Was there an open election?' I asked.

He tut-tutted impatiently. 'There *can't* be an open election. Bishops are seen as part of the apostolic succession.'

Not being a churchgoer, I asked for an explanation.

'It's God's will. When Judas Iscariot blotted his copybook he had to be replaced. They let the Holy Ghost decide.'

I was mystified. 'How did he make his views known?'

'By drawing lots,' said Peter.

'So can't we let the Holy Ghost decide this time?' I asked, looking for a way out of this awkward decision.

Peter and Bernard looked at each other. Clearly my suggestion was not on. Bernard tried to explain. 'No one', he said, 'is confident that the Holy Ghost would understand what makes a good Church of England bishop.'

I asked how this 'choice' emerged. Peter informed me enigmatically that soundings were taken.

'Peter,' I said with a smile. 'When I was a student I used to play poker. I can recognise a stacked deck when I see one.'

Bernard stood up, and reminded me that I was due to meet Sir Humphrey. He suggested that Peter and I continue the discussion tomorrow. Peter looked thankful and left.

While Humphrey came in and I poured end-of-the-day drinks, Bernard went off to get Mike Stanford's career details, having whispered to me that appointing Mike Stanford might be a bit of an own goal.

Humphrey and I wished each other Good Health and relaxed in the comfy study armchairs. I asked him what was *really* meant by a Modernist.

He misunderstood, and asked me whether I was referring to Shostakovich or Marcel Duchamp. I told him that I was referring to Mike Stanford.

As I expected, he knew exactly. 'In the Church of England the word Modernist is code for non-believer.'

'An atheist?' I asked with surprise.

'Oh no, Prime Minister,' he replied wickedly. 'An atheist clergy-man couldn't continue to draw his stipend. So when they stop believing in God they call themselves modernists.'

I was staggered. 'How can the Church of England recommend an atheist as Bishop of Bury St Edmunds?'

Humphrey crossed his legs and sipped his drink. 'Very easily,' he smiled. 'The Church of England is primarily a social organisation, not a religious one.'

This was news to me. But then I don't come from a very 'social' background.

'Oh, yes,' Humphrey continued knowledgeably. 'It's part of the rich social fabric of this country. Bishops need to be the sort of chaps who speak properly and know which knife and fork to use. They are someone to look up to.'

So that, I realised, is what Peter meant by Stanford having an eminently suitable wife.

I asked Humphrey if there are no other suitable candidates. He said that there aren't at the moment. Apparently there were a couple of better jobs available recently. I couldn't think what could be better than a bishop, other than a rook! But apparently the Dean of Windsor is a better job. So is the Dean of Westminster. Humphrey explained that such preferment enables one to be on intimate terms with the royals.

It was all becoming clear to me. 'So being a bishop', I summed up, 'is simply a matter of status. Dressing up in cassocks and gaiters.'

Humphrey nodded. 'Yes, Prime Minister. Though gaiters are now worn only at significant religious events – like the royal garden party.'

I wondered why cassocks and gaiters are now out of style.

'The church is trying to be more relevant,' said Humphrey.

'To God?' I asked.

'Of *course* not, Prime Minister. I meant relevant in sociological terms.'

What he was saying, in effect, is that the ideal candidate from the church's point of view is a cross between a socialite and a socialist.

Bernard came back with Mike Stanford's career details. He was right. They were very instructive. After he left theological college he became Chaplain to the Bishop of Sheffield. He moved on to be the Diocesan Adviser on Ethnic Communities and Social Responsibility. He organised conferences on Inter-faith interface, and interface between Christians and Marxists, and between Christians and the

Women of Greenham Common. [*This was a part feminist/part lesbian encampment of anti-nuclear/pacifist/Marxist women that stationed itself illegally outside the gates of an American airbase near Newbury, where Cruise missiles were kept. Only women and children were allowed to take part in the protest, which was against nuclear weapons, America and men, possibly in the reverse order. Nuclear missiles were seen as a form of phallic symbol. The Women were regarded by Freudians as suffering from a severe case of penis envy. Expressing support, even limited support, for the Women of Greenham Common was perceived as a 'progressive stance' – Ed.*] Subsequently Stanford became University Chaplain at the University of Essex, then Vice Principal of a theological college, and he is now the Secretary to the Disarmament Committee of the British Council of Churches.

There was one significant gap in his CV.[1] 'Has he ever been an ordinary vicar in a parish?' I asked.

Bernard was surprised by the question. 'No, Prime Minister. Clergymen who want to be bishops try to avoid pastoral work.'

'He's a high flyer,' remarked Humphrey.

'So was Icarus,' replied Bernard mysteriously.[2]

'Anyway, I don't want him if he's a political troublemaker,' I decided.

Bernard nodded wisely. 'What peevish fool was that of Greece who taught his son the office of a fowl.' I told Bernard to stop quoting Greek at me. [*Hacker was incorrect. Bernard Woolley was quoting Shakespeare's* Henry VI Part III *– Ed.*]

Humphrey responded with cautious agreement to my decision. He said that Stanford would have the added nuisance value of speaking with the authority of a bishop and as a member of the Lords.

'He's exactly the sort of person I don't want,' I explained 'It's no good all these bishops exhorting me to spend more on welfare. You can't always solve problems by throwing money at them, especially other people's money. What this country needs is a greater spirit of responsibility and self-reliance.'

Humphrey smiled at me. 'Isn't it interesting how nowadays politicians talk about morals and bishops talk about politics?'

He's right. Bernard gave us an example from Stanford's career. 'He designed a new church in south London. On the plans there were places for dispensing orange juice, and family planning, and organis-

[1] Curriculum vitae, i.e. the story of his life.
[2] Icarus was the son of Daedalus. He flew too near the sun and his wings melted. Thus he put himself out of the running by his ambition, like Canon Stanford.

ing demonstrations – but no place for Holy Communion.' He added, in all fairness, that there was a dual-purpose hall in which a service could be held.

I asked my two officials if the Church approved of this design.

'Oh yes,' said Humphrey. 'You see, the church is run by theologians.'

'What does that mean?' I asked.

'Well,' he smiled, 'theology's a device for helping agnostics stay within the church.'

'Perhaps I'm naïve,' I said, 'but . . .'

'Perish the thought, Prime Minister,' interrupted Humphrey.

Stupid flattery! Couldn't he tell it was false modesty? Of course I don't think I'm naïve. I waved him to shut up, and continued. 'I think the church should be run by simple men who believe in God, not worldly politicians seeking preferment.'

'You could argue,' said Humphrey amiably, 'that those who seek preferment feel that they can be of greater service to the community in a more important job.'

'That's hypocritical twaddle,' I said.

He shrugged. 'Just as you yourself only wanted to serve your country here in Number Ten.'

Suddenly I saw what he meant. He's right. But I still don't want Stanford.

Humphrey explained to me that I can turn both candidates down, although it would be exceptional and not advised.

'Even if one candidate wants to get God out of the Church of England and the other wants to get the Queen out of it?'

'The Queen,' said Humphrey, 'is inseparable from the Church of England.'

'Is she?' I asked. 'And what about God?'

'I think He is what is called an optional extra,' replied my Permanent Secretary, finishing off his drink.

June 9th

An interesting development about that nurse in Qumran tonight. There's been nothing from the Foreign Office for days. This is not really a surprise – the Foreign Office aren't there to do things, they are there to explain why things can't be done.

I was trying to explain this to Annie over dinner. She had difficulty in grasping the concept. She kept asking irrelevant questions like 'Don't they care?'

'No,' I said. She had difficulty in grasping that answer.

'Isn't that rather awful?' she asked.

Obviously it *is* awful. It's doing the government a lot of damage. Yet all the Foreign Office does is shrug its shoulders and say we mustn't upset the Qumranis. 'The FO simply can't see beyond its narrow selfish interests,' I said.

'It must be ghastly for her,' said Annie.

'Who?' I asked. Then I realised she meant that nurse. 'Yes,' I agreed.

Annie stared at me coldly. 'You don't care about her any more than the Foreign Office do.'

I don't think that's entirely fair. [*Not* entirely *fair, perhaps – Ed.*] Annie seemed to think that just as the Foreign Office is worried about its popularity with the Arabs, I'm worried about my popularity with the voters. That's not wholly true – but in so far as it *is* true, what's wrong with it? I'm an elected representative – isn't it right and proper that in a democracy I should be concerned with pleasing the electorate?

Bernard came to the flat. I was irritated. It doesn't seem possible any more to have a quiet drink with my wife without being interrupted. He was wearing his coat and was clearly on his way home.

He apologised for the intrusion, but said it was important. 'The Foreign Office have just rung to say that the Bishop of Banbury and the Church Missionary Society have announced that we are sending the Dean of Baillie College to Qumran on a mercy mission to plead for that nurse.'

This was good news. But I couldn't see why they were sending an Oxford don. Bernard explained that the man has faith in the Arabs.

'It's good to hear of a senior member of the Church of England who has faith in anything,' I said. 'But isn't this rather a hopeless journey?'

Bernard thought not. 'Although he's a Christian he's an expert on Islam. It's a faith to faith meeting.'

I smiled, and told Bernard to tell the Foreign Office that I'm happy to support the trip. Bernard shook his head vigorously. 'No, no,' he said, 'actually the Foreign Office want you to stop it. They're furious. They say it's a futile gesture and will only impair our relationships with a friendly country.'

This was really too much. I had no intention of stopping it. It's an excellent idea. At the very least it will look as though we're doing something about her, and it might even save her. I sent Bernard home, after he reminded me that Lambeth Palace were pressing me for a decision about Bury St Edmunds.

Annie was curious. She asked what he meant.

'I've got to decide who should be appointed to the see.'

'Isn't that a job for the First Lord of the Admiralty?'

'No, Annie,' I explained patiently, 'I'm choosing a bishop.'

She laughed uproariously. 'You?' she gasped eventually. 'That's ridiculous.' She wiped her eyes, weak from laughing.

I couldn't quite see what was so ridiculous about it. I know I'm not religious, but religion manifestly has nothing to do with it. I'm Prime Minister. Annie couldn't see why religion has nothing to do with bishops so I explained to her that they are basically managers in fancy dress.

I showed her the papers from my red box. The Church of England has over 172,000 acres of land, thousands of tenants and leaseholds, and property and investments worth a total of £1.6 billion, comprising industrial, commercial and residential property, and agricultural land and woodland. So, really, the ideal bishop is a corporate executive – a sort of merchant banker, personnel manager and estate agent.

Annie wasn't impressed. 'Speaking as a churchgoer,' she said, 'I'd prefer you to choose a man of God.'

'I was offered one of them,' I explained. 'But he wants to turn the Church of England into a religious movement.'

'I see.'

'The other one, the one they're trying to force on me, is a modernist.'

Annie, being a churchgoer, knew the code. 'You mean a Marxist or an atheist?'

'Both,' I revealed. 'Nobody minds the atheist bit, apparently. But being a Marxist could cause me a lot of trouble when he starts making speeches in the Lords.'

'Can't you reject him?' asked Annie.

'I'd like to. But it will look political.'

Annie was confused. 'But haven't you just been explaining that the Church *is* political?'

I was patient. 'Yes, Annie, but it mustn't look it.'

She considered this for a few moments. 'So why don't you turn him down on religious grounds?'

I couldn't see what she meant exactly. She explained. 'Does he believe in Heaven and Hell?'

'Of course not,' I said.

'The Virgin Birth?' she asked.

'Nope.'

'The Resurrection?' asked Annie.

'Nope.' I was beginning to see what a great idea this was.

'Isn't that enough to be going on with?' she enquired. She's brilliant. Simple common sense. It suddenly became clear to me that I can do what Humphrey suggested and ask for more candidates *without it looking like political discrimination*. Wonderful!

'What I really need,' I said to Annie, 'is a candidate who can get along with everyone.'

'You mean he mustn't have strong views on anything?'

Annie puts it a little cynically, but that is basically right. But there is a proviso. I think it would help if he were *inclined* towards Christianity. That couldn't do any real harm. So what I actually want is a sort of closet Christian.

[*A few days later amid much publicity the Dean of Baillie, the Rev. Christopher Smythe, embarked on his mercy mission to Qumran. When he arrived there he dropped out of sight for three days. Suddenly he re-emerged into the full glare of publicity to announce that he had succeeded in obtaining the release of Fiona McGregor, the young British nurse held there in prison. They were expected back in England the following day. This was thrilling news in Britain, especially in view of the fact that the pound had had another bad day. Sir Richard Wharton, the Permanent Secretary of the Foreign Office, made an entry in his private diary – which was marked 'Private and Strictly Confidential'. The diary was found recently in a basement in Carlton Gardens – Ed.*]

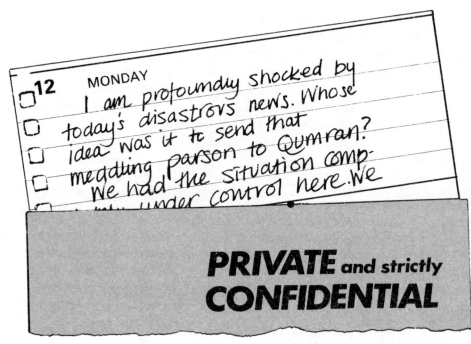

I am profoundly shocked by today's disastrous news. Whose idea was it to send that meddling parson to Qumran?

We had the situation completely under control here. We had made our protest, the nurse would have been quietly flogged and stuffed away in some Qumrani jail, and in a couple of weeks the press would have forgotten all about it.

June 12

I am profoundly shocked by today's disastrous news. Whose idea was it to send that meddling parson to Qumran?

We had the situation completely under control here. We had made our protest, the nurse would have been quietly flogged and stuffed away in some Qumrani jail, and in a couple of weeks the press would have forgotten all about it.

The upshot is that there's terrific damage to the Foreign Office. We had almost got agreement to set up a signals listening post in Qumran. We had told them we wouldn't make any more fuss about the nurse if they signed. Now we have lost our best bargaining counter.

The only good thing to have resulted from this whole silly rescue is that it has got that nurse's ghastly mother off my back. She's been phoning and writing and telling the press we weren't doing enough. And incredibly, the press took her side. They have been going on about how the Foreign Office should be more patriotic. This is nonsense. Our job is to get along with other countries. People have said a lot of unpleasant things about the Foreign Office but no one has *ever* accused us of patriotism.

It is hard to believe that the newspapers have such abject ignorance of diplomatic realities.

Now I foresee that there will be a problem with the PM, because we advised him against letting that clergyman go out there. He will say that we were wrong to tell the Cabinet it was impossible to get the nurse released. But we were right – if they'd left it to the Foreign Office it *would* have been impossible.

[The following day Sir Richard received a note from Sir Humphrey Appleby – Ed.]

---

70 WHITEHALL, LONDON SW1A 2AS

From the Secretary of the Cabinet and Head of the Home Civil Service

13 June

Dear Dick,

    I believe that the F.O. is about to have a P.R. problem.

    The press will say that the church succeeds where the F.O. fails. They may dig out all the old clippings about ambassadors' Rolls Royces, five million pound embassies, school fees at Eton subsidised by the taxpayer, and what does Britain get from it all?

    What do you propose?

SIR BERNARD WOOLLEY RECALLS:[1]

I was summoned to an urgent private meeting with Humphrey, shortly after that nurse was rescued from Qumran.

He knew that the Foreign Office had been against the Dean of Baillie's mercy mission, and he knew that *I* knew.

But in order to forestall hostile press coverage of the FO's passive role in

---

[1] In conversation with the editors.

the proceedings, Sir Richard Wharton had proposed that the FO tell the press that it was Hacker's initiative to send the Dean. The PM would enjoy taking the credit. (And incidentally, there would be no danger of Hacker denying a favourable story just because it was not true.)

Then for the Sunday papers, the Foreign Office would leak the idea that they had suggested this course to the PM when they found the diplomatic channels were blocked. Thus no one would get the blame and everyone would share the credit.

It was a sensible plan. As the PM's Principal Private Secretary my co-operation was needed. I gave it without hesitation.

[*After his meeting with Bernard Woolley, Sir Humphrey received a phone call from the Master of Baillie College. The meeting with Woolley is only referred to* en passant *in the diary, but there are brief notes about the phone call and about a subsequent meeting with Peter Harding, the Appointments Secretary – Ed.*]

Tuesday 13 JUNE

2.30   Successful meeting with B.W. about F.O. press plans.

2.45.   Master of Baillie telephoned, excited that the news of Fiona McGregor's release might help our friend towards preferment.

I was able to inform him that we might not have to wait for a vacancy in another Bishopric. The battle of Bury St Edmunds is not over.

2.30 Successful meeting with BW about FO press plans.

2.45 Master of Baillie telephoned, excited that the news of Fiona McGregor's release might help our friend towards preferment.

I was able to inform him that we might not have a wait for a vacancy in another Bishopric. The battle of Bury St Edmunds is not over. My intention is to get the Dean up to the starting gate as a late entry.

3.00 Peter Harding came to discuss Bury St Edmunds. The Crown Appointments Commission is meeting tomorrow morning.

He was put out that a further candidate has to be submitted to the PM now that he has seen fit to break with tradition by insisting upon a bishop who believes in the Resurrection.

Peter promised me a possible candidate, Stephen Soames. He was regretful because Soames was being saved up for Truro. [*Truro is very remote. It is to the Church what the Vehicle Licensing Centre in Swansea is to the Civil Service – Ed.*]

Soames has been waiting for a bishopric for years. Long time, no See? He is rather a nuisance. He keeps on about his 'duty to God' and that sort of thing. The Church really wants him out of the way. But if the PM wants a religious bishop he is about the only candidate around.

I told Peter that there is a snag. The PM wants *two* more names put up to him. Actually, the PM does not yet know that he wants two more names, but he will realise it as soon as the idea has been put to him. After all, it is only right that the Prime Minister should be given the feeling that he is making a choice.

Therefore, Peter is obliged to put up a second candidate. I encouraged him to find someone plausible but unacceptable. Peter was concerned. He had only till tomorrow morning to think of yet another candidate.

I suggested the Dean of Baillie College. Peter felt he was too implausible even to be suggested, on the grounds that he is unbelievably vain and hopelessly incompetent.

I explained to Peter that the PM doesn't think it's silly to appoint people who are vain and incompetent. Look at the Cabinet. Furthermore, as the Dean has just had some good publicity he must be a plausible second choice.

This made Peter more concerned. This time he was worried at the danger that the Dean might therefore *get* the job.

I was able to smooth ruffled feathers by telling him of the PM's stated view that a devout Christian should be appointed. As the Dean is known to believe only in Islam, the MCC and steam engines, Peter felt relaxed about making him the second name on the list.

I shall have to smooth more ruffled feathers when Hacker recommends the Dean for the bishopric. However, tomorrow is another day.

[*Hacker's diary continues – Ed.*]

June 14th
The morning newspapers were a triumph.

$\mathfrak{Daily}$ $\mathfrak{Mail}$

20p

ANGEL OF MERCY WAS SENT BY PM

By FRANK THOMPKIN

Prime Minister's envoy secures nurse's release

JIM'S DEAN SAVES FIONA FROM LASH

I was given the full credit for it all on the news last night as well. I'm not quite sure why. I suppose it *must* have all been my doing, really. After all, it says so in the papers. I did stop the Foreign Office from stopping the Dean, which comes to the same thing.

Still, it's strange. One normally has such a battle in public life to get the proper credit for anything good one has achieved. Yet here the glory's being handed to me on a plate, when my role in it was peripheral to say the least.

Anyway, there's no point in asking for corrections when the story has come out so thoroughly to my advantage. I suppose I should count my blessings.

I had a final meeting first thing this morning, to discuss the vacant bishopric. Apparently the Palace is now waiting. When Humphrey and Bernard came in, though, I first asked why – in their opinion – the Foreign Office press office gave me the credit for the rescue.

Humphrey took the view that they couldn't take any credit themselves because of their protest. But by giving me the credit, it looks like a government achievement instead of a church achievement.

I suppose that must be it! The first sentence of the Telegraph leader reinforces that view.

16 THE DAILY TELEGRAPH.

The Daily Telegraph

135, FLEET STREET, LONDON EC4P 4BL. TEL: 01-353 4242. TELEX: 22874/5/6
TRAFFORD PARK, MANCHESTER M17 1SL. TEL: 061-872 5939 TELEX: 668891

Imaginative diplomacy

IT DOES the Prime Minister great credit that he has not let himself be bound by the shackles of orthodox diplomacy.

We moved on to the question of the new Bishop of Bury St Edmunds. I was initially in favour of Stephen Soames. Peter likes him too. And although the Dean of Baillie did a pretty good job in Qumran he is said to be fairly eccentric. In fact, I've heard he's barking mad. But when I asked for Humphrey's opinion, his response really frightened me. 'I'm sure Soames is the choice the Crown Commissioners are hoping you'll make, Prime Minister.'

An ominous warning sign. Peter hasn't been levelling with me. I asked Humphrey what the problem is with Soames.

231

'I've heard it said that he's an extremist.'

What, I wondered, is *extremist* the code word for. 'You mean that he believes in God?' I was groping wildly.

Bernard tried to explain. 'He's *very* religious, Prime Minister.'

I was still groping. 'That's all right for a bishop, isn't it?'

'Well . . . yes and no,' said Humphrey carefully. 'He tends to raise issues that governments often would prefer not to be raised. He is a trenchant critic of abortion, contraception for the under-sixteens, sex education, pornography, Sunday trading, easy divorce and bad language on television.'

Quite a catalogue. This is serious. I don't want some loud-mouth, self-righteous cleric challenging the government on all these subjects.

It wouldn't be so bad if we had a policy about any of them. But they are all matters about which the government is trying to avoid having a policy. Our policy is not to have a policy.

I went over this with Humphrey. 'Quite,' he replied. 'He is against your "no policy" policy.'

Bernard, presumably in the interests of clarity, piped up. 'He would demand that you ban abortion, Sunday trading, contraception for the under-sixteens, sex education . . .'

'Thank you, Bernard, I've got the gist,' I said.

Humphrey said he had more bad news about Soames. 'He's also against oppression and persecution in Africa.'

I saw no problem with that. 'So are we.'

'Yes,' he agreed. 'But Soames is against it when practised by black governments as well as white ones.'

So he's a racist! [*This curious leap in logic is explained by the fact that Hacker had been a* Guardian *reader when in opposition – Ed.*]

I really didn't know what to do. Sympathetically, Humphrey murmured that I could still choose Soames if I wanted to. Obviously I *didn't* want to – but how could I turn down *another* two names?

So we looked again at the Dean of Baillie. I listed the arguments against him. 'He's not really up to it. He's said to be lazy, vain, and totally uninterested in Christianity.'

'Yes,' said Humphrey, 'but he's not *against* it! I think he'd make a thoroughly suitable British bishop – cricket, steam engines, and a complete ignorance of theology. Theology can seriously damage your faith.'

My problem was that he was basically unqualified. The submission said that he has never done a real church job. He's spent his whole life in Oxford. On the other hand, he did very well in Qumran, and so his appointment might be a very popular choice with the voters.

Then Humphrey dropped a bombshell. 'There is a problem,' he said. 'I gather that he is thinking of telling the press that the Qumran visit wasn't your idea. I gather he has a letter from the Bishop of Banbury dated some time before your involvement.'

This was *dreadful* news! It would be an incredible embarrassment. It would look as if I were trying to take the credit for something I didn't do! I can just imagine the headlines. PRIME MINISTER TAKES CREDIT FOR DEAN'S MERCY MISSION. Or JIM DIDN'T FIX IT!

So the question was, how could we stop the Dean from making this embarrassing revelation? It seemed, according to Humphrey's information, that the Dean is peeved because he felt that he hasn't been given enough recognition for his role in Qumran. Or the church hasn't. Or something!

On the face of it, there was an easy answer. I told Bernard to invite the Dean here for drinks this evening. It'll be a very nice photo opportunity for the press, too.

Humphrey, however, said that this would be improper: whilst I am considering two candidates for the vacancy in Bury St Edmunds I can hardly, in his view, invite just one of them here for drinks.

I saw his point. But I had to do *something* to stop him blabbing to the press.

Then Humphrey, thank God, had a brainwave. 'If you had already *given* him the job, then it would be perfectly proper.'

And then, the more I thought about it, the more I began to feel that the Dean might be rather a *good* choice of bishop. After all, he is an enterprising chap. And, as I explained to Bernard, eccentricity can be a virtue: you just call it individualism.

Bernard agreed wholeheartedly. 'It's one of those irregular verbs, isn't it? "I have an independent mind, you are eccentric, he is round the twist?"'

We discussed it further, and agreed that we need people in the House of Lords who understand the Arab world. And cricket. And steam engines. So, after mature consideration, I made the Rev. Christopher Smythe, Dean of Baillie College, Oxford, my choice. I told Bernard to convey my recommendation to the Palace, fast! I wanted the appointment announced by lunchtime, the Dean informed at once, and I wanted him round here for drinks, with a photographer, by six o'clock this evening.

And that's what happened. The crisis was averted. We have a new

Bishop of Bury St Edmunds, the nurse was freed from Qumran, and I got the credit all round.

Humphrey was delighted too. He told me that the appointment of the Dean was an act of wisdom. In fact, he was *so* pleased that I began to wonder why.

I suddenly remembered that Baillie was Humphrey's old college. Perhaps that was why he knew so much about the Dean and why he was so pleased. So I asked him if this was another case of jobs for the boys.

He denied it indignantly. 'On the contrary, Prime Minister. I hardly know him. In fact, I know he dislikes me. You can ask him this evening, if you like. I don't like him much either.'

'So you have nothing to gain from this appointment?'

'How could I have?' he asked.

I couldn't see how. But it all seemed a little coincidental. So while we were having our photos taken by the press in front of the fireplace in the White Sitting Room, I asked the Dean if he liked Humphrey Appleby. 'Can't stand him, quite frankly,' the Dean whispered to me. 'I think he's smug.'

So Humphrey was telling the truth. I am really very grateful to him, for giving me helpful, impartial advice in the best traditions of the Civil Service.

9
One Of Us

June 20th

I had an absolutely sensational Prime Minister's Question Time in the House this afternoon. Members were attacking me from all sides about my controlling expenditure on defence, but I really made mincemeat of them all.

So after I finished work I hurried upstairs to the flat to see the TV News. Annie was watching it, it had started already. I asked her if it was the lead story, but they hadn't mentioned it.

'Typical BBC,' I said.

'It's not the BBC.'

'Typical ITV,' I said.

'It's Channel Four,' she said.

'Oh well,' I said, 'what do you expect?'

I watched what was left of the news, which was entirely devoted to the fate of Benjy, an Old English Sheepdog who has somehow got

Family snapshot.

under the wire and on to a Ministry of Defence artillery range on Salisbury Plain.

According to Channel Four News, Benjy belongs to an eight-year-old orphan called Linda Fletcher. Linda lost both her parents in a car crash last year, a crash that only she and Benjy survived.

The artillery range where Benjy is lost is full of unexploded shells and is highly dangerous except for one fixed road through it. Benjy is a long way from the road. The News showed shots of *Danger* signs, telephoto shots of the dog running around and sitting down, and a tearful little orphan girl looking through the wire fence and being comforted by relatives.

The story finished with the Army expressing their regrets but saying that there is nothing they can do unless the dog comes to the wire of his own accord. It seems inevitable that Benjy will either starve to death or be blown up.

That was the end of the news. I couldn't believe it – there was nothing about me at all! I asked Annie if she could have missed it.

'I watched the whole news,' she said, en route to the kitchen to dish up dinner, 'but you know how it is when one watches it – one sort of mentally tunes out the boring bits.'

'Thanks,' I said, and got myself a Scotch.

She was instantly apologetic. 'No, not you, darling. You're not boring, not to me, even if you are to the rest of the country.' She doesn't mean me *personally*, of course, she just means that some people are bored by politicians.

I was a bit fed up, though. Instead of showing the viewers a significant triumph in the House of Commons they give them a pathetic story about a kid and a dog.

[*Although Hacker regarded the debate in the House as a significant triumph, it is possible that Channel Four News took the view that the debate merely consisted of some juvenile rowdies bickering with each other – Ed.*]

'I thought that the story about the dog was interesting,' said Annie, slicing tomatoes for the salad.

'But it's totally unimportant,' I explained, as I struggled with the tray of ice cubes.

'Why is the story about Parliamentary Question Time more important?' she wanted to know.

'Quite simply,' I said, with all due modesty, 'because it was about me. I am Prime Minister, after all. Doesn't that impress anyone in the media?'

'You seem to be quite impressed enough for all of us,' said Annie. I couldn't understand why she was taking this attitude.

'Annie,' I remonstrated with her, 'the future of Britain's defence was being thrashed out in the great forum of the nation and what do the viewers get offered? Lassie Come Home.'

'But what was decided in the great forum of the nation?'

Annie sometimes asks the stupidest questions. Obviously nothing was decided. You can't leave decisions to MPs. She was just being silly. The real importance of the debate is that *I won it*! And I think that the media should let my people know. [*Hacker was apparently developing a Moses complex after five months in Number Ten – Ed.*] I told her that the media people don't live in the real world, and that I'd like to drop the subject.

But Annie wouldn't let it go. 'I think that a kid losing a dog is much more real than a lot of overgrown schoolboys shouting insults at each other. I think the army ought to rescue that dog.'

Bloody stupid idea! Spend thousands and thousands of pounds in a dog rescue operation when you could replace it for nothing from Battersea Dogs' Home? Kids lose dogs every day. Should the army mount rescue operations for all of them? It's just a television sob story.

Annie told me I don't understand how ordinary people feel.

'I happen to be an ordinary person myself,' I replied loftily.

'Surely not!'

I tried to explain to her that I am in charge of the responsible control of public money. 'It's not for me to spend taxpayers' money to buy a bit of easy popularity.'

'If popularity's so easy' said Annie, hitting straight below the belt, 'how come you're so low in the opinion polls?' She argued that to save the dog would cost a fraction of a penny per taxpayer, they'd all like it done, and that sometimes you have to do things that aren't economic if you live in a civilised humane society.

I told her to write a paper on that and submit it to the Treasury. We don't get a lot of laughs in the Cabinet Economic Committee.

June 23rd

I've had some shocks and surprises during my time in politics, but today I think I had the greatest surprise ever.

The Director-General of MI5 came to see me. Sir Geoffrey Hastings, by name. A tall, shambling St Bernard dog of a man, with mournful brown tired eyes and wobbly droopy jowls.

Bernard showed him in to my study, and I invited them to sit down. Hastings looked pointedly at Bernard. I told him that I always have Bernard present at my meetings.

'Not this time, Prime Minister,' he said gently but firmly.

On reflection, I realise that I don't always have Bernard present at my meetings, and I let him go. After he'd gone I realised that I hadn't been given any papers for the meeting. But Hastings indicated that this was on his instructions. Apparently the meeting was too serious for papers. In other words, there should be no record of it at all. This is almost unheard of in Whitehall, where *everything* is minuted.

I was agog. And my agogness was soon to be rewarded.

'We've just received some information,' murmured Hastings.

I was somewhat perplexed. 'Isn't that what you're supposed to do?'

He nodded. 'You know Sir John Halstead?' I nodded. I never *knew* Halstead personally, but everyone knows he was Head of MI5 in the sixties. And he died last month. 'He left a whole lot of his personal papers to us. We've started to go through them. It's very clear he was passing government secrets to Moscow for several years in the fifties and sixties.'

I found it hard to believe what I was being told. The Head of MI5 a Russian agent? Incredible.

Geoffrey Hastings seemed a little embarrassed to be telling me this at all. I'm not surprised. I asked him why Halstead left the papers to MI5.

'His Will says it's a final act of conscience. But I think he just wanted to do a bit of posthumous gloating. Show us he got away with it. But it's a shattering blow.' And Geoffrey certainly looked shattered. The bags under his eyes extended halfway down his cheeks.

'How much did he tell the Russians?' I asked.

'That hardly matters,' said Geoffrey. 'I mean, what with Burgess and Maclean and Philby and Blake and Fuchs and the Krogers, so many people were telling them things that one more didn't really make much difference.'

'So what is the point?' If it didn't matter about the secrets, I couldn't see *any* reason why it should matter.

How wrong I was! Geoffrey Hastings gazed gloomily at me, his salt and pepper moustache flapping in the breeze. I've hardly ever seen a more lugubrious figure. 'The point is,' said Geoffrey in a voice of profound melancholy, 'he was one of us.'

'One of us?'

He could see that I didn't quite get the full significance. 'He joined

MI5 straight from Oxford. Been in the Civil Service all his life. If this ever gets out, all of us who were recruited by him will be suspects for ever.'

Suddenly I saw the seriousness of it all. 'I see,' I said, and eyed him speculatively. 'And you're not a Russian agent, are you?' Geoffrey stared at me coldly, so I hastened to reassure him. 'Only joking,' I said, 'but you're not, are you?' He remained silent. I realised that, if I ever got an answer out of him I wouldn't know if it were true or not anyway. 'No, of course you're not,' I said, and then told him that, embarrassing or not, in my opinion I ought to make this information public.

He begged me not to. He said there were tremendous security implications. I couldn't see why, if the information itself was unimportant. But Hastings said that it's absolutely vital to keep it secret from our enemy that we can't keep secrets.

'I shouldn't have thought that was much of a secret,' I said with unanswerable logic. After all, it must have been mentioned by Burgess and Maclean and Philby and Blake and the Krogers. But it turned out that the Russians weren't the enemy he had in mind. He was talking about our real enemy – the press.

'We had an internal security investigation into John Halstead in the seventies. There was a lot of media speculation. You remember?'

'Vaguely,' I told him.

'It was all terribly irresponsible and ill-informed,' Geoffrey reminded me bitterly.

'You mean,' I asked, 'the press hinted that Halstead was a spy?'

'Yes.'

'But he *was* a spy.'

Geoffrey sighed impatiently. 'Yes, but they didn't know that! They were being typically ignorant and irresponsible. They just happened to be accurate, that's all. Anyway, the enquiry cleared him. Completely. Clean bill of health. But they missed some rather obvious questions and checks. So obviously that, well . . . one *wonders.*'

This was uttered with tons of significance. He really ladled it on. What does one wonder? I wondered. I couldn't guess, so I had to ask him.

'One wonders about the chaps who cleared him, whether they were . . . you know . . .'

'Stupid, you mean,' I said, then suddenly realised what he was driving at. 'My God . . . you mean, *they could be spies too*??' He nodded, and shrugged helplessly. 'Who headed the inquiry?' I asked.

'Old Lord MacIver. But he was ill most of the time.'

'Ill?' I wanted clarification.

'Well . . . ga-ga, really. So effectively it was the Secretary who conducted it.'

'Who was the Secretary?' I asked.

Geoffrey Hastings gave me a woebegone stare, looked around nervously, and apologetically mumbled, 'Sir Humphrey Appleby, I'm afraid.'

I wasn't sure I'd heard him correctly. 'Humphrey?'

'Yes, Prime Minister.'

'You think he may have been spying for the Russians too?'

'It's a remote possibility, but very unlikely. After all, he's one of us.'

'So was John Halstead,' I pointed out.

He couldn't deny it. 'Well . . . yes. But there's no other evidence at all, not against Humphrey.'

I tried to collect my thoughts. 'Might he have been covering up for one of us . . .' I corrected myself. 'One of *them* . . . er, one of *you*?'

Geoffrey thought that this was a very remote possibility. He actually believes that Humphrey is completely loyal, and that all that Humphrey is guilty of is hideous incompetence.

That's bad enough, though. After all, it's a matter of the highest national security. I asked Hastings what he recommended that I should do about Humphrey.

'It's up to you, Prime Minister. We still haven't got through all the papers. You could set up an inquiry into Sir Humphrey.'

This is rather an enjoyable prospect, I must say. But when I questioned Geoffrey closely it turned out that he didn't really recommend it. 'Not at this stage. Things might get out. We don't want any more irresponsible ill-informed press speculation.'

'Even if it's accurate,' I commented.

'*Especially* if it's accurate,' agreed Geoffrey. 'There's nothing worse than *accurate* irresponsible ill-informed press speculation. But you could send Humphrey off on gardening leave while we examine the rest of the Halstead papers.'

This was also an appealing thought. But Humphrey is fairly useful, in spite of his many faults. And he is the Cabinet Secretary. I felt that I should keep him on unless his loyalty were really in question.

Geoffrey Hastings sees no problem in that. He handed me a file marked TOP SECRET: FOR THE PRIME MINISTER'S EYES ONLY and told me that I could confront Humphrey with all the substantive evidence it contains.

But I didn't really want to interrogate Humphrey. 'If you don't seriously suspect him, shouldn't we just forget it?' I asked.

He looked very doubtful indeed. 'Obviously it's your decision,' he rumbled in a sepulchral tone. 'On the other hand, if you did nothing and it emerged later that Sir Humphrey . . . that he was . . . one of *them* . . . well, it might not look too good. Not to mention the fact that as Cabinet Secretary he co-ordinates all of our security services. There are no secrets from him.'

I was forced to agree. Geoffrey rose from his chair, and straightened his baggy pinstripe suit. 'Personally,' he concluded, 'I find it hard enough to believe that *one* of us was one of them. But if *two* of us were one of them . . .' he realised that this was a logical impossibility and tried to correct himself. '*Two* of them, then all of us could be . . . could be . . .'

He had painted himself into a corner. 'All of them?' I suggested helpfully as I escorted him to the door. 'Thank you, Geoffrey, I've heard enough.'

June 26th

I couldn't talk to Humphrey about Sir John Halstead on Friday. I had appointments all day and so had he. But this morning we had a meeting already pencilled in.

It was to be about the defence cuts that I'm looking for. I decided to have the meeting as planned, and then have a private word with Humphrey afterwards.

I've been trying to find as many small savings in the defence budgets as I can. Defence expenditure in this country is completely out of hand. By the mid-1990's we shall only be able to afford half a frigate. This, I surmise, will be inadequate for our naval defences. The Secretary of State for Defence is getting nowhere so I have decided to take a look myself.

A simple way has emerged of saving three million pounds, for instance, and the Service Chiefs say it can't be done. Humphrey is backing them, of course, with the argument that *any* defence savings can be dangerous.

Ironically, the suggestion being made by the Service Chiefs is to close a hundred miles of coastal Radar Stations. And I know *why* they're suggesting that particular economy: because it *is* dangerous, and therefore they know that I won't agree to it! But *I'm* suggesting

241

that they start eating some of their forty-three years' supply of strawberry jam instead of buying more.

Humphrey couldn't – or wouldn't – see how that would help. 'As I understand it, Prime Minister, the Army haven't got any strawberry jam. It's the Navy that's got it.'

He's right. But the army have seventy-one years' supply of tinned meat. And the RAF, which has no strawberry jam lake and no tinned meat mountain, has fifty-six years' supply of baked beans. So I am trying to get across to Humphrey and the MOD that the Army and the RAF should eat the Navy's strawberry jam, and the Navy and the RAF should eat the Army's tinned meat, and the Army and the Navy should eat the RAF's baked beans. And if they did that with all the other surpluses too we'd save £3 million a year for four years. And I do not believe that the defence of the realm is imperilled by soldiers eating sailors' jam!

Bernard had an objection. 'The RAF's baked beans are in East Anglia and the Army's tinned meat is in Aldershot and the Navy's jam is in Rosyth. So it would mean moving the beans from . . .'

I stopped him there. 'Bernard,' I asked, 'if our armed forces can't move a few tins of baked beans around Britain, how can they intercept guided missiles?'

Bernard seemed perplexed by the question. 'But you don't intercept missiles with baked beans, you have long pointy things which go . . .' I told him to shut his mouth. At which point Humphrey reluctantly agreed that it *could* be done, but added that it would be extremely complicated. 'The administrative costs would outweigh the savings.'

But no one's even worked out the administrative costs. And why? Because there's no need – they *know* that they can make the administrative costs outweigh the savings, if they really put their minds to it.

As the meeting drew uneventfully to a close, a messenger arrived with the latest opinion polls. They contained bad news. I'm down another three points. Not the government – just my personal rating.

I wonder what I'm doing wrong. Humphrey believes it proves that I'm doing things right – politically popular actions, in his view, are usually administrative disasters.

I wonder if it's caused by my failure to get the defence cuts through. Maybe. Though in all honesty I'm not sure that defence cuts are the principal topic of conversation in the supermarkets of Britain. No, the lead story in the newspapers is that bloody lost dog on Salisbury Plain. Perhaps I should forget about my defence policy for the moment and think up a lost dog policy.

Anyway, the meeting was over. And there was nothing for it, I could postpone it no longer: I had to have my private word with Humphrey. I told Bernard that I had to discuss a top secret security matter with Humphrey, and nodded to the door. 'Would you mind, Bernard?'

He went to the door and, suddenly, threw it open! Then he looked up and down the landing to see if anyone was eavesdropping. I realised he had misunderstood me. So I explained that I wished him to leave us alone.

He seemed a little crestfallen. I can see why. That's two meetings in two days that he's been asked to leave. But Geoffrey had no choice, and nor do I – I can hardly let Bernard know that Humphrey, of *all* people, is a security risk at the moment.

After Bernard left us, probably wondering if *he* was considered a security risk all of a sudden, Humphrey and I were left alone. I didn't quite know how to begin, so it was a minute or so before I spoke. Humphrey waited patiently.

'Humphrey,' I began eventually, 'there's something I want to talk about. Something very secret.'

I was stuck. Humphrey leaned forward helpfully. 'Would it be easier if I wasn't here?' he asked.

'It's something very serious,' I replied.

He assumed an appropriately serious expression. 'Very serious and very secret?'

I nodded. 'Humphrey, does the name Sir John Halstead ring a bell?'

'Of course, Prime Minister. He died only three weeks ago. And he was the subject of a security enquiry ten years ago. I had to conduct it myself, virtually. Old MacIver was ga-ga.'

So far so good. I asked Humphrey if he'd found evidence of anything incriminating.

'Of course not.' He smiled confidently.

'Why of course not?' I asked.

'Well, in the first place John Halstead was one of us. We'd been friends for years. In the second place the whole story was got up by the press. And in the third place, the whole object of internal security enquiries is to find no evidence.'

'Even if the security of the realm is at risk?'

He laughed. 'Prime Minister, if you really believe the security of the realm is at risk you call in the Special Branch. Government security enquiries are only used for killing press stories. Their sole

243

purpose is to enable the Prime Minister to stand up in the House and say, 'We have held a full enquiry and there is no evidence to substantiate these charges.'

'But suppose you find something suspicious?'

'Prime Minister, practically everything that happens in government is suspicious. The fact that you asked Bernard to leave us alone together for a secret conversation could be construed as suspicious.'

This surprised me. But it shouldn't have, he's obviously right. Anyway, Humphrey went on to say that the whole story was nonsense, typical Fleet Street sensationalism.

He was so confident that it was inevitable that he would feel really stupid when I revealed what I knew. I was beginning to enjoy myself thoroughly.

'There is *no* possibility,' I asked carefully, 'that Sir John Halstead ever passed any information to Moscow?'

'Impossible,' he asserted. 'Out of the question.'

'You'd stake your reputation on that?'

'Without hesitation.'

I went for the kill. 'Well, Humphrey, I'm afraid I have to tell you that he was spying for Russia for a considerable part of his career.'

Humphrey was silenced. But only for a moment. 'I don't believe it,' he said defiantly. 'Who says so?'

I gave him an apologetic smile. 'He says so himself. He left all his papers to the government with a detailed confession. MI5 says it's absolutely true. It checks out all along the line.'

Humphrey was speechless. This is a sight that I've never seen before, and I must say I thoroughly enjoyed it. He spluttered a bit, and tried to put together a sentence. Finally he said: 'But, good Lord, I mean, well, he was . . .'

'One of us?' I put in helpfully.

'Well . . . yes.' He began to pull himself together. 'Well, that certainly leaves a lot of questions to be asked.'

'Yes,' I agreed, 'and I'm asking you the first one. *Why* didn't you ask him a lot of questions?' Humphrey didn't see what I was getting at. 'Why, Humphrey, did your enquiry exonerate him so quickly?'

He suddenly realised how my questions affected *him*. 'You don't mean . . . surely nobody is suggesting . . .' He went very pale.

So I pointed out to Humphrey that it was all very suspicious. I asked why he hadn't held a proper enquiry. After all, according to the TOP SECRET file, Humphrey had been given evidence of Halstead's surprisingly long stay in Yugoslavia. And shortly after Halstead left Yugoslavia several of our MI5 agents behind the Iron Curtain were rounded up and never seen again.

And there was one specific interpreter with whom Halstead spent a lot of time. I asked Humphrey what he'd found out about this interpreter.

'She turned out to be a Russian agent. We knew that. Most Yugoslav interpreters are Russian agents. Those who aren't in the CIA, that is.'

'But you never followed her up.'

'I had better things to do with my time,' he said defensively.

I stared at him accusingly. 'Three months later she moved to England and settled in Oxford, a hundred and fifty yards from Sir John Halstead's house. They were neighbours for the next eleven years.'

Humphrey was completely demoralised. He tried to defend himself. 'You can't check up on everything. You don't know what you might find out. I mean, if you've got that sort of suspicious mind you ought to . . .'

'Conduct security enquiries.' I finished his sentence for him.

Humphrey's defence, in a nutshell, was that Halstead gave him his word. The word of a gentleman. And you don't go checking up on the word of a gentleman, especially when you were at Oxford together.

I asked him if he'd have checked up on Anthony Blunt. Humphrey said that was totally different. Blunt was at Cambridge.

I listened patiently. Then I was forced to tell him that I had a problem with him.

He was horrified. 'But you don't think . . . you *can't* think . . . I mean, I mean, I don't speak a word of Russian.'

'But you must admit,' I said, 'that it looks as if it must have been incompetence or collusion. Either way . . .'

I left the sentence unfinished. The implications were clear enough. Humphrey was dreadfully upset. 'Collusion? Prime Minister, I give you my word there was no collusion.'

'Is that the word of a gentleman?' I asked ironically.

'Yes. An Oxford gentleman,' he added hastily.

I wasn't really satisfied. 'How's the garden?' I asked.

He relaxed and began to tell me about his roses when he realised the full force of my question. 'No, no, I beseech you, Prime Minister, not gardening leave!'

'Why not?'

'I have my reputation to think of.'

'I thought you'd already staked that on Sir John Halstead's innocence.'

I told Humphrey that I would have to think long and hard about what to do. I indicated that I would talk to Sir Arnold Robinson, his predecessor as Cabinet Secretary, for advice on handling a security enquiry into a Cabinet Secretary. And I cautioned him against speaking to Arnold until after I've spoken to him.

He assured me that he wouldn't dream of it.

[*What possessed Hacker to warn Sir Humphrey that he would be discussing the matter with Sir Arnold? And why did he believe Sir Humphrey's assurance that he would not speak to Sir Arnold himself? These are questions over which historians will ponder for ever. Suffice to say that Sir Humphrey met Sir Arnold for a drink that very evening, at the Athenaeum Club. Sir Arnold's private diary relates what happened in full detail – Ed.*]

Met a flustered and anxious Appleby at the club. After one brandy he revealed the cause of his panic. Apparently the Prime Minister and Geoffrey Hastings of MI5 both think he might be a spy, because he cleared Halstead and Halstead has now confessed all.

Humphrey asked me what he should do. I told him that depends on whether he actually was spying or not. He seemed shocked that I could entertain the suspicion, but I explained that one must keep an open mind.

Humphrey advanced several compelling arguments in his own favour.

1. He was not at Cambridge.
2. He is a married man.
3. He is one of us.
4. He has been in the Civil Service all his life.
5. Unlike John Halstead, he has never believed in things like *causes*. Humphrey argues correctly that he has never believed in anything in his life.
6. He, unlike Halstead, has never had ideas – especially original ideas.

These arguments are all persuasive – but not conclusive.

However, it seemed to me that whether Humphrey Appleby is a spy is immaterial in the short term. I agree with him that, whether he is or isn't, we have to see that it doesn't get out.

Of course, now that I am President of the Campaign for Freedom of Information I am in a very good position to prevent sensitive information from reaching the press. Giving information to Moscow is serious – but giving information to anyone is serious. In fact, giving information to the Cabinet could be more serious than giving it to Moscow.

The key point is that a scandal of this nature could gravely weaken the authority of the Service. This could result in letting the politicians in – as in

America, they might decide to make their party hacks into Permanent Secretaries and Deputy Secretaries. Even Under Secretaries. The top jobs in the Civil Service would be filled with people who would just do what they were asked by the politicians. This would be unthinkable! There are no secrets that anyone could pass to Moscow that would cause one-tenth of the damage that Britain would suffer if it were governed the way the Cabinet wanted. Therefore Humphrey certainly must not confess, even if he is guilty, and I told him so.

He reiterated that he has nothing to confess. Be that as it may, there is still the other possibility. Nevertheless, I asked him to assume, for the sake of argument, that he is innocent.

He thanked me profusely. I repeated that I was making that assumption for the sake of argument only, without prejudice. Unfortunately, however, if he is innocent of espionage, he is plainly guilty of incompetence.

He denied incompetence. He reminded me that I had appointed him Secretary of the Halstead enquiry. And he suggested that I had hinted to him that he was expected to find no evidence against Halstead.

Naturally *I* denied this. He has no written evidence – I made sure of that at the time. And of course I sent him the memorandum that I always sent, the one instructing him to leave no stone unturned, to be no respecter of persons, and to pursue the truth however unpalatable.

In fact, I left a copy of this memorandum in the Cabinet Office files, so there can be no credence given to Humphrey's claim.

Nonetheless, I asked him to assure me that we shall hear no more about my alleged complicity. He gave me that assurance, and we returned to the question of *his* incompetence. I told him that although *we* might both know that he did the job that he was required to do, it would be hard to explain that to the politicians.

He asked me if the politicians have to know. We agreed that it should be avoided, if possible. But the main danger is the Prime Minister: he may want to go around telling people about it all.

Clearly Humphrey must not allow this to happen. It must be stopped. The Prime Minister might tell the Cabinet. They might decide to suspend Humphrey. They might remove him to the Chairmanship of the War Graves Commission!

Humphrey had not considered any of these dire possibilities. He should have. Frankly, I do not mind what happens to Humphrey. He is expendable, and I told him so. He denied it emotionally, but it is true nonetheless.

But even though Humphrey personally is expendable, we dare not allow politicians to establish the principle that Senior Civil Servants can be removed for incompetence. That would be the thin end of the wedge. We could lose dozens of our chaps. Hundreds, maybe. Even thousands!

Therefore I advised Humphrey that he should make himself so valuable to the Prime Minister in the next few days that he cannot be let go. We discussed what the PM is really dead set on at the moment: popularity, of course, which is what all politicians are dead set on all the time.

The biggest current news story is about a lost dog on Salisbury Plain. I advised him to find an angle on this.

[*Sir Humphrey's diary makes only a brief reference to the above conversation with Sir Arnold. Perhaps he wished there to be no record of the fact that Sir Arnold considered him expendable, which may have hurt him even more than the suggestion that he might have been a spy. However, Sir Humphrey notes a meeting with Sir Norman Block[1] the following day, at which he made a proposal clearly based on Sir Arnold Robinson's advice – Ed.*]

Met Arnold at the club yesterday. He made one or two valuable suggestions, chiefly that I find some way to help the PM increase his ratings in the opinion polls before the end of the week.

The only answer seems to be for Hacker to help the lost dog on Salisbury Plain. Arnold seemed to be suggesting that I should get the Prime Minister to crawl all over Salisbury Plain with a mine detector in one hand and a packet of Winalot in the other. At least it would probably do Britain less harm than anything else he would be likely to be doing.

Today Norman popped in to see me. He was curious as to how his Secretary of State acquitted himself in Cabinet. [*Sir Humphrey Appleby, as Cabinet Secretary, was present at all Cabinet meetings. Other Permanent Secretaries were generally not present unless specially invited, a rare occurrence – Ed.*]

I told Norman that, even though the Cabinet are being resentful, his Secretary of State refused to agree to defence cuts. Norman was very encouraged.

I told him that I needed a favour, on a very sensitive issue. He assumed that I would be referring to Cruise Missiles or chemical warfare, and was surprised when I revealed that I was concerned about the lost dog on Salisbury Plain.

Norman was confident that there were no problems, and that everything was under control. The dog, he predicted, will have starved to death by the weekend. Then the army will recover the body and give it a touching little funeral and bury it just outside the gates. He has made plans for pictures of the guards resting on reversed arms, and to set up a photo session of the Commanding Officer comforting the weeping orphan girl. He says the telly would love it, and there would be pictures in all the Sundays.

I listened carefully, and then proposed that we rescue the dog.

Norman's reaction was explosive. He said it would be highly dangerous. It would take:

a) A squadron of Royal Engineers with mine detectors.

b) A detachment of the Veterinary Corps with stun darts.

c) A helicopter (possibly two helicopters) with winching equipment.

d) A bill for hundreds of thousands of pounds.

All for a dog that could be replaced for a fiver in the local petshop.

I know all this anyway, and I persisted. I asked Norman if the dog *could* be rescued, technically. Norman didn't think twice. He told me that *anything* can be done technically, if you've got the money. But he argued that it would

[1] Permanent Secretary of the MOD.

be madness: he is under great pressure from the PM to cut spending, why on earth should he waste hundreds of thousands in full view of the world's press just to save a dog?

Norman was only seeing the *problem*. I flipped it over, and showed him the *opportunity*: if the Prime Minister authorised the rescue, if it were Hacker's initiative, it would make it much harder for him to insist on defence cuts subsequently.

Norman was silenced. Then he smiled a beatific smile. It is clear to me that I have regained my touch. I told Norman the conditions:

1) The real cost of the rescue must not be known to Hacker until after the rescue.
2) The rescue operation should be put on immediate standby, in strict confidence.
3) The PM must get the credit – a Number Ten job.

He agreed instantly.

[*Appleby Papers 28/13/GFBH*]

[*Hacker's diary continues – Ed.*]

June 27th

Sir Arnold Robinson returned to Number Ten today for the first time since his retirement, for a confidential meeting with me about Humphrey. He had been briefed by MI5. He thinks that it was a bad business, an unfortunate business. I went further, and said it was disastrous. Arnold seemed to feel that I was overstating it.

'Not disastrous, surely, Prime Minister. It will never come out.'

'You mean,' I asked, 'things are only disastrous if people find out?'

'Of course.'

Perhaps he's right. If nobody finds out I suppose it's merely an embarrassment rather than a disaster. [*If the Cabinet Secretary were a spy it would be a* grave *political embarrassment – Ed.*]

But happily it turned out that it was not a disaster because new evidence has emerged. Sir Arnold brought with him proof that Sir Humphrey was not a spy.

'MI5 have just come across this document in the Halstead papers. From his private diary.'

He handed it to me, and I read it with a mixture of feelings that I cannot quite describe: relief, joy and glee, perhaps.

October 28th.

Another session with that prize goof Appleby. Fooled him completely. He never asked any of the difficult questions. Didn't seem to have read the MI5 report. So much wool in his head, its child's play to pull it over his eyes.

Nothing I have ever read has ever given me so much pleasure.

Arnold assumed that my delight was due to the fact that Humphrey was now exonerated. He wanted to take the Halstead diary back, but I insisted on keeping it.

Arnold then suggested that the matter was closed as there was nothing further to investigate. But I pointed out that the question of incompetence remains.

'We all make mistakes,' said Arnold feebly.

'Not on this scale,' I replied severely. 'Do you think I should sack him?'

Arnold didn't seem to think that this suggestion was even worthy of discussion. Dismissively he replied, 'I hardly think so.'

'Why not?' I asked. 'Do you think Civil Servants should never be sacked?'

Arnold replied with care. 'If they deserve it, of course they should. In principle. But not in practice.'

At first I was sceptical. But he explained that before Humphrey could be sacked there would have to be an enquiry. And all enquiries into the incompetence of civil servants somehow seemed to lead back to mistakes by ministers. However, he offered to chair an impartial enquiry.

I had second thoughts. Since I have been Humphrey's minister for some years I decided that discretion is the better part of valour. I thanked Arnold for his contribution, let him go, and sent for Humphrey.

I put Humphrey out of his misery as soon as he arrived. I told him he had been cleared of spying. Naturally he was extremely relieved, and asked how.

'Something Sir John Halstead wrote,' I told him.

'That's very gratifying,' he said.

I was enjoying myself. '*Isn't* it?' I said. 'I knew you'd be pleased.'

'May one see the document?' he asked.

'Indeed one may, Humphrey. Better still, one can have it read to one.' And one read it aloud to him.

'"October 28th. Another session with that prize goof Appleby. Fooled him completely."'

Humphrey went very pink. 'I see. Thank you, Prime Minister.' And he reached for the diary.

'No, Humphrey, it goes on,' I said. 'Clears you even more. "He never asked any of the difficult questions. Didn't seem to have read the MI5 report. So much wool in his head, it's child's play to pull it over his eyes."' I looked up at Humphrey and beamed at him. 'Isn't that wonderful? You must be *very* happy.'

He pursed his lips. He was visibly seething with indignation. 'I always said John Halstead was a hopeless judge of character,' he snarled.

I pretended to be worried. 'You mean . . . we can't believe it? He's lying?'

Humphrey was cornered. He realised he had no choice but to admit the truth. Very reluctantly he agreed that Halstead's account was absolutely true, but he insisted that Halstead wasn't bright enough to understand Humphrey's subtle questioning techniques. The non-confrontational approach.

I nodded understandingly. 'You were lulling him into a true sense of security,' I remarked.

'Yes,' said Humphrey. 'No,' said Humphrey, as he realised what I meant. 'Anyway,' he added, 'I take it that it's all over now.'

'The collusion charge? Of course,' I said. Humphrey relaxed. 'But we're left with the incompetence.'

He licked his lips nervously. 'Prime Minister, I do urge you . . .'

'Humphrey,' I said. 'Would you condone this sort of incompetence in someone working for you?'

'It was a long time ago,' he pleaded. 'A period of great strain. I had many other onerous duties.'

'You have many other onerous duties now,' I said, threateningly.

But then he redeemed himself. Humphrey with his back to the wall is a valuable man. 'Prime Minister,' he began, 'I have been giving some thought to how you might increase your popularity rating.'

Naturally I was immediately interested. I waited for him to continue.

'A strong government needs a popular Prime Minister.'

How true! I waited for more.

'I think you should do something really popular.'

I was getting impatient. 'Of *course* I should,' I said. 'But what?'

His suggestion was not what I expected. 'I was going to suggest that you intervene personally to save that poor little doggy on Salisbury Plain.'

At first I didn't think he was serious. 'It would certainly be popular, but surely it would also be rather expensive?'

'Surely not?' replied Humphrey.

[*Civil Service watchers will note this skilful reply – not a lie, but hardly revealing the truth – Ed.*]

He told me that time was running out. 'The decision has to be taken right away, this morning, before poor little Benjy starves to death.' I was undecided. Then Humphrey appealed to my emotions. 'There are times when you have to act from the heart. Even as Prime Minister.'

He was right! I gave him the go-ahead. He phoned Sir Norman right away. He told me that he had already put the army on a three-hour standby, and that he was merely waiting for my clearance.

I was delighted. I had just one worry. 'Humphrey, it's not a question of buying cheap popularity, is it?'

'By no means, Prime Minister,' he replied emphatically, and then was put through to Sir Norman at the MOD. 'Norman? Walkies.'

Apparently this was the codeword to begin Operation Lassie Come Home.

June 28th

They saved Benjy today. And I expect to be *very* popular tomorrow.

I watched it all on the Six O'Clock News. It was rather thrilling, feeling like the Commander-in-Chief of a major military operation. I felt like Mrs Thatcher during the Falklands, only more so – almost Churchillian really. The country needs a strong, decisive, tough leader like me.

The operation began on 'B' range early this morning. Four detachments of the Royal Engineers with mine detectors set off from different parts to close in on the area where Benjy was last sighted. It took over an hour to locate him. Then the Royal Veterinary Corps fired a stun dart. We saw him keel over, temporarily unconscious.

The troops couldn't enter the area without detonating shells, which might have injured the dog. So an RAF helicopter was flown in, and an air rescue team lowered a man to pick Benjy up without crossing dangerous ground. He was flown to safety and reunited with his little orphan Linda, who was overjoyed to see him. I think she'd given up hope of ever seeing him again. I was so profoundly moved by my own wisdom and kindness that I cried a little. I'm not ashamed to admit it.

Annie was delighted. I hadn't told her that I'd arranged for them to rescue the dog. When we last spoke about it I'd told her it would be a waste of money.

Her little face was glowing with pleasure and happiness for that child.

I told her that I'd thought again. 'I thought about what *you* said. And I thought "government is about caring".'

'Caring for votes?' she asked.

I was a bit put out. 'That's not very kind, Annie. I thought about that little girl and what the dog must mean to her. Individuals do count – even in a world of budgets and balance sheets. Some people may criticise me for using the army that way, but I don't care. Sometimes, doing the right thing means risking unpopularity.'

I was pleased with the sound of that. I shall use it at question time in the House tomorrow – it's bound to come up.

Annie was totally taken by it. [*It is possible that Hacker said taken 'in' by it, but his words are unclear on the cassette, due to what sounds like an emotional and excitable state of mind – Ed.*]

She gave me a kiss and told me that she *certainly* wouldn't criticise me for it. 'For the first time since we moved into Number Ten, I can see the point of being Prime Minister.' She is weird.

June 29th
The press coverage was wonderful this morning. Even better than I'd hoped.

I showed them to Humphrey. He was delighted as well. Even the leading articles were favourable. '*Today Britain discovered that a real human heart beats inside Number 10 Downing Street.*' I showed it to Bernard. His response was a typical quibble. 'Actually, seventy-four human hearts beat inside Number Ten.' But he was smiling.

I made a slight tactical error with Humphrey. I told him I'd been right and that I have an instinct for what the people want. That's perfectly true, of course – but in this instance it was actually Humphrey who had suggested the rescue, and when he reminded me I graciously gave him full credit. Although, in fact, he mostly has crummy ideas and the credit is *really* due to me for spotting that, for once, his idea was a good one. Still, I let him feel he was responsible for it, as that's always good for morale.

As he had been so helpful on this matter I readily granted the favour that he asked of me. He wanted the question of his incompetence in the Halstead enquiry to be dropped. I agreed at once. Why not? No harm had been done.

Then we moved on to Cabinet Agenda, after we gloated over a few more of the newspaper stories. Wonderful quotes. Linda said: '*My vote goes to Mr Hacker*.' The BBC and ITV reported a flood of phone calls approving my decision to rescue Benjy. And, according to *The Times*, the Leader of the Opposition was not available for comment. I bet he wasn't! He has to choose between supporting me or being in favour of leaving dogs to starve to death! I really got him there!

When we finally turned to the Agenda, Humphrey suggested that we postponed item 3 – the defence cuts. He wanted to refer them to OPD.[1] I couldn't see the sense of this – I wanted a decision at Cabinet, not a sixty-page submission nine months from now.

But then the bombshell hit me. Humphrey revealed that saving Benjy had cost £310,000. It seemed impossible! And yet these were the MOD figures, on a true-cost basis.

My breath was taken away. 'Humphrey,' I said, aghast, 'we must do something!'

'Put the dog back?' suggested Bernard.

On balance, shocked though I was, I still felt it was the right decision – it may have cost £310,000 but I'd won a lot of public support. [*It might have been more accurate for Hacker to say that he had bought a lot of public support. With public money – Ed.*]

But then the full horror dawned on me. At least, it didn't exactly dawn – Humphrey explained it. 'You do not have to postpone the defence cuts, but that would be a very courageous decision.'

My heart sank. 'Courageous? Why?'

'If there are defence cuts, the cost of rescuing the dog is bound to be leaked to the press.'

'Surely not,' I said feebly, but I knew he was right.

He shook his head and smiled a rueful smile. 'Of course, Prime Minister, if you have complete faith in the defence staff's confidentiality and loyalty . . .'

What a ridiculous idea! How could I have? They leak like sieves.

Humphrey rubbed salt into the wound. 'I can see the headlines now. PRIME MINISTER SAVES DOG AT THE EXPENSE OF BRITAIN'S AIR DEFENCES. It would be quite a story.'

'A shaggy dog story,' added Bernard facetiously. Sometimes I'd like to kill Bernard.

I contemplated the situation miserably. For months I've been struggling to make these defence cuts. And now, because of one

[1] The Overseas Policy and Defence Committee of the Cabinet.

impulsive, good-hearted decision, I was screwed.

'Of course,' murmured Humphrey, 'it would only come out if . . .' And he gazed at me.

I suddenly wondered if this had been a plot, if Humphrey could have persuaded me to rescue the dog to secure postponement of the defence cuts.

But I quickly realised that this was sheer paranoia. Humphrey is not clever enough for that, nor would he do that to me.

He was simply telling me that somebody in the MOD would inevitably leak the story unless I dropped the defence cuts. He was right. Someone would be sure to see the opportunity to blackmail me.

'I'm not going to be blackmailed,' I told Humphrey firmly.

'I should hope not,' he said. And waited.

And as I thought it all through, I realised I have no choice. So I put the best face on it that I could.

'On the other hand,' I began carefully, 'one can't cut defence too far back. Defence of the Realm, the first duty of government. And there are always unexpected emergencies: Korea, the Falklands, Benjy.'

'Benjy!' echoed Bernard and Humphrey with approval.

'Yes,' I concluded, 'perhaps I have been a bit hasty.' So I told Humphrey that in my considered opinion Item 3 – the Defence Cuts – possibly needs a little more thought. I instructed Humphrey to refer it to committee.

I could see from Humphrey's respectful expression that he thought that I had made a right decision.

'And tell them there's no particular hurry, would you?'

'Yes Prime Minister.'